Resource Book

Teacher's Edition Part Three
Grade 6

Editorial Offices: Glenview, Illinois • Parsippany, New Jersey • New York, New York
Sales Offices: Needham, Massachusetts • Duluth, Georgia • Glenview, Illinois
Coppell, Texas • Sacramento, California • Mesa, Arizona

ISBN: 0-382-36628-X

4 5 6 7 8 9 10 V039 09 08 07 06 05

Program Authors

Jane Beethoven

Susan Brumfield

Patricia Shehan Campbell

David N. Connors

Robert A. Duke

Judith A. Jellison

Rita Klinger

Rochelle Mann

Hunter C. March

Nan L. McDonald

Marvelene C. Moore

Mary Palmer

Konnie Saliba

Will Schmid

Carol Scott-Kassner

Mary E. Shamrock

Sandra L. Stauffer

Judith Thomas

Jill Trinka

Resource Book Contributing Authors

Jane Beethoven	Activity Masters
Susan Brumfield	Music Reading Worksheets Music Reading Practice
David N. Connors	Orff
Alice-Ann Darrow	Signing
Robert A. Duke	Assessment
Martha F. Hilley	Keyboard
Debbie Burgoon Hines	Pronunciation Practice Guides
Judith A. Jellison	Assessment
Rita Klinger	Music Reading Worksheets Music Reading Practice
Shirley Lacroix	Recorder
Rochelle Mann	Music Reading Worksheets Music Reading Practice
Konnie Saliba	Orff
Julie K. Scott	Orff Recorder
Judith Thomas	Orff
Jill Trinka	Music Reading Worksheets Music Reading Practice
CP Language Institute	Pronunciation Practice Guides

Master Table of Contents

PRONUNCIATION PRACTICE GUIDES

Recorded Pronunciation Practice tracks are provided in the CD package.

Table of Contents

Pronunciation Practice 1

Bắt kim thang (Setting Up the Golden Ladder)

Traditional Song from Vietnam

Verse 1

Phrase

① *Bắt kim thang cà lang bí rợ.*
buhk'n kihm tayng kah layng bee ruhr.

② *Cột qua kèo kèo qua cột.*
koht'n kwah kay‿oh kay‿oh kwah koht'n.

③ *Chú bán dầu qua cầu mà té.*
choo bayn yee‿oh kwah kah‿oh mah teh‿ehr.

④ *Chú bán ếch ở lại làm chi.*
choo bayn eht'n ehr ll‿ee lehm chee.

⑤ *Con le le đánh trống thổi kèn.*
kohn leh‿eer leh‿eer duhn trawng thoh-ee kehn.

⑥ *Con bìm bịp thổi*
kohn bihm bihp'm thoh‿ee

⑦ *tò tí te tò te.*
taw tee teh‿ehr taw teh‿ehr.

ay = long *a* sound

PRONUNCIATION PRACTICE 2

Magnolia

Words and Music by Tish Hinojosa

Verse 1

Phrase ① *Tem-pra-no‿en la ma-ña-na‿un pa-ja-ri-to can-ta,*
tehm-prah-noh‿ehn lah mah-nyah-nah‿oon pah-hah-ree-toh kahn-tah,

② *des-pier-ta la mag-no-li-a.*
dehs-pee‿ehrr-tah lah mahg-noh-lee-ah.

③ *Su can-ción me ha-bla,*
soo kahn-see‿ohn meh ah-blah,

④ *dul-ce y tan cla-ra,*
dool-seh ee tahn klah-rrah,

⑤ *ba-jo la mag-no-li-a.*
bah-hoh lah mahg-noh-lee-ah.

⑥ *Flor blan-ca‿y bo-ni-ta*
flohr blahn-kah‿ee boh-nee-tah

⑦ *ho-jas bien bri-lla-das,*
oh-hahs bee‿ehn bree-yah-dahs,

⑧ *cre-cen en mag-no-li-a.*
kreh-sehn ehn mahg-noh-lee-ah.

⑨ *En pri-ma-ve-ra so-la,*
ehn prree-mah-veh-rrah soh-lah,

⑩ *yo sue-ño por ho-ras,*
yoh soo‿weh-nyoh pohr oh-rrahs,

⑪ *ba-jo la mag-no-li-a.*
bah-hoh lah mahg-noh-lee-ah.

⑫ *Hmm y mi-ro‿el cie-la‿a-llá.*
hmm ee mee-roh‿ehl see‿eh-lah‿ah-yah.

Pronunciation Practice 2 (continued)

⑬ *Hmm y pien-so to-do‿a-mar.*
hmm ee pee‿ehn-soh toh-doh‿ah-mahr.

⑭ *El vien-to bai-la mag-no-li-a por mí.*
ehl vee‿ehn-toh bah‿ee-lah mahg-noh-lee-ah pohrr mee.

Verse 2

Phrase

① *Ve-ra-no se a-ca-ba*
veh-rah-noh seh ah-kah-bah

② *tam-bién el jue-go pa-ra,*
tahm-bee‿ehn ehl wheh-goh pah-rrah,

③ *ba-jo la mag-no-li-a.*
bah-hoh lah mahg-noh-lee-ah.

④ *Ho-jas caen de‿e-to-ño,*
oh-hahs kahn deh‿eh-toh-nyoh,

⑤ *a-nun-cian-do‿in-vier-no,*
ah-noon-see‿ahn-doh‿een-vee‿ehrr-noh,

⑥ *ba-jo la mag-no-li-a.*
bah-hoh lah mahg-noh-lee-ah.

⑦ *Mi‿her-ma-ni-ta‿y yo con*
mee‿ehrr-mah-nee-tah‿ee yoh kohn

⑧ *té y de-sa-yu-no,*
teh ee deh-sah-yoo-noh,

⑨ *ba-jo la mag-no-li-a.*
bah-hoh lah mahg-noh-lee-ah.

⑩ *Pre-ten-dien-do ho-jas,*
preh-tehn-dee‿ehn-doh oh-yahs,

PRONUNCIATION PRACTICE 2 (CONTINUED)

⑪ *ta-cos bien sa-bro-sos,*
tah-kohs bee‿ehn sah-brroh-sohs,

⑫ *ba-jo la mag-no-li-a.*
bah-hoh lah mahg-noh-lee-ah.

⑬ *Hmm vie-nen a vi-si-tar.*
hmm vee‿eh-nehn ah vee-see-tahr.

⑭ *Hmm John, Rin-go, George, y Paul.*
hmm Jahn, Reen-goh, Jorj, ee pahl.

⑮ *Ri-en-do ve-mos mag-no-li-a bai-lar.*
ree-ehn-doh veh-mohs mahg-noh-lee-ah bah‿ee-lahr.

Pronunciation Practice 3

El condor pasa

Music by Daniel Almonica Robles

Phrase

1. *El a-mor co-mo‿un con-dor ba-ja-rá,*
ehl ah-mohr koh-moh‿oon kohn-dohr bah-hah-rah,

2. *mi co-ra-zón,*
mee koh-rah-sohn,

3. *gol-pea-rá,*
gohl-pee‿yah-rah,

4. *des-pués se‿i-rá.*
dehs-pwehs seh‿ee-rah.

5. *La lu-na‿en el de-sier-to bri-lla-rá.*
lah loo-nah‿ehn ehl deh-syehr-toh bree-yah-rah.

6. *Tú ven-drás.*
too vehn-drahs.

7. *So-la-men-te‿un be-so,*
soh-lah-mehn-teh‿oon beh-soh,

8. *me de-ja-rás.*
meh deh-hah-rahs.

9. *¿Quién sa-be si ma-ña-na vol-ve-rás,*
kee‿ihn sah-beh see mah-nyah-nah vohl-veh-rahs,

10. *qué ha-rás,*
keh hah-rahs,

11. *no pen-sa-rás?*
noh pehn-sah-rahs?

12. *Yo sé que nun-ca vol-ve-rás,*
yoh seh keh noon-kah vohl-veh-rahs,

13. *más pien-so que*
mahs pee‿yehn-soh keh

14. *no vi-vi-ré*
noh bee-bee-ray

15. *co-mo po-dré.*
koh-moh poh-dreh.

Pronunciation Practice 4

La paloma se fué (The Dove that Flew Away)

Folk Song from Puerto Rico

Phrase

① *¿Se-ño-res no‿han vis-to*
seh-nyoh-rehs noh‿ahn vee-stoh

② *la pa-lo-ma que vo-ló del pa-lo-mar?*
lah pah-loh-mah keh voh-loh dehl pah-loh-mahrr?

③ *¿Se-ño-res no‿han vis-to*
seh-nyoh-rehs noh‿ahn vee-stoh

④ *la pa-lo-ma que vo-ló del pa-lo-mar?*
lah pah-loh-mah keh voh-loh dehl pah-loh-mahrr?

⑤ *Se fué la pa-lo-ma, se fué la pa-lo-ma,*
seh fweh lah pah-loh-mah, seh fweh lah pah-loh-mah,

⑥ *se fué pa-ra no vol-ver.*
seh fweh pah-rah noh vohl-vehrr.

⑦ *Se fué la pa-lo-ma, se fué la pa-lo-ma,*
seh fweh lah pah-loh-mah, seh fweh lah pah-loh-mah,

⑧ *se fué pa-ra no vol-ver.*
seh fweh pah-rah noh vohl-vehrr.

Pronunciation Practice 5

Adiós, amigos (Goodbye, My Friends)

Folk Song from New Mexico

Verse 1

Phrase

① *A-diós a-mi-gos,*
ah-dee‿ohs ah-mee-gohs,

② *que duer-man muy bien,*
keh dwehrr-mahn moo‿ee bee‿ehn,

③ *Que vie-nen los án-ge-les*
keh vee‿eh-nehn lohs ahn-heh-lehs

④ *pa-ra guar-dar.*
pah-rrah gwahrr-dahrr.

⑤ *A-diós, a-diós,*
ah-dee‿ohs, ah-dee‿ohs,

⑥ *a-diós, a-diós.*
ah-dee‿ohs, ah-dee‿ohs.

PRONUNCIATION PRACTICE 6

La mariposa (The Butterfly)

Folk Song from Bolivia

Chorus

Phrase

① *La la la la lai la lai la lai la lai lai lai lai lai,*
lah lah lah lah lah‿ee lah lah‿ee lah lah‿ee lah lah‿ee lah‿ee lah‿ee lah‿ee lah‿ee,

② *La la la la lai la lai la lai la lai la la la la la lai lai lai.*
lah lah lah lah lah‿ee lah lah‿ee lah lah‿ee lah lah‿ee lah lah lah lah lah lah‿ee lah‿ee lah‿ee.

Verse 1

Phrase

① *Al son de las ma-tra-cas*
ahl sohn deh lahs mah-trah-kahs

② *to-dos can-tan y bai-lan*
toh-thos kahn-tahn ee bah‿ee-lahn

③ *La mo-re-na-da.*
lah moh-reh-nah-dah.

④ *Con las pal-mas,*
kohn lahs pahl-mahs,

⑤ *Con los ta-cos.*
kohn lohs tah-kohs.

⑥ *¡Vi-va la fies-ta!*
vee-vah lah fyehs-tah!

Pronunciation Practice 7

Yü guang guang (Moonlight Lullaby)

Folk Song from Hong Kong

Phrase ① *Yü gwahng gwahng*
yew gwahng gwahng

② *tsee-oo day-ee tong*
tsee-oo day-ee tahng

③ *Hah tzai nay gwai gwai*
hah tzah‿ee neh gwah‿ee gwah‿ee

④ *fuhn lah-oo tchong*
fuhn lah-oo tchahng

⑤ *teeng dsee-yoo ah mah*
tehng tsee-yoo ah mah

⑥ *yee‿oo gong tsah(p) yong law*
yee‿oo gahng tsah pyoong law

⑦ *ah yeh tai ngow*
ah yeh tah‿een (n)yow

⑧ *koy tsü(ng) sahn gong.*
kuh‿ee tsuh(ng) sahn gahng.

PRONUNCIATION

Pronunciation Practice 8

Hava nashira (Sing and Be Joyful)

Round from Israel

Phrase ① *Ha-va na-shir-a, shir hal-le-lu-jah.*
hah-vah nah-shee-rah, sheer hah-leh-loo-yah.

② *Ha-va na-shir-a, shir hal-le-lu-jah.*
hah-vah nah-shee-rah, sheer hah-leh-loo-yah.

③ *Ha-va na-shir-a, shir hal-le-lu-jah.*
hah-vah nah-shee-rah, sheer hah-leh-loo-yah.

Pronunciation Practice 9

Dona nobis pacem

Traditional Canon

Phrase ① *Do-na no-bis pa-cem, pa-cem,*
doh-nah noh-bees pah-chehm, pah-chehm,

② *Do-na no-bis pa-cem.*
doh-nah noh-bees pah-chehm.

③ *Do-na no-bis pa-cem,*
doh-nah noh-bees pah-chehm,

④ *Do-na no-bis pa-cem.*
doh-nah noh-bees pah-chehm.

⑤ *Do-na no-bis pa-cem,*
doh-nah noh-bees pah-chehm,

⑥ *Do-na no-bis pa-cem.*
doh-nah noh-bees pah-chehm.

Pronunciation Practice 10

Lo yisa (Vine and Fig Tree)

Hebrew Words from the Book of Isaiah
Music by Shalom Altman

Verse 1

Phrase

① *Lo yi-sa goy el goy che-rev,*
loh yee-sah goy ehl goy hkheh-rehv,

② *Lo yil-m'-du od mil-cha-ma.*
loh yihl-muh-doo ohd mihl-hkhah-mah.

③ *Lo yi-sa goy el goy che-rev,*
loh yee-sah goy ehl goy hkheh-rehv,

④ *Lo yil-m'-du od mil-cha-ma.*
loh yihl-muh-doo ohd mihl-hkhah-mah.

⑤ *Lo yi-sa goy el goy che-rev,*
loh yee-sah goy ehl goy hkheh-rehv,

⑥ *Lo yil-m'-du od mil-cha-ma.*
loh yihl-muh-doo ohd mihl-hkhah-mah.

oy = as in b<u>oy</u>

Pronunciation Practice 11

El payo (The Cowpoke)

Folk Song from Mexico

Verse 1

Phrase

① *Es-ta-ba‿un pa-yo sen-ta-do.*
ehs-tah-bah‿oon pah-yoh sehn-tah-thoh.

② *En tran-cas de‿un co-rral;*
ehn trahn-kahs deh‿oon koh-rahl;

③ *Y‿el ma-yor-do-mo le di-jo,*
ee‿yehl mah-yohr-doh-moh leh dee-hoh,

④ *"No es-tés tris-te, Ni-co-lás."*
"noh ehs-tehs trees-teh, nee-koh-lahs."

PRONUNCIATION PRACTICE 11 (CONTINUED)

⑤ *"Si quie-res que no‿es-té tris-te*
"see kee‿eh-rehs keh noh‿ehs-teh trees-teh

⑥ *Lo que pi-da me‿has de dar."*
loh keh pee-tha meh‿ahs deh dahr."

⑦ *Y‿el ma-yor-do-mo le di-jo,*
ee‿yehl mah-yohr-doh-moh leh dee-hoh,

⑧ *"Ve pi-dien-do, Ni-co-lás."*
"veh pee-dee‿ehn-do, nee-koh-lahs."

Verse 2

Phrase ① *"Necesito treinta pesos,*
"neh-seh-see-toh treh‿een-tah peh-sohs,

② *Una cuera y un gabán."*
oon-ah koo‿eh-rah ee‿oon gah-bahn."

③ *Y‿el mayordomo le dijo,*
ee‿yehl mah-yohr-doh-moh leh dee-hoh,

④ *"No‿hay dinero, Ni-co-lás."*
"noh‿ah‿ee dee-neh-roh, nee-koh-lahs."

⑤ *"Ne-ce-si-to trein-ta pesos*
"neh-seh-see-toh treh‿een-tah peh-sohs

⑥ *Pa-ra po-der-me ca-sar."*
pah-rah poh-dehrr-meh kah-sahr."

⑦ *Y‿el ma-yor-do-mo le di-jo,*
ee‿yehl mah-yohr-doh-moh leh dee-hoh,

⑧ *"Ni‿un real ten-go, Ni-co-lás."*
"nee‿oon reh‿ahl tehn-goh, nee-koh-las."

Pronunciation Practice 12

Hava nagila

Jewish Folk Song

Phrase

① *Ha-va na-gi-la, ha-va na-gi-la,*
hah-vah nah-gee-lah, hah-vah nah-gee-lah,

② *ha-va na-gi-la, v'-nis-m'-cha.*
hah-vah nah-gee-lah, veh-nees-meh-hkhah.

③ *Ha-va n'-ra-n'-na, ha-va n'-ra-n'-na,*
hah-vah neh-rrah-neh-nah, hah-vah neh-rrah-neh-nah,

④ *ha-va n'-ra-n'-na, v'-nis-m'-cha.*
hah-vah neh-rrah-neh-nah, veh-nees-meh-hkhah.

⑤ *U-ru, u-ru a-chim,*
oo-roo, oo-roo ah-hkheem,

⑥ *u-ru a-chim b'-lev sa-me-ach, u-ru a-chim b'lev sa-me-ach,*
oo-roo ah-hkheem beh-lehv sah-meh-ahkh, oo-roo ah-hkheem beh-lehv sah-meh-ahkh,

⑦ *u-ru a-chim b'-lev sa-me-ach, u-ru a-chim b'lev sa-me-ach,*
oo-roo ah-hkheem beh-lehv sah-meh-ahkh, oo-roo ah-hkheem beh-lehv sah-meh-ahkh,

⑧ *u-ru a-chim, u-ru a-chim b'lev sa-me-ach.*
oo-roo ah-hkheem, oo-roo ah-hkheem beh-lehv sah-meh-ahkh.

PRONUNCIATION PRACTICE 13

O lê lê O Bahía (O Le O La)

Folk Song from Brazil

Phrase ① *Da Ba-hí-a me man-da-ram*
dah bah-ee-ah mee mahn-dah-rahm

② *O lê lê O Ba-hí-a*
oh leh leh oh bah-ee-ah

③ *Um ces-ti-nho de ca-já,*
oom sehs-tchee-nyoh djeh kah-zhah,

④ *O lê lê O Ba-hí-a*
oh leh leh oh bah-ee-ah

⑤ *E man-da-ram per-gun-tar*
ee mahn-dah-rahm pehr-goon-tahr

⑥ *O lê lê O Ba-hí-a,*
oh leh leh oh bah-ee-ah,

⑦ *Se eu que-ri-a me ca-sar.*
see oh kee‿eh-ree-ah mee kah-sahr.

⑧ *O lê lê O Ba-hí-a,*
oh leh leh oh bah-ee-ah,

⑨ *O le o la, O lê lê O Ba-hí-a,*
oh leh oh lah, oh leh leh oh bah-ee-ah,

⑩ *O le o la, O lê lê O Ba-hí-a.*
oh leh oh lah, oh leh leh oh bah-ee-ah.

Pronunciation Practice 14

Así es mi tierra (This Is My Land)

Words and Music by
Ignacío Fernandez Esperón

Phrase

① *A-sí‿es mi tie-rra,*
ah-see‿ehs mee tyeh-rrah,

② *mo-re-ni-ta‿y lu-mi-no-sa;*
moh-reh-nee-tah‿ee loo-mee-noh-sah;

③ *A-sí‿es mi tie-rra,*
ah-see‿ehs mee tyeh-rrah,

④ *tie-ne‿el al-ma‿he-cha de‿a-mor.*
tyeh-nehl ahl-mah‿eh-chah deh‿ah-mohr.

⑤ *A-sí‿es mi tie-rra,*
ah-see‿ehs mee tyeh-rrah,

⑥ *a-bun-dan-te‿y ge-ne-ro-sa;*
ah-boon-dahn-teh heh-neh-roh-sah;

⑦ *¡Ay, tie-rra mí-a*
ah‿ee, tyeh-rrah mee-ah

⑧ *co-mo‿es gra-to tu ca-lor!*
koh-moh‿ehs grah-toh too kah-lohr!

⑨ *Sus al-bo-ra-das*
suhs ahl-bor-rah-thahs

⑩ *tan lle-ni-tas, de‿a-le-grí-a.*
thahn yeh-nee-tahs, deh‿ah-leh-gree-ah.

⑪ *Sus se-re-na-tas*
suhs seh-reh-nah-tahs

⑫ *tan pro-pi-ci‿as al a-mor.*
thahn proh-pee-cee‿ahs ahl ah-mohr.

⑬ *A-sí‿es mi tie-rra,*
ah-see‿ehs mee tyeh-rrah,

⑭ *flor de la me-lan-co-lí-a.*
flohr deh lah meh-lahn-koh-lee-ah.

⑮ *¡Ay, tie-rra mí-a*
ah‿ee, tyeh-rrah mee-ah

⑯ *co-mo‿es gra-to tu ca-lor!*
koh-moh‿ehs grah-toh too kah-lohr!

PRONUNCIATION PRACTICE 15

Habemos llegado (We Have Arrived)

Folk Song from Puerto Rico

Verse 1

Phrase

① *Ha-be-mos lle-ga-do‿a su‿a-ma-do ho-gar.*
ah-beh-mohs djeh-gah-doh‿ah soo‿ah-mah-doh oh-gahrr.

② *Ha-be-mos lle-ga-do‿a su‿a-ma-do ho-gar.*
ah-beh-mohs djeh-gah-doh‿ah soo‿ah-mah-doh oh-gahrr.

③ *Con con-chas, con per-las, con bri-sas del mar;*
kohn kohn-chahs, kohn pehrr-lahs, kohn brree-sahs dehl mahrr;

④ *Con con-chas, con per-las, con bri-sas del mar.*
kohn kohn-chahs, kohn pehrr-lahs, kohn brree-sahs dehl mahrr.

Verse 2

Phrase

① *Oí-ga-me, se-ño-ra, le ven-go‿a can-tar.*
oh‿ee-gah-meh, seh-nyoh-rah, leh vehn-goh‿ah kahn-tahrr.

② *Oí-ga-me, se-ño-ra, le ven-go‿a can-tar.*
oh‿ee-gah-meh, seh-nyoh-rah, leh vehn-goh‿ah kahn-tahrr.

③ *Que‿es u-na pro-me-sa que quie-ro pa-gar;*
keh‿ehs oo-nah proh-meh-sah keh kyeh-roh pah-gahrr;

④ *Que‿es u-na pro-me-sa que quie-ro pa-gar.*
keh‿ehs oo-nah proh-meh-sah keh kyeh-roh pah-gahrr.

Pronunciation Practice 16

Siyahamba

Traditional Freedom Song from South Africa

Verse 1

Phrase

① *Si-ya-hamb'-e-ku-kha-nye-ni kwen-khos'.*
see-yah-hahm-beh-koo-khah-nyeh-nee kgwehn-kohs.

② *Si-ya-hamb'-e-ku-kha-nye-ni kwen-khos'.*
see-yah-hahm-beh-koo-khah-nyeh-nee kgwehn-kohs.

③ *Si-ya-hamb'-e-ku-kha-nye-ni kwen-khos'.*
see-yah-hahm-beh-koo-khah-nyeh-nee kgwehn-kohs.

④ *Si-ya-hamb'-e-ku-kha-nye-ni kwen-khos'.*
see-yah-hahm-beh-koo-khah-nyeh-nee kgwehn-kohs.

⑤ *Si-ya-ham-ba Si-ya-ham-ba*
see-yah-hahm-bah see-yah hahm-bah

⑥ *Si-ya-hamb'-e-ku-kha-nye-ni kwen-khos'.*
see-yah-hahm-beh-koo-khah-nyeh-nee kgwehn-kohs.

⑦ *Si-ya-ham-ba Si-ya-ham-ba*
see-yah-hahm-bah see-yah hahm-bah

⑧ *Si-ya-hamb'-e-ku-kha-nye-ni kwen-khos'.*
see-yah-hahm-beh-koo-khah-nyeh-nee kgwehn-kohs.

PRONUNCIATION PRACTICE 17

Ise oluwa

Yoruba Folk Song from Nigeria

Verse 1

Phrase

1. *I-se o-lu-wa*
   ee-sheh oh-loo-wah

2. *ko le ba-je-oh;*
   koh leh bah-jeh-oh;

3. *I-se o-lu-wa*
   ee-sheh oh-loo-wah

4. *ko le ba-je-oh.*
   koh leh bah-jeh-oh.

5. *Ko le ba-je-oh,*
   koh leh bah-jeh-oh,

6. *ko le ba-je-oh.*
   koh leh bah-jeh-oh.

7. *I-se o-lu-wa*
   ee-sheh oh-loo-wah

8. *ko le ba-je-oh.*
   koh leh bah-jeh-oh.

9. *I-se o-lu-wa*
   ee-sheh oh-loo-wah

10. *ko le ba-je-oh.*
    koh leh bah-jeh-oh.

Pronunciation Practice 18

Riendo el río corre (Run, Run, River)

Words and Music by Tish Hinojosa

Refrain

Phrase

① *Co-rre, co-rre,*
koh-rreh, koh-rreh,

② *co-rre‿el río,*
koh-rreh‿ehl ree‿oh,

③ *Ri-en-do‿el rí-o co-rre.*
ree-ehn-doh‿ehl rree-oh koh-rreh.

④ *Co-rre, co-rre,*
koh-rreh, koh-rreh,

⑤ *co-rre‿el río,*
koh-rreh‿ehl ree‿oh,

⑥ *Ri-en-do‿el rí-o co-rre.*
rree-ehn-doh‿ehl rree-oh koh-rreh.

Verse 1

Phrase

① *Cuén-ta-me de las mon-ta-ñas*
kwehn-tah-meh deh lahs mohn-tah-nyahs

② *de tu em-pe-sar,*
deh too ehm-peh-sahrr,

③ *Cuén-ta-me de pie-dra‿y pe-na*
kwehn-tah-meh deh pyeh-drah‿ee peh-nah

④ *que lle-vas al mar.*
keh djeh-vahs ahl mahrr.

Pronunciation Practice 18 (continued)

Verse 2

Phrase ① *Sa-bes tú de la dis-tan-cia*
sah-behs too-deh lah dees-tahn-see‿yah

② *que pien-sas al-can-zar,*
keh pyehn-sahs ahl-kahn-sahrr,

③ *Co-mo sue-ño de la lu-na*
koh-moh-sweh-nyoh deh lah loo-nah

④ *que me das pa-ra so-ñar.*
keh meh dahs pah-rah soh-nyahrr.

Refrain

Phrase ① *Co-rre, co-rre,*
koh-rreh, koh-rreh,

② *corre‿el río,*
koh-rreh‿ehl ree‿oh,

③ *Ri-en-do‿el rí-o co-rre.*
rree-ehn-doh‿ehl ree-oh koh-rreh.

④ *Co-rre, co-rre,*
koh-rreh, koh-rreh,

⑤ *corre‿el río,*
koh-rreh‿ehl ree‿oh,

⑥ *Ri-en-do‿el rí-o co-rre.*
rree-ehn-doh‿ehl ree-oh koh-rreh.

Pronunciation Practice 19

Banuwa

Folk Song from Liberia

Phrase

① *Ba-nu-wa, ba-nu-wa, ba-nu-wa yo.*
bah-noo-wah, bah-noo-wah, bah-noo-wah yoh.

② *Ba-nu-wa, ba-nu-wa, ba-nu-wa yo.*
bah-noo-wah, bah-noo-wah, bah-noo-wah yoh.

③ *Ba-nu-wa, ba-nu-wa, ba-nu-wa yo.*
bah-noo-wah, bah-noo-wah, bah-noo-wah yoh.

④ *A-la-no, neh-ni a-la-no.*
ah-lah-noh, neh-nee ah-lah-noh.

⑤ *A-la-no, neh-ni a-la-no.*
ah-lah-noh, neh-nee ah-lah-noh.

PRONUNCIATION PRACTICE 20

Má Teodora

Folk Song from Cuba

Unison and Melody

Phrase ① *¿Dón-de‿es-tá la Má Teo-do-ra?*
dohn-deh‿ehs-tah lah mah teh‿oh-doh-rah?

② *Rajando la le-ña‿es-tá.*
rah-hahn-doh lah leh-nyehs-tah.

③ *¿Con su pa-lo‿y su ban-do la?*
kohn soo pah-loh‿ee soo bahn-doh lah?

④ *Ra-jan-do la le-ña‿es-tá.*
rah-hahn-doh lah leh-nyehs-tah.

⑤ *¿Dón-de‿es-tá que no la ve-o?*
dohn-deh‿ehs-tah keh noh lah veh-oh?

⑥ *Ra-jan-do la le-ña‿es-tá.*
rah-hahn-doh lah leh-nyehs-tah.

⑦ *Ra-jan-do la le-ña‿es-tá.*
rah-hahn-doh lah leh-nyehs-tah.

⑧ *Ra-jan-do la le-ña‿es-tá.*
rah-hahn-doh lah leh-nyehs-tah.

Unison and Harmony

Phrase ① *¿Don-de‿es-tá la Má Teo-do-ra?*
dohn-deh‿ehs-tah lah mah teh‿oh-doh-rah?

② *Rajando la le-ña‿es-tá.*
rah-hahn-doh lah leh-nyehs-tah.

③ *¿Con su pa-lo‿y su ban-do-la?*
kohn soo pah-loh‿ee soo bahn-doh-lah?

④ *Ra-jan-do la le-ña‿es-tá.*
rah-hahn-doh lah leh-nyehs-tah.

⑤ *¿Don-de‿es-tá que no la ve-o?*
dohn-deh‿ehs-tah keh noh lah veh-oh?

⑥ *Ra-jan-do la le-ña‿es-tá.*
rah-hahn-doh lah leh-nyehs-tah.

⑦ *Ra-jan-do la le-ña‿es-tá.*
rah-hahn-doh lah leh-nyehs-tah.

⑧ *Ra-jan-do la le-ña‿es-tá.*
rah-hahn-doh lah leh-nyehs-tah.

Pronunciation Practice 21

Asadoya

Folk Song from Okinawa

Phrase ① *A A-sa-do-ya nu*
ah‿ah-sah-doo-yah noo

② *Ku-ya-ma ni yo*
koo-yah-mah nee yoh

③ *sa yu-i yu-i,*
sah yoo-ee yoo-ee,

④ *A-n chu-ra sa na*
ah-(n) choo-rah sah nah

⑤ *u-ma-ri ba-shi-o.*
oo-mah-ree bah-shee-oh.

⑥ *Ma-ta ha-ri-nu*
mah-tah hah-ree-noo

⑦ *chin-da-ra, ka-nu-sya-ma yo.*
cheen-dah-rah, kah-noo-shyah-mah yoh.

PRONUNCIATION PRACTICE 22

Alumot (Sheaves of Grain)

Harvest Song from Israel

Phrase ① *Ye-la-dim na-gi-la*
yeh-lah-deem! nah-gee-lah

② *ve-na-sov bim-cho-lot!*
veh-nah-sohv beem-hoh-loht!

③ *Shi-bo-lim hiv-shi-lu.*
shee-boh-leem heev-shee-loo.

④ *Ne´ e-sof a-lu-mot!*
neh heh-sohv ah-loo-moht!

⑤ *A-lu-mot shel za-hav,*
ah-loo-moht shehl zah-hahv,

⑥ *ha-sa-deh ra-chav, ra-chav.*
hah-sah-deh rah-hahv, rah-hahv.

⑦ *Ba-sa-deh u-va-nir,*
bah-sah-deh oo-vah-nihrr,

⑧ *shi-ru ze-mer la-ka-tsir!*
shee-rroo zeh-mehrr lah-kah-tsihrr!

Pronunciation Practice 23

Oye

By Jim Papoulis

Verse 1

Phrase

① *Es-tán só-los, llo-ran-do*
eh-stahn soh-lohs, djoh-rahn-doh

② *en si-len-cio, en la‿os-cu-ri-dad.*
ehn see-lehn-see-oh, ehn lah‿oh-skoo-ree-dahd.

③ *Es-tán so-ñan-do, de-se-an-do*
eh-stahn soh-nyahn-doh, deh-seh-ahn-doh

④ *con es-per-an-za, por la‿opp-or-tun-i-dad.*
kohn eh-speh-rahn-sah, pohrr lah‿oh-pohrr-too-nee-dahd.

⑤ *Es-cú-cha-los, es-cú-cha-los, ell-os te lla-man.*
ehs-koo-chah-lohs, ehs-koo-chah-lohs, eh-djohs teh djah-mahn.

Refrain

Phrase

① *Oye.*
oh-yeh.

Verse 2

Phrase

① *Es-cú-cha-los, mí-ra-los*
ehs-koo-chah-lohs, mee-rah-lohs

② *es-cu-cha lo que tra-tan de de-cir.*
ehs-koo-chah loh keh trah-tahn deh deh-seer.

③ *Es-tán en bús-que-da, del ca-mi-no*
eh-stahn ehn boo-skeh-dah, dehl kah-mee-noh

④ *pe-que-ñas vo-ces, lla-man-do-te.*
peh-keh-nyahs voh-sehs, djah-mahn-doh-teh.

Pronunciation Practice 24

Corta la caña (Head for the Canefields)

Folk Song from Puerto Rico

Phrase ① *Yo ven-go de mon-te‿a-den-tro*
yoh vehn-goh deh mohn-teh‿ah-dehn-troh

② *de cor-tar ca-ña, ca-ñe-ro,*
deh kohrr-tahrr kah-nyah, kah-nyeh-rroh,

③ *por más ca-ña que se cor-te*
pohrr mahs kah-nyah keh seh kohrr-teh

④ *nun-ca se ga-na‿el di-ne-ro.*
noon-kah seh gah-nah‿ehl dee-neh-rroh.

⑤ *To-do‿el mun-do la pro-cla-ma*
toh-doh‿ehl moon-doh lah proh-klah-mah

⑥ *que‿es muy fá-cil de cor-tar,*
keh‿ehs moo-ee fah-seel deh kohrr-tahr,

⑦ *cuan-do se ja-la la mo-cha*
kwahn-doh seh hah-lah lah moh-chah

⑧ *na-die quie-re tra-ba-jar.*
nah-dee‿eh kee‿eh-rreh trah-vah-hahrr.

⑨ *Cor-ta la ca-ña, ca-ñe-ro,*
kohrr-tah lah kah-nyah, ka-nyeh-rroh,

⑩ *cór-ta-la.*
kohrr-tah-lah.

⑪ *Cor-ta la ca-ña, ca-ñe-ro,*
kohrr-tah lah kah-nyah, ka-nyeh-rroh,

⑫ *cór-ta-la.*
kohrr-tah-lah.

Pronunciation Practice 25

Cuando pa' Chile me voy (Leavin' for Chile)

Cueca from Chile

Verse 1

Phrase

① *Cuan-do pa' Chi-le me voy,*
kwahn-doh pah chee-leh meh voi,

② *Cru-zan-do la cor-di-lle-ra,*
kroo-sahn-doh lah kohr-dee-yeh-rah,

③ *Cuan-do pa' Chi-le me voy,*
kwahn-doh pah chee-leh meh voi,

④ *Cru-zan-do la cor-di-lle-ra,*
kroo-sahn-doh lah kohr-dee-yeh-rah,

⑤ *La-te‿el co-ra-zón con-ten-to,*
lah-teh‿ehl koh-rah-sohn kohn-tehn-toh,

⑥ *Pues u-na chi-le-na me‿es-pe-ra.*
pwehs oo-nah chee-leh-nah meh‿ehs-peh-rah.

⑦ *La-te‿el co-ra-zón con-ten-to,*
lah-teh‿ehl koh-rah-sohn kohn-tehn-toh,

⑧ *Pues u-na chi-le-na me‿es-pe-ra.*
pwehs oo-nah chee-leh-nah meh‿ehs-peh-rah.

⑨ *Y cuan-do vuel-vo de Chi-le,*
ee kwahn-doh vwehl-voh deh chee-leh,

⑩ *En-tre ce-rros y que-bra-das,*
ehn-treh seh-rohs ee keh-brah-thahs,

⑪ *Y cuan-do vuel-vo de Chi-le,*
ee kwahn-doh vwehl-voh deh chee-leh,

⑫ *En-tre ce-rros y que-bra-das,*
ehn-treh seh-rohs ee keh-brah-thahs,

oy = as in b<u>oy</u>

Pronunciation Practice 25 (continued)

⑬ *La-te‿el co-ra-zón con-ten-to,*
lah-teh‿ehl koh-rah-sohn kohn-tehn-toh,

⑭ *Pues me‿es-pe-ra u-na cu-ya-na.*
pwehs meh‿es-peh-rah oo-nah koo-yah-nah.

⑮ *La-te‿el co-ra-zón con-ten-to,*
lah-teh‿ehl koh-rah-sohn kohn-tehn-toh,

⑯ *Pues me‿es-pe-ra u-na cu-ya-na.*
pwehs meh‿es-peh-rah oo-nah koo-yah-nah.

Refrain

Phrase ① *Vi-van el bai-le y la dan-za,*
vee-vahn ehl bI-leh ee lah dahn-sah,

② *vi-van la cue-ca‿y la zam-ba,*
vee-vahn lah kweh-kah‿ee lah sahm-bah,

③ *Dos pun-tas tie-ne‿el ca-mi-no*
dohs poon-tahs tyeh-neh‿ehl kah-mee-noh

④ *y‿en las dos al-guien me‿a-guar-da.*
ee‿ehn lahs dohs ahl-ghee‿yehn me‿ah-gwahr-thah.

⑤ *Dos pun-tas tie-ne‿el ca-mi-no*
dohs poon-tahs tyeh-neh‿ehl kah-mee-noh

⑥ *y‿en las dos al-guien me‿a-guar-da.*
ee‿ehn lahs dohs ahl-ghee‿yehn me‿ah-gwahr-thah.

Verse 2

Phrase ① *En Chi-le bai-lo la cue-ca,*
ehn chee-leh bI-loh lah kweh-kah,

② *En Cu-yo bai-lo la zam-ba,*
ehn koo-joh bI-loh lah sahm-bah,

③ *En Chi-le bai-lo la cue-ca,*
ehn chee-leh bI-loh lah kweh-kah,

Pronunciation Practice 25 (continued)

④ *En Cu-yo bai-lo la zam-ba,*
ehn koo-joh bI-loh lah sahm-bah,

⑤ *En Chi-le con las chi-le-nas,*
ehn chee-leh kohn lahs chee-leh-nahs,

⑥ *Con las o-tras en Ca-lin-ga-sta.*
kohn lahs oh-trahs ehn kah-leen-gah-stah.

⑦ *En Chi-le con las chi-le-nas,*
ehn chee-leh kohn lahs chee-leh-nahs,

⑧ *Con las o-tras en Ca-lin-ga-sta.*
kohn lahs oh-trahs ehn kah-leen-gah-stah.

⑨ *Vi-da trist, vi-da a-le-gre,*
vee-thah treest vee-thah ah-leh-greh,

⑩ *Es la vi-da del a-rri-er-o,*
ehs lah vee-thah dehl ah-rree-eh-roh,

⑪ *Vi-da trist, vi-da a-le-gre,*
vee-thah treest vee-thah ah-leh-greh,

⑫ *Es la vi-da del a-rri-e-ro,*
ehs lah vee-thah dehl ah-rree-eh-roh,

⑬ *Pe-ni-tas en el ca-mi-no,*
peh-nee-tahs ehn ehl kah-mee-noh,

⑭ *Y ri-sas al fin del sen-de-ro.*
ee ree-sahs ahl feen dehl sehn-deh-roh.

⑮ *Pe-ni-tas en el ca-mi-no,*
peh-nee-tahs ehn ehl kah-mee-noh,

⑯ *Y ri-sas al fin del sen-de-ro.*
ee ree-sahs ahl feen dehl sehn-deh-roh.

Refrain (Repeat)

PRONUNCIATION PRACTICE 26

Fais do do (Go to Sleep)

Acadian Folk Song

Vocal Part 1 (beginning at m.9)

Phrase ① *Fais do do, 'co-las mon p'tit frè-re,*
feh doh doh, koh-lah, mo(n) p'tee freh-ruh,

② *fais do do, t'au-ras du lo lo.*
feh doh doh, toh-rah doo loh loh.

③ *Ma-man est en haut*
mah-maw eh taw(n) oh

④ *qui fait des gâ-teaux,*
kee feh doo gah-toh,

⑤ *pa-pa est en bas qui fait du cho-co-lat.*
pah-paw eh taw(n) bah kee feh doo shah-koh-lah.

⑥ *Fais do do, 'co-las mon p'tit frè-re,*
feh doh doh, koh-lah mo(n) p'tee freh-ruh,

⑦ *fais do do, t'au ras du lo lo.*
feh doh doh, toh rah doo loh loh.

⑧ *pa-pa est en bas, qui fait du cho-co-lat.*
pah-paw eh taw(n) bah, kee feh doo shah-koh-lah.

⑨ *Oh, fais do do, 'co-las mon p'tit frè-re,*
oh feh doh doh, koh-lah mo(n) p'tee freh-ruh,

⑩ *Fais do do, t'au-ras du lo lo.*
feh doh doh, toh-rah doo loh loh.

Vocal Part 2 (beginning at m.9)

Phrase ① *Fais do do, 'co-las, mon p'tit frè-re,*
feh doh doh, koh-lah, mo(n) p'tee freh-ruh,

② *fais do do, t'au ras du lo lo.*
feh doh doh, toh rah doo loh loh.

Pronunciation Practice 26 (continued)

③ *Ma-man est en haut*
mah-maw eh taw(n) oh

④ *qui fait des gâ-teaux,*
kee feh doo gah-toh,

⑤ *pa-pa est en bas qui fait du cho-co-lat.*
pah-paw eh taw(n) bah kee feh doo shah-koh-lah.

⑥ *Fais do do, 'co-las mon p'tit frè-re,*
feh doh doh, koh-lah mo(n) p'tee freh-ruh,

⑦ *fais do do, t'au-ras du lo lo.*
feh doh doh, toh-rah doo loh loh.

⑧ *Ma-man est en haut*
mah-maw eh taw(n) oh

⑨ *qui fait des gâ-teaux,*
kee feh doo gah-toh,

⑩ *pa-pa, fait du cho-co-lat.*
pah-paw, feh doo shah-koh-lah.

⑪ *Oh, fais do do, t'au-ras du lo lo.*
oh, feh doh doh, toh-rah doo loh loh.

Vocal Part 3 (beginning at m.9)

Phrase ① *Fais do do, 'Co-las, mon p'tit frè-re,*
feh doh doh, koh-lah, mo(n) p'tee freh-ruh,

② *fais do do, t'au-ras du lo lo.*
feh doh doh, toh-rah doo loh loh.

③ *Ma-man est en haut*
mah-maw eh taw(n) oh

PRONUNCIATION PRACTICE 26 (CONTINUED)

④ *qui fait des gâ-teaux,*
kee feh doo gah-toh,

⑤ *pa-pa est en bas qui fait du cho-co-lat.*
pah-paw eh taw(n) bah kee feh doo shah-koh-lah.

⑥ *Fais do do, 'co-las mon p'tit frè-re,*
feh doh doh, koh-lah mo(n) p'tee freh-ruh,

⑦ *fais do do, t'au-ras du lo lo.*
feh doh doh, toh-rah doo loh loh.

⑧ *Ma-man est en haut,*
mah-maw eh taw(n) oh,

⑨ *qui fait des gâ-teaux,*
kee feh doo gah-toh,

⑩ *pa-pa est en bas qui fait du cho-co-lat.*
pah-paw eh taw(n) bah kee feh doo shah-koh-lah.

⑪ *Oh, fais do do, 'co-las mon p'tit frè-re,*
oh, feh doh doh, koh-lah mo(n) p'tee freh-ruh,

⑫ *fais do do, t'au-ras du lo lo.*
feh doh doh, toh-rah doo loh loh.

Pronunciation Practice 27

Shalom aleichem

Traditional Jewish Song

(Harmony)

Phrase ① *Sha-lom a-lei-chem mal-a-chei ha-sha-ret*
shah-lohm ah-leh-hkhehm mahl-ah-hkheh ah-shah reht

② *mal-a-chei el-yon*
mahl-ah-hkheh ehl-yohn

③ *mi me-lech mal-a-chei ham-la-chim*
mee meh-lehkh mahl-ah-hkheh hahm-lah-hkheem

④ *ha-ka-dosh ba-ruch hu*
hah-kah-dohsh bah-roohkh hoo

⑤ *Bo-a-chem l´-sha-lom*
boh-ah-hkhehm luh-shah-lohm

⑥ *mal-a-chei ha-sha-lom*
mahl-ah-hkheh hah-shah-lohm

⑦ *mal-a-chei el-yon*
mahl-ah-hkheh ehl-yohn

⑧ *mi-me-lech mal-a-chei ham-la-chim*
mee-meh-lehkh mahl-ah-hkheh hahm-lah-hkheem

⑨ *ha-ka-dosh ba-ruch hu*
hah-kah-dohsh bah-roohkh hoo

⑩ *Bo-a-chem bo-a-chem l´-sha-lom*
boh-ah-hkhehm boh-ah-hkhehm luh-shah-lohm

⑪ *mal-a-chei ha-sha-lom*
mahl-ah-hkheh hah-shah-lohm

⑫ *mal-a-chei el-yon*
mahl-ah-hkheh ehl-yohn

⑬ *mal-a-chei el-yon*
mahl-ah-hkheh ehl-yohn

⑭ *mi-me-lech mal-a-chei ham-la-chim*
mee meh-lehkh mahl-ah-hkheh hahm-lah-hkheem

⑮ *ha-ka-dosh ba-ruch hu*
hah-kah-dohsh bah-roohkh hoo

PRONUNCIATION PRACTICE 28

Cantaré, cantarás (I Will Sing, You Will Sing)

Words and Music by Albert Hammond and Juan Carlos Calderón

Verse 1

Phrase

1. *Te da-ré*
teh dah-reh
2. *cuan-to pue-do dar,*
kwahn-toh pweh-thoh dahr,
3. *Só-lo sé can-tar*
soh-loh seh kahn-tahr
4. *y pa-ra tí‿es mi can-to*
ee pah-rah tee‿ehs mee kahn-toh
5. *Y mi voz,*
ee mee vohs,
6. *Jun-to‿a los de-más,*
hoon-toh‿ah lohs deh-mahs,
7. *En la‿in-men-si-dad*
ehn lah‿een-mehn-see-thath
8. *se‿es-tá es-cu-chan-do.*
seh‿ehs-tah ehs-koo-chahn-doh.

Refrain

Phrase

1. *Can-ta-ré*
kahn-tah-reh
2. *can-ta-rás*
kahn-tah-rahs
3. *Y‿e-sa luz al fi-nal*
ee‿eh-sah loos ahl fee-nahl
4. *del sen-de-ro.*
dehl sehn-deh-roh.
5. *Bri-lla-rá*
bree-yah-rah
6. *co-mo‿un sol*
koh-moh‿oon sohl
7. *Que‿i-lu-mi-na el mun-do en-te-ro.*
keh‿ee-loo-mee-nah ehl moon-doh ehn-teh-roh.
8. *Ca-da vez*
kah-thah vehs
9. *so-mos más*
soh-mohs mahs
10. *Y si‿al fin nos da-mos la ma-no*
ee see‿ahl feen nohs dah-mohs lah mah-noh
11. *Siem-pre‿ha-brá*
see‿ehm-preh ah-brah
12. *un lu-gar*
oon loo-gahr
13. *Pa-ra to-do ser hu-ma-no.*
pah-rah toh-doh sehr oo-mah-noh.

Pronunciation Practice 29

Vem kan segla? (Who Can Sail?)

Folk Song from Finland

PART 1

Verse 1

Phrase ① *Vem kan seg-la,*
vehm kahn see-gklah,

② *vem kan skil-jas*
vehm kahn sheel-ee‿yahs

③ *u-tan tå-rar?*
yew-tahn toh-rahrr?

Verse 2

Phrase ① *Jag kan seg-la,*
yahg kahn see-gklah,

② *men ej skil-jas*
mehn eh sheel-ee‿yahs

③ *u-tan tå-rar.*
yew-tahn toh-rahrr.

PART 2

Verse 1

Phrase ① *Vem kan seg-la för-u-tan vind,*
vehm kahn see-gklah fehr-yew-tahn veend,

② *vem kan ro u-tan å-ror?*
vehm kahn roo yew-tahn oh-roorr?

③ *vem kan skil-jas från vän-nen sin*
vehm kahn sheel-ee‿yahs frahn vehn-nehn seen

④ *u-tan att fäl-la tå-rar?*
yew-tahn aht fehl-lah toh-rahrr?

Pronunciation Practice 29 (continued)

Verse 2

Phrase

① *Jag kan seg-la för-u-tan vind,*
yahgk kahn see-gklah fohr-yew-tahn veend,

② *jag kan ro u-tan å-ror,*
yahgk kahn roh yew-tahn oh-roorr,

③ *men ej skil-jas från vän-nen min*
mehn eh sheel-ee‿yahs frohn vehn-nehn meen

④ *u-tan att fäl-la tå-rar.*
yew-tahn aht fehl-lah toh-rahrr.

PART 3

Verse 1

Phrase

① *Vem kan seg-la og*
vehm kahn see-gklah oh

② *vem kan ro u-tan å-ror?*
vehm kahn roo yew-tahn oh-roorr?

③ *vem kan, vem kan skil-jas*
vehm kahn, vehm kahn sheel-ee‿yahs

④ *för-u-tan fäll-da tå-rar?*
fehr-yew-tahn fehl-dah toh-rahrr?

Pronunciation Practice 29 (continued)

Verse 2

Phrase

① *Jag kan seg-la og*
yahgk kahn see-gklah oh

② *jag kan ro u-tan å-ror,*
yahgk kahn roh yew-tahn oh-roorr,

③ *men ej, men ej skil-jas*
mehn eh, mehn eh sheel-ee‿yahs

④ *för-u-tan fäll-da tå-rar.*
fohr-yew-tahn fehl-dah toh-rahrr.

PRONUNCIATION PRACTICE 30

Loigratong

Folk Song from Thailand

Phrase ① *Wan pen deup sip song*
wahn peh(n) duhp sihp sahng

② *nam gau nong tem ta-ling*
nahm goh nahng tehm tah-leeng

③ *rao tang lai chai ying*
rah‿ow tahng lah‿ee shah‿ee yeeng

④ *sa-nook gan-jing wan loi-gra-tong*
sah-nook gahn-jeeng wahn loy-krah-tuhng

⑤ *loi loi-gra-tong loi loi-gra-tong*
loy loy-krah-tuhng loy loy-krah-tuhng

⑥ *loi-gra-tong gan lah-ow*
loy-krah-tuhng gahn lah-ow

⑦ *koh churn nong kay‿oh ock ma lum wong*
koh chuhrn nahng key‿oh ohk mah luhm wahng

⑧ *lum wong wan loi-gra-tong lum wong wan loi-gra-tong*
luhm wahng wahn loy-krah-tuhng luhm wahng wahn loy-krah-tuhng

⑨ *boon ja song hey rao sook jai*
boon jah sahng heh‿ee rah‿ow sook jah‿ee

⑩ *boon ja song hey rao sook jai*
boon jah sahng heh‿ee rah‿ow sook jah‿ee

oy = as in b<u>oy</u>

Pronunciation Practice 31

S´vivon (Dreydl)

Hebrew Words by L. Kipnis
Folk Song from Israel

Phrase ① *S´-vi-von, sov, sov, sov,*
seh-vee-vahn, sahv, sahv, sahv,

② *Cha-nu-kah hu-chag tov.*
hah-noo-kah hoo-hkhahg tahv.

③ *Cha-nu-kah hu chag tov,*
hkhah-noo-kah hoo-hkhahg tahv,

④ *S´-vi-von sov, sov, sov.*
seh-vee-vahn sahv, sahv, sahv.

⑤ *Chag sim-chah hu la am*
hahg seem-hkhah hoo lah ahm

⑥ *nes ga-dol ha-ya sham.*
nehs gah-dohl hah-yah shahm.

⑦ *nes ga-dol ha-ya sham,*
nehs gah-dohl hah-yah shahm,

⑧ *chag sim-chah hu la am.*
hkhahg seem-hkhah hoo lah ahm.

PRONUNCIATION PRACTICE 32

Gloria, Gloria

Music by Franz Joseph Haydn

Part 1

Phrase
1. *Glo-ri-a, Glo-ri-a*
   gloh-ree-ah, gloh-ree-ah
2. *in ex-cel-sis Glo-ri-a*
   een ex-shehl-sees gloh-ree-ah
3. *Et in ter-ra*
   eht een tehr-rah
4. *pax ho-mi-ni-bus.*
   pahx oh-mee-nee-boos.

Part 2

Phrase
1. *Glo-ri-a, Glo-ri-a*
   gloh-ree-ah, gloh-ree-ah
2. *in ex-cel-sis Glo-ri-a*
   een ex-shehl-sees gloh-ree-ah
3. *Et in ter-ra*
   eht een tehr-rah
4. *pax ho-mi-ni-bus.*
   pahx oh-mee-nee-boos.

Part 3

Phrase
1. *Glo-ri-a, Glo-ri-a*
   gloh-ree-ah, gloh-ree-ah
2. *in ex-cel-sis Glo-ri-a*
   een ex-shehl-sees gloh-ree-ah
3. *Et in ter-ra*
   eht een tehr-rah
4. *pax ho-mi-ni-bus.*
   pahx oh-mee-nee-boos.

Pronunciation Practice 33

Eres tú (Touch the Wind)

Music by Juan Carlos Calderón

Verse 1

Phrase ① *Co-mo‿u-na pro-me-sa, e-res tú, e-res tú.*
koh-moh‿oo-nah proh-meh-sah, eh-rehs too, eh-rehs too.

② *Co-mo‿u-na ma-ña-na, de ve-ra-no.*
koh-moh‿oo-nah mah-nyah-nah, deh veh-rah-noh.

③ *Co-mo‿u-na son-ri-sa, e-res tú, e-res tú,*
koh-moh‿oo-nah sohn-rhee-sa, eh-rehs too, eh-rehs too,

④ *A-sí, a-sí, e-res tú.*
ah-see, ah-see, eh-rehs too.

Verse 2

Phrase ① *To-da mi‿es-pe-ran-za, e-res tú, e-res tú.*
toh-thah mee‿ehs-peh-rahn-sah, eh-rehs too, eh-rehs too.

② *Co-mo llu-via‿fres-ca en mis ma-nos.*
koh-moh yoo-vee‿ah frehs-kah ehn mees mah-nohs.

③ *Co-mo fuer-te bri-sa, e-res tú, e-res tú,*
koh-moh fwehr-teh bree-sah, eh-rehs too, eh-rehs too,

④ *a-sí, a-sí, e-res tú.*
ah-see, ah-see, eh-rehs too.

Refrain

Phrase ① *E-res tú,*
eh-rehs too,

② *co-mo‿el a-gua de mi fuen-te.*
koh-moh‿ehl ah-gwah deh mee fwehn-teh.

③ *E-res tú,*
eh-rehs too,

④ *el fue-go de mi‿ho-gar.*
ehl fweh-goh deh mee‿oh-gahr.

Pronunciation Practice 33 (continued)

Melody only

Phrase ① *E-res tú,*
eh-rehs too,

② *co-mo‿el fue-go de mi‿ho-gue-ra.*
koh-moh‿ehl fweh-goh deh mee‿oh-gahr.

③ *E-res tú,*
eh-rehs too,

④ *el tri-go de mi pan.*
ehl tree-goh deh mee pahn.

Verse 3

Phrase ① *Co-mo mi po-e-ma, e-res tú, e-res tú.*
koh-moh mee poh-eh-mah, eh-rehs too, eh-rehs too.

② *Co-mo‿u-na gui-ta-rra en la no-che.*
koh-moh‿oo-nah ghee-tah-rrah ehn lah noh-cheh.

③ *Co-mo mi ho-ri-zon-te, e-res tú, e-res tú,*
koh-moh mee oh-ree-zohn-teh, eh-rehs too, eh-rehs too,

④ *a-sí, a-sí, e-res tú.*
ah-see, ah-see, eh-rehs too.

Refrain

Phrase ① *E-res tú,*
eh-rehs too,

② *co-mo‿el a-gua de mi fuen-te,*
koh-moh‿ehl ah-gwah deh mee fwehn-teh,

③ *E-res tú,*
eh-rehs too,

Pronunciation Practice 33 (continued)

④ *el fue-go de mi‿ho-gar.*
ehl fweh-goh deh mee‿oh-gahr.

Countermelody Only

Phrase ① *Al-go‿a-sí e-res tú,*
ahl-goh‿ah-see eh-rehs too,

② *oo*
oo

③ *Al-go‿a-sí, co-mo‿el fue-go*
ahl-goh‿ah-see, koh-moh‿ehl fweh-goh

④ *de mi‿ho-gue-ra.*
deh mee‿oh-geh-rrah.

⑤ *Al-go‿a-sí e-res tú,*
ahl-goh‿ah-see eh-rehs too,

⑥ *oo*
oo

⑦ *Sí, al-go‿a-sí e-res tú,*
see, ahl-goh‿ah-see eh-rehs too,

PRONUNCIATION PRACTICE 34

Las mañanitas

Folk Song from Mexico

Phrase ① *Es-tas son las ma-ña-ni-tas*
ehs-tahs sohn lahs mah-nyah-nee-tahs

② *Que can-ta-ba‿el Rey Da-vid,*
keh kahn-tah-bah‿ehl reh dah-veed,

③ *A las mu-cha-chas bo-ni-tas*
ah lahs moo-chah-chahs boh-nee-tahs

④ *Se las can-ta-mos a-quí.*
seh lahs kahn-tah-mohs ah-kee.

⑤ *Des-pier-ta, mi bien, des-pier-ta,*
dehs pyehr-tah, mee byehn, dehs-pyehr-tah,

⑥ *Mi-ra que ya‿a-ma-ne-ció;*
mee-rah keh yah‿ah-mah-neh-see‿oh;

⑦ *Ya los pa-ja-ri-llos can-tan,*
yah lohs pah-hah-ree-yohs kahn-tahn,

⑧ *La lu-na ya se me-tió.*
lah loo-nah yah seh meh-tee‿oh.

Pronunciation Practice 35

El carnavalito humahuaqueño (The Little Humahuacan Carnival)

Folk Song from Argentina

Phrase ① *Lle-gan-do‿es-tá‿el car-na-val,*
djeh-gahn-doh‿ehs-tah‿ehl kahr-nah-vahl,

② *que-bra-de-ño mi cho-li-ta.*
keh-brah-deh-nyoh mee choh-lee-tah.

③ *Lle-gan-do‿es-tá‿el car-na-val,*
djeh-gahn-doh‿ehs-tah‿ehl kahr-nah-vahl,

④ *que-bra-de-ño mi cho-li-ta.*
keh-brah-deh-nyoh mee choh-lee-tah.

⑤ *Fies-ta de la que-bra-da*
fyeh-stah deh lah keh-brah-thah

⑥ *hu-ma-hua-que-ña pa-ra can-tar.*
oo-mah-wah-keh-nyah pah-rah kahn-tahr.

⑦ *Er-que, cha-ran-go‿y bom-bo*
ehr-keh, chah-rahn-goh‿ee bohm-boh

⑧ *car-na-val-i-to pa-ra bai-lar.*
kahr-nah-vah-lee-toh pah-rah bah‿ee-lahr.

⑨ *Bom-bo-ro bom-bom, bom-bo-ro bom-bom, bom-bo-ro bom bom bom.*
bohm-boh-roh bohm-bohm, bohm-boh-roh bohm-bohm, bohm-boh-roh bohm bohm bohm.

Pronunciation Practice 36

Phonetic Pronunciation for Choral Singing of Non-English Songs

ah	as in father
ah‿ee	as in light (diphthong; a long *ah* sound with a hint of *ee* at close)
aw	as in awe
eh‿ee	as in day (diphthong; a long *eh* sound with a hint of *ee* at close)
b	as in button
ch	as in church
d	as in dad
dj	as in judge
ee	as in seed
eh	as in let
ew	used for French u (pronounce a bright *ee* and round the lips as if to whistle)
f	as in face
g	as in goat
h	as in hat
hkh	guttural, aspirant h of German, Hebrew ch, and Spanish j
ih	as in fit
I	as in light (a harsh *i* sound, where possible an *ah‿ee* has been suggested for singing the I sound)
k	as in kite
l	as in let
ll	prolonged l sound
m	as in man
(m)	French nasal m, not articulated as a distinct letter but as an open nasal sound
n	as in note
(n)	French nasal n, not articulated as a distinct letter, but as an open nasal sound
(ng)	as in sang (sometimes sounded as a prolonged nasal tone)
oh	as in tone
oo	as in spoon
ow	as in powder
p	as in pat
r	as in ran
(r)	as in turn (combined with another vowel sound in German)
rr	rolled r
rrrr	extended trilled r
s	as in song
t	as in tell
th	as in that
thh	as in feather
uh	as in up
v	as in van
w	as in way
wh	as in what
y	as in yes (not a vowel sound)
z	as in zone
zh	as in azure

Teacher Notes

Assessment

Table of Contents

Assessment

Name ______________________ Class ____________

Assessment 1: Unit 1

Show What You Know!

Show what you know about rhythm. Perform this counter-rhythm as you sing the song *Bắt kim thang* on the syllable *loo*.

Show What You Know!

Create movements that follow the melodic contour to "Gonna Build a Mountain." Then have the class perform your movements with the song.

Name ______________________ Class ______________

Assessment 1: Unit 1

Review, Assess, Perform, Create

What Do You Know?

1. For each term on the left, circle the type of musical expression on the right.

Performance	**Musical Expression**	
a. fast	dynamics	tempo
b. loud	dynamics	tempo
c. soft	dynamics	tempo
d. slow	dynamics	tempo

2. Circle the downbeats in this rhythm. How many downbeats are there? Underline the pickups (anacrusis) in this rhythm. How many pickups are there?

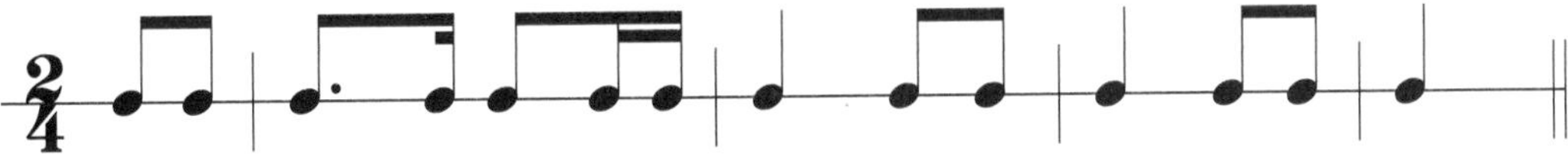

Assessment

Name ______________________ Class ______________

ASSESSMENT 1: UNIT 1 (CONTINUED)

What Do You Hear? 1A Vocal Timbre

Listen to these recordings of vocal timbres. Identify the correct vocal performance for each selection. Write your answers in the blanks provided.

Excerpt	**Vocal Performance**
1. ________	**a.** opera chorus
2. ________	**b.** women's "barbershop" chorus
3. ________	**c.** Tibetan monks of Central Asia
4. ________	**d.** boys' choir
5. ________	**e.** men's and women's chorus of Tahiti
6. ________	**f.** sacred harp singing

What Do You Hear? 1B Form

Listen to the recording of "Lean on Me." Circle the correct form for the selection, using the form symbols on the right.

Form	**Form Symbols**
a. ABBA	**A** Verse
b. BABA	**B** Refrain
c. ABAB	

Name ______________________ Class ______________________

Assessment 1: Unit 1 (continued)

What You Can Do

Sing Melodic Patterns

Using pitch syllables, read and perform these melodic patterns.

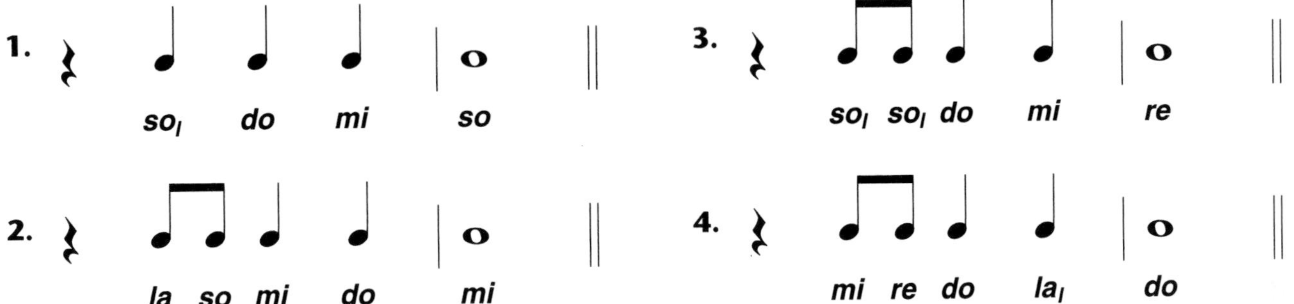

Play and Create Textures with Ostinatos

Select and perform one of the ostinatos for "Hey, Ho! Nobody Home" on page 29. Then, create a new ostinato and notate it on the staff below. When ready, perform your ostinato as a new texture to the song.

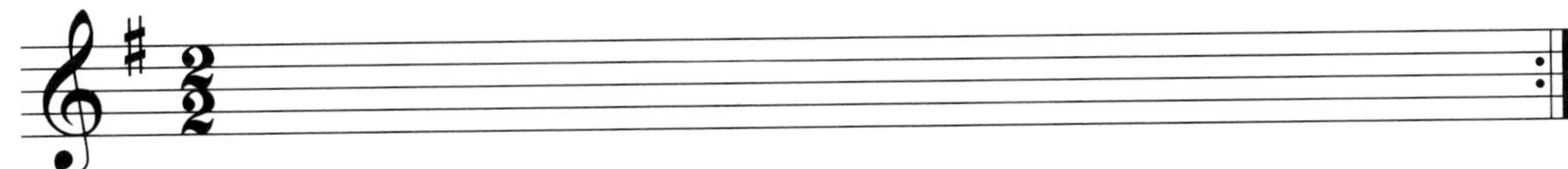

Assessment

Name ______________________ Class ______________

Assessment 2: Unit 2

Show What You Know!

Read and clap these patterns using rhythm syllables. Then find one pattern used in "Farewell to Tarwathie," on page 43, and one pattern used in "Barb'ry Allen," on page 44.

1.

2.

3.

4.

5. 

6. 

7.

8.

Show What You Know!

Create rhythm patterns using the notes in the scales below. Play these patterns on a mallet instrument. Label the scales "major" or "minor." Write and label the major and minor scales on the staves below.

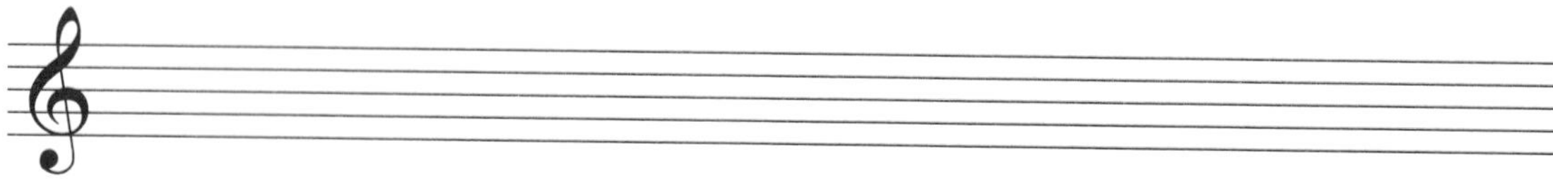

Name ______________________ Class ______________________

Assessment 2: Unit 2 (continued)

Review, Assess, Perform, Create

What Do You Know?

1. For the following terms, match the Italian term to the correct definition. Write the correct answer in the blanks provided next to the definition. Then, write the symbol for each term in the space provided to the right of the term.

Vocabulary	**Definition**
a. *mezzo forte* = _______	_________ very soft
b. *piano* = _______	_________ loud
c. *pianissimo* = _______	_________ very loud
d. *forte* = _______	_________ moderately soft
e. *mezzo piano* = _______	_________ soft
f. *fortissimo* = _______	_________ moderately loud

2. Look at the notation for the songs below. Circle the name of the scale on which each melody is based. Identify *do* in each song and write your answers in the blanks provided.

Song	**Page**	**Scale**	**Tonic**
a. *"Adiós, amigos"*	57	Major or Minor	*do* = _______
b. *"El condor pasa"*	46	Major or Minor	*do* = _______
c. *"La mariposa"*	58	Major or Minor	*do* = _______
d. "Farewell to Tarwathie"	43	Major or Minor	*do* = _______

What Do You Hear? 2A Texture/Harmony

Listen to the recording and melodic themes of Bizet's *Farandole* on page 68. For each selection, select the melodic themes that you hear from the list on the right and write your answers in the blanks provided.

Excerpt	**Melodic Themes**
1. _________	**a.** theme 1
2. _________	**b.** theme 2
3. _________	**c.** themes 1 & 2
4. _________	

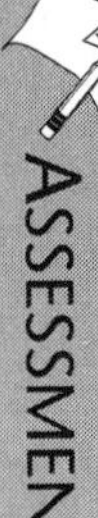

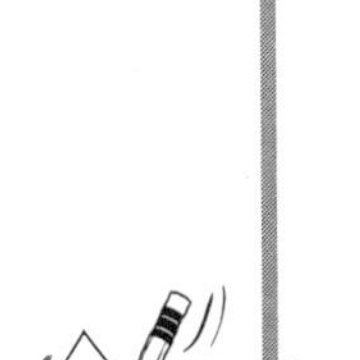

Name ______________________ Class ____________

Assessment 2: Unit 2 (continued)

What Do You Hear? 2B Timbre

Listen to two recordings of *What a Wonderful World.* As you listen, select the words that describe the timbres of the voices and instruments on the recordings from the list on the right. Write your answers in the blanks provided.

Excerpt

1. ____________

2. ____________

Timbre

a. smooth violins

b. piano

c. trumpet

d. soft guitar

e. buzzy voice

f. mellow drums

g. clear voice

h. children's voices

What You Can Do

Move to Show Form

Analyze and describe the form of "*El condor pasa,*" page 46. Create two movements (A and B) that go with the song. Perform the movements to accompany each section of the song.

Read and Play Rhythms in Meter in 3

Follow the notation of "Farewell to Tarwathie," page 43, and conduct the beat in meter in 3. Play the rhythms in the song on a nonpitched rhythm instrument. Create new rhythms in meter in 3 that can be performed with the song. Notate the rhythms on the staves below.

$\frac{3}{4}$ ____

$\frac{3}{4}$ ____

Name ______________________________ Class ______________________

ASSESSMENT 3: UNIT 3

Show What You Know!

Follow these directions to show what you know about augmentation and diminution.

1. Conduct and say the rhythm syllables for the pattern notated below.

2. Conduct and say the syllables for a rhythmic augmentation of this pattern. Write your augmentation below. See Resource Book p. J-17 for additional manuscript paper.

3. Conduct and say the syllables for rhythmic diminution of this pattern. Write your diminution below.

augmentation ______________________________

diminution ______________________________

Here is the motive used in the song "I Got Rhythm."

1. How many times is it used in the piece? ______________

2. What happens to the melody of the motive in measures 3 and 4? ______________

Using a keyboard or other melody instrument, play the four notes used in the motive—D, E, G, and A. Create your own motive by adding a new rhythm to these same notes. Write your motive on the staff below.

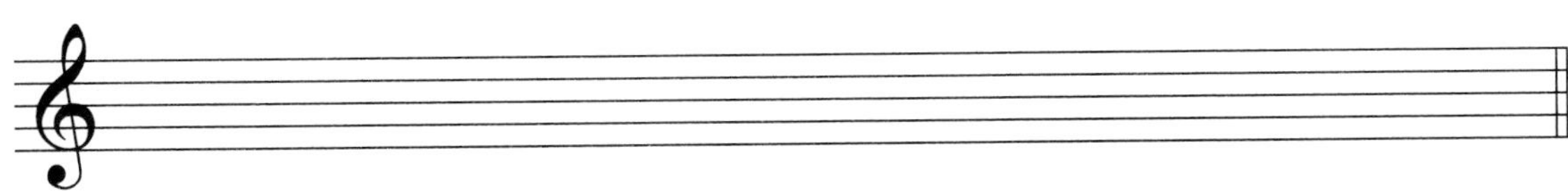

ASSESSMENT

Name ______________________________ Class ______________

Assessment 3: Unit 3 (continued)

Review, Assess, Perform, Create

What Do You Know?

1. Match each vocabulary word to its correct definition. Write the correct answer in the blanks provided next to the definition. Then draw the musical symbols to the right of the dynamic terms.

Vocabulary	**Definition**
a. *crescendo* = _______	_________ a short musical idea
b. *sforzando* = _______	_________ gradually getting louder
c. *decrescendo* = _______	_________ suddenly loud
d. motive = _______	_________ gradually getting softer

2. Look at the rhythms below. Circle the rhythm on the right that is the augmentation of the rhythm in the left column.

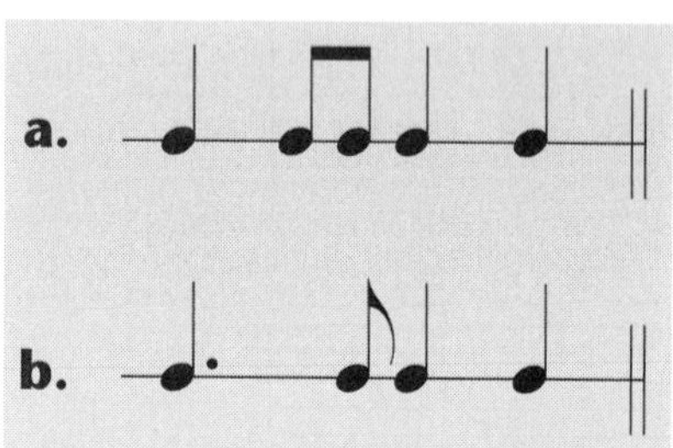

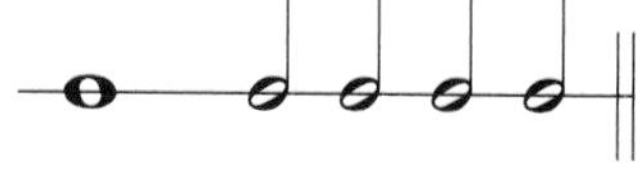

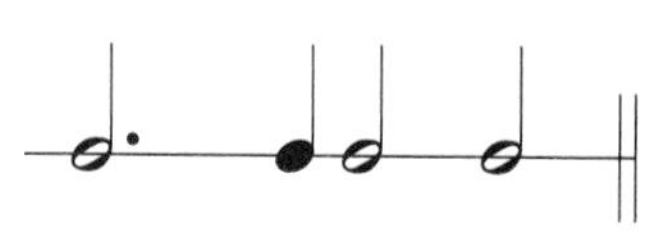

3. Look at the rhythms below. Circle the rhythm on the right that is the diminution of the rhythm in the left column.

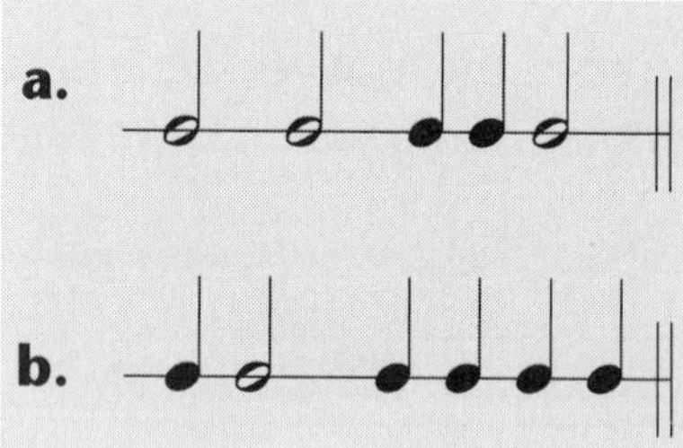

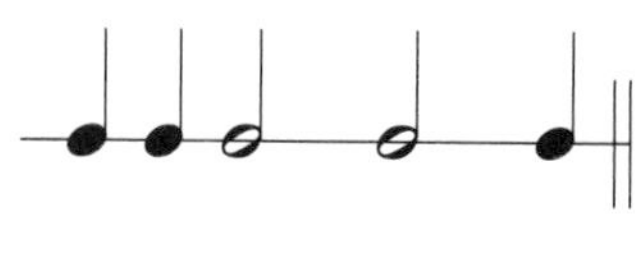

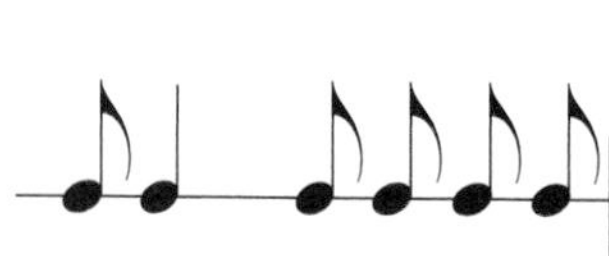

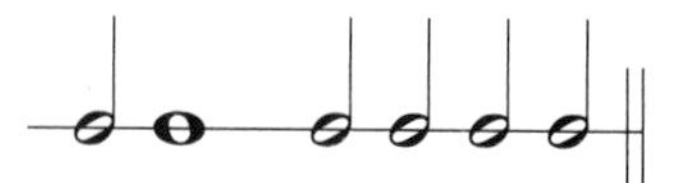

Name ______________________ Class ______________________

Assessment 3: Unit 3 (continued)

What Do You Hear? 3 **Timbre**

Listen to these examples of string instruments playing. For each selection, identify which techniques of producing sound are used by placing a check mark in the correct column. Selections may use more than one string technique.

String Techniques				
Excerpt	Bowing *(arco)*	Strumming	Plucking *(pizzicato)*	Tremolo
1. *Symphony No. 5*				
2. *The Moon Mirrored in the Pool*				
3. *Shchedryk*				
4. *Concerto No. 2, "Summer"*				

Assessment

Name ______________________ Class ____________

ASSESSMENT 3: UNIT 3 (CONTINUED)

What You Can Do

Show Form with Movement

Listen to the song "Bridges," page 86. Identify the form of the song using letter names **a** and **b**. Create a movement for each letter name and then perform the movements to the appropriate phrases of the song.

Sing Modes

Sing "Harrison Town" on page 97 using pitch syllables. Use *ta* to indicate the flatted seventh of the scale. Then, sing the song with lyrics using hand signs each time you sing the motive *ta-la-so*. Notate and label the motive *ta-la-so* in the key of C major on the staff below.

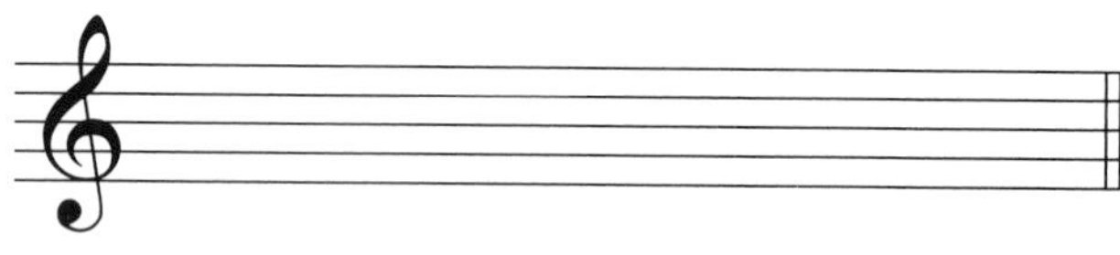

Sing Textures

As a class, sing "Going upon the Mountain" on page 105. Form small groups and perform the countermelodies as the class sings the song. As a challenge, sing "Harrison Town" as a countermelody to "Going upon the Mountain."

Name ____________________ Class ____________________

ASSESSMENT 4: UNIT 4

Show What You Know!

Play these rhythm patterns. Tap the beat note and identify the type of meter (simple or compound). Circle your answer. Then sing the melody using pitch syllables.

a. simple or compound

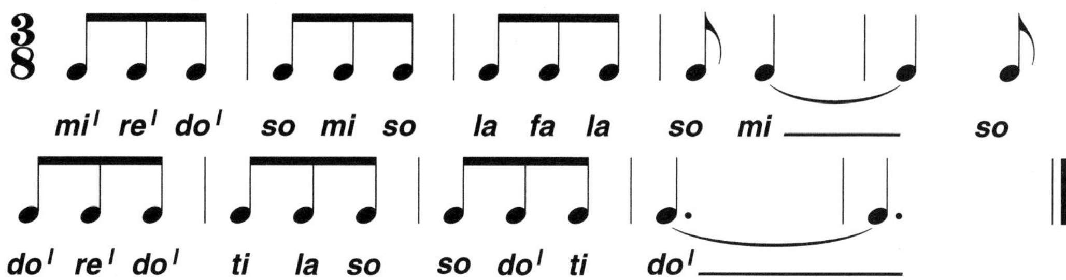

b. simple or compound

Show What You Know!

Find this motive in "Strike Up the Band" and identify the sequences based on this motive. Create one additional sequence for this motive.

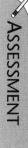

ASSESSMENT

Name ______________________________ Class ______________

Assessment 4: Unit 4 (continued)

What Do You Know?

Match the notation on the left with the correct definition or symbol on the right. Write the letters of the correct answers in the blanks provided.

Notation

1. ________ ♫ ♩ ♫

2. ________ $\frac{4}{4}$

3. ________ $\frac{2}{2}$

4. ________ ♪♪♪ ♩. ♪♪♪

Definition/Symbol

a. 𝄴

b. simple meter

c. compound meter

d. 𝄵

What Do You Hear? 4A Form

Listen to the following selections. Identify the term in the right column that best describes the form of the selection. Write the letters of the correct answers in the blanks provided.

Selection

1. ________ "Dance for the Nations"

2. ________ *Canon for Violin and Cello*

3. ________ "Barb'ry Allen"

4. ________ *"Little" Organ Fugue in G Minor*

Form

a. verse form (ballad form)

b. fugue

c. round

d. canon

Name ______________________________ Class ______________________________

Assessment 4: Unit 4 (continued)

Timbre

Listen to the timbre of these selections and match each with the correct musical ensemble. Write the letters of the correct answer in the blanks provided.

Selection	Musical Ensemble
1. ________ *Suite No. 2 in F*	**a.** big band
2. ________ *The Stars and Stripes Forever*	**b.** concert band
3. ________ "Alexander's Ragtime Band"	**c.** polka band
4. ________ *Kerenski*	

What You Can Do

Sing with Expression

As a class, sing "Swanee," page 118, with the recording. Follow the notation and conduct a two-beat pattern. Sing the song without the recording at a slow tempo, and then again at a fast tempo. Circle the correct Italian terms below for "slow" and "fast."

moderato *adagio* *prestissimo* *allegro*

Sing Sequences

Sing the melody of "Alleluia," page 133. Perform small steady-beat movements as you sing. Find the melodic sequence in the second line of the music. Is this sequence ascending or descending? Circle your answer.

ascending descending

Play Chords

Play the D and A chords on guitar or keyboard. Sing "Give a Little Love," page 140, with the recording. Add harmony by playing the accompaniment part on guitar or keyboard with the recording. Play the chords accurately and in time with the song.

Name ____________________ Class ____________

ASSESSMENT 5: UNIT 5

Show What You Know!

Perform these syncopated rhythms. Then, create your own eight-beat syncopated rhythm and perform it on a percussion instrument of your choice.

1.

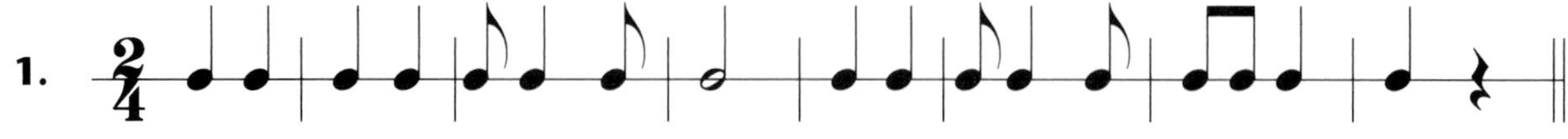

2.

Show What You Know!

Notate the E-major scale on the staff below. Then, play it on a keyboard or other instrument. Identify each of these intervals: second, third, fourth, fifth, and octave. Draw brackets and label each interval.

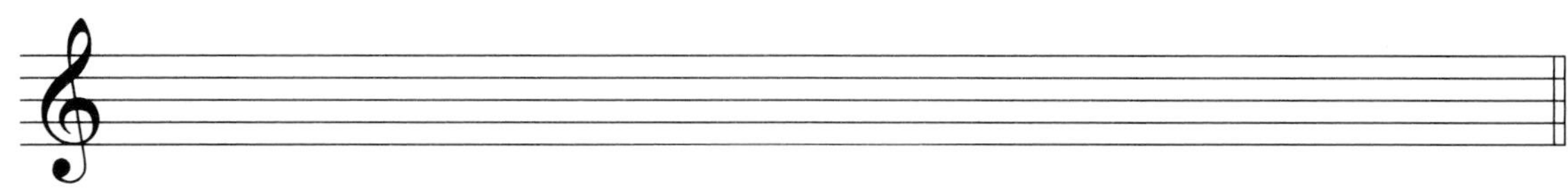

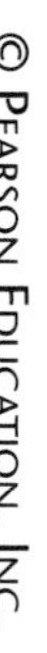

Name ______________________ Class ______________________

ASSESSMENT 5: UNIT 5 (CONTINUED)

Review, Assess, Perform, Create

What Do You Know?

1. Read the rhythms below. Circle the rhythms that contain syncopation.

a.

b. 

c. 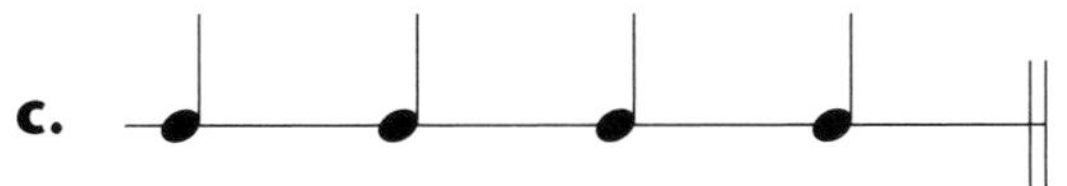

d. 

e. 

f. 

2. Select the correct term for each musical interval. Write the answers underneath the notated intervals in the blanks provided.

octave fifth fourth third second

a. ________ **b.** ________ **c.** ________ **d.** ________ **e.** ________

ASSESSMENT

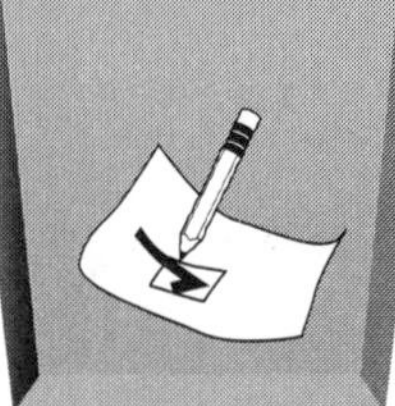

Name ______________________ Class ____________

Assessment 5: Unit 5 (continued)

What Do You Hear? 5A Timbre

Listen to *Vocal Timbres Around the World,* page 170. Match the most appropriate description to each musical style. Write the letters of the correct answers in the blanks provided.

Musical Style	Description
1. ________ country-western	**a.** folksy and rough vocal timbres, blues progression, guitar accompaniment
2. ________ folk blues	**b.** solo vocal answered by three-part response, drum accompaniment
3. ________ vocal imitation	**c.** solo vocal with vocal inflections, three-part harmony in refrain, country sound
4. ________ African call and response	**d.** voice imitates instruments

What Do You Hear? 5B Form

Listen to *Variations on "The Carnival of Venice,"* page 161. Identify the most appropriate description for each excerpt. Write the letters of the correct answers in the blanks provided.

Excerpt	Description of Variation
1. ________	**a.** fast descending notes
2. ________	**b.** main theme; *legato*
3. ________	**c.** melody as low notes, plus high notes
4. ________	**d.** many fast notes
5. ________	**e.** theme with just a little ornamentation

Name ______________________________ Class ____________________

Assessment 5: Unit 5 (continued)

What You Can Do

Sing Harmony

Sing either of the following songs in two-part harmony.

"*Así es mi tierra*," page 172

"*Habemos llegado*," page 174

Move to Show Expression

Perform the movements to "*Hava nagila*," page 153. Make your movements expressive. When you hear an *accelerando*, match your movements to the pace of the music. Then, create new movements that can be used with the song.

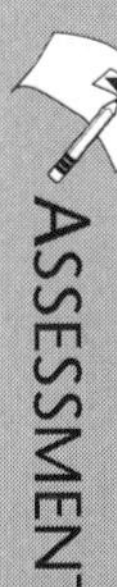

Assessment

Name ______________________ Class ______________

Assessment 6: Unit 6

Show What You Know!

Perform the following patterns that use syncopation and mixed meters. Then, compose your own rhythms and mixed meters and perform them on a nonpitched percussion instrument of your choice.

1.

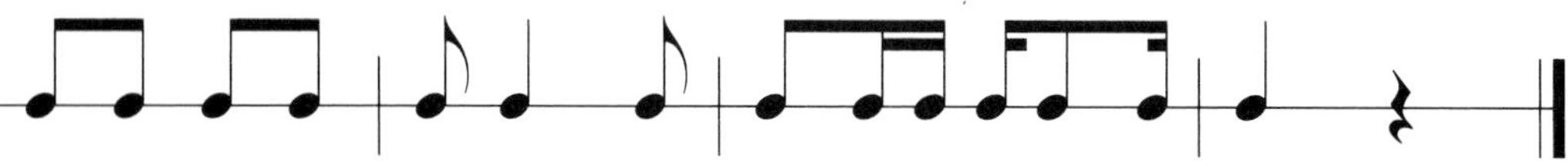

2.

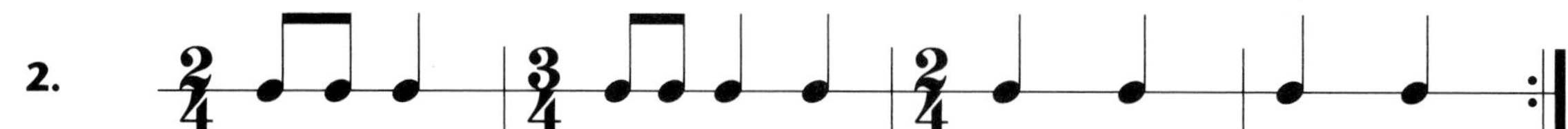

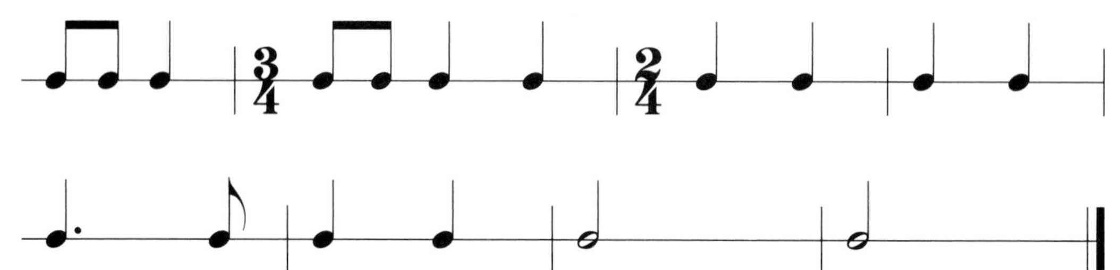

Show What You Know!

Analyze the notation of "Blue Mountain Lake" on page 205. Write the pitch set of the intervals used in the song on the staff below. Then, draw an interval chart of the intervals and indicate the interval (melodic distance) between each pair of pitches.

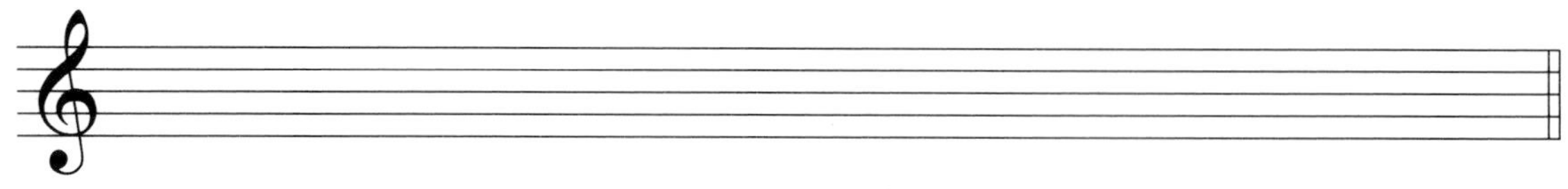

Name ______________________ Class ______________________

ASSESSMENT 6: UNIT 6 (CONTINUED)

Review, Assess, Perform, Create

What Do You Know?

1. Identify the intervals of a fourth and fifth. Write your answers in the blanks provided.

a. ______ **b.** ______ **c.** ______ **d.** ______ **e.** ______ **f.** ______

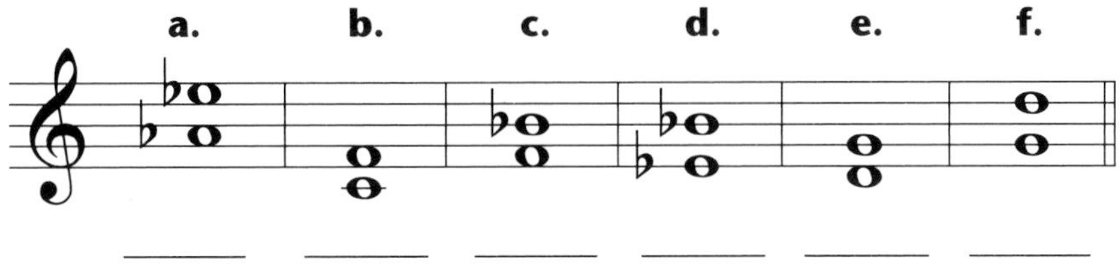

2. Match each term with its definition. Write your answers in the blanks provided next to the definition.

Term		Definition
a. through-composed	________	a change in tempo in which the music pushes ahead and/or pulls back slightly to allow greater expression
b. *a capella*	________	a musical piece in which the musical sections do not repeat
c. *rubato*	________	a musical texture in which two or more melodic parts occur at the same time, creating layers of harmony
d. polyphonic	________	vocal music performed without instrumental accompaniment

ASSESSMENT

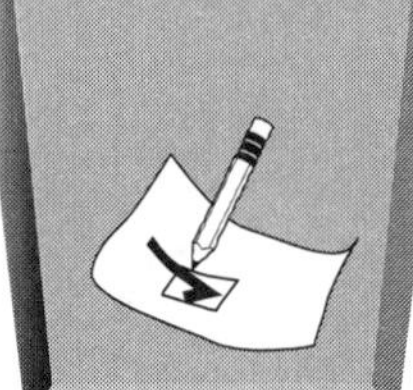

Name ______________________ Class ____________

ASSESSMENT 6: UNIT 6 (CONTINUED)

What Do You Hear? 6A Form

Listen to the following sections. Analyze the form of each, using letter names for the sections in the music. Match the correct form to each listening selection. Write your answers in the blanks provided.

Selection	Description of Form
1. ________ "Skye Boat Song"	**a.** through-composed
2. ________ *"Kyrie"*	**b.** chance music
3. ________ *"Vive l'amour"*	**c.** ABA
4. ________ *Concert for Piano and Orchestra*	**d.** AB
5. ________ "Your Friends Shall Be the Tall Wind"	**e.** round

What Do You Hear? 6B Timbre

Listen to the following choral selections. Match the correct description of the timbre that best describes each listening selection. Write your answers in the blanks provided.

Selection	Description of Timbre
1. ________ *Gloria in excelsis*	**a.** African chorus
2. ________ *Lo, How a Rose E'er Blooming*	**b.** chorus and orchestra
3. ________ *"Siyahamba"*	**c.** *a cappella* chorus
4. ________ "America, the Beautiful"	

Name ______________________ Class ______________

Assessment 6: Unit 6 (continued)

What You Can Do

Analyzing Texture

Review the use of texture in your choice of *Responsory: Alleluia* on page 217, or *Overture to Candide* on page 218. You may wish to listen to the recording you choose. Then, describe the texture of your selection using the words *homophonic* or *polyphonic*. Write your description in your music journal.

Play Syncopated Rhythms

Play the percussion parts on page 197, following the notation. First perform the rhythms using body percussion, and then again using percussion instruments.

Perform with Expression

Select a song from this unit. Decide where to use *rubato* in the song. Perform the song with the class, using *rubato* to add expression to the music. Discuss the effect of *rubato* on the character of the song.

Assessment

Name ______________________ Class ______________

Assessment: Introduction

Introduction for the Music Teacher

Checklists

Checklists are provided for performance skills (singing, playing instruments, reading, improvising, moving) and non-performance skills (composing/arranging/notating, listening). Have individual students demonstrate each of the items on the checklists. Guide the students in selecting music and tasks that will permit them to meet all of the goals outlined in the checklists.

You may consider assembling small ensembles in which students with different skill levels all perform a given piece together, but with students playing parts that are appropriate for their various skill levels. When reviewing students' work, continue to refer to the items on the checklists and point out ways their work does or does not meet each of the criteria. For students who do not perform as well as they are capable, provide opportunities to perform small sections of their pieces again. Have the students pay attention to one or two specific points that will improve their work. In this way, assessment becomes an important and contributing part of the learning process.

Rubrics

The rubrics are designed to be used together with the checklists. The goal of performance skills is for all students to perform well, regardless of the difficulty of the material they perform. The goal of non-performance skills is for all students to demonstrate competence, regardless of the difficulty of the composing, arranging, and listening tasks that they are assigned. Of course, some items on the checklists are more important than others, but all of them work together to create successful, expressive music performances, compositions, or informed listening experiences. If you wish to summarize your evaluations of the students' performances or work in a way that allows you to place each student or small group on a graded scale, you may use the rubrics for describing their performances or work.

Name ______________________ Class ______________________

Assessment: Performance Skills

Singing

Checklist for Singing

❑ Posture is upright and relaxed.
❑ Jaw and mouth are relaxed and open.
❑ Breath is inhaled with natural, relaxed expansion of the body.
❑ Tone is free, open, and even throughout range.
❑ Singing is accurate and in tune.
❑ Rhythm is precise and sung with inflection.
❑ Diction is clear (all words are understood).
❑ Volume level is balanced with other members of the ensemble.
❑ Dynamic and rhythmic variations are used to create expressive effects.

Rubric for Singing

❑ **Fluent** The student sings with fluency and ease. There are few errors. All items on the checklist are consistently demonstrated. The performance is confident, beautiful, and expressive.

❑ **Competent** The student sings with relative ease, but several errors or hesitations are present. Most items on the checklist are consistently demonstrated. The performance is confident and expressive.

❑ **More Practice Needed** The student has difficulty performing evenly and in time. Hesitations and errors are clearly evident. Only some of the checklist items are demonstrated. The performance does not convey the expressive intent of the piece performed.

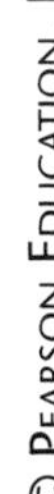

Name ____________________ Class ____________

Assessment: Performance Skills

Playing Instruments

Checklist for Playing Instruments

- ❑ Posture is upright and relaxed.
- ❑ Instruments, sticks, and mallets (when used) are held loosely and comfortably.
- ❑ Arms, hands, and fingers move easily (no tension evident).
- ❑ Playing motion is efficient and smooth.
- ❑ Instrument tone is open, resonant, and even.
- ❑ Notes are performed accurately and in tune.
- ❑ Rhythm is accurate and precise.
- ❑ Tempo is steady and even.
- ❑ Volume level is balanced with other members of the ensemble.
- ❑ Dynamic and rhythmic variations are used to create expressive effects.

Rubric for Playing Instruments

❑ **Fluent** The student plays with fluency and ease. There are few errors. All items on the checklist are consistently demonstrated. The performance is confident, beautiful, and expressive.

❑ **Competent** The student plays with relative ease, but several errors or hesitations are present. Most items on the checklist are consistently demonstrated. The performance is confident and expressive.

❑ **More Practice Needed** The student has difficulty performing evenly and in time. Hesitations and errors are clearly evident. Only some of the checklist items are demonstrated. The performance does not convey the expressive intent of the piece performed.

Name ________________________ Class ________________________

Assessment: Performance Skills

Reading

*Checklist for Reading

*❑ Selects appropriate tempo at which to perform unfamiliar music.
*❑ Identifies passages that are not immediately interpretable or technically difficult.
❑ Rehearses difficult or unfamiliar elements in isolation.
❑ Pitches are performed accurately.
❑ Rhythm is accurate and precise.
❑ Rhythm is performed with appropriate inflection.
❑ Style of articulation (if applicable) is accurate and consistent.
❑ Dynamic levels are accurate.
❑ Tempo is steady and even when appropriate.
❑ Rhythmic and dynamic variations are used to create expressive effects.

* Refer to tasks involved in learning unfamiliar music.

Rubric for Reading

❑ Fluent The student reads with fluency and ease. There are few errors. All items on the checklist are consistently demonstrated. The performance is confident, beautiful, and expressive.

❑ Competent The student reads with relative ease, but several errors or hesitations are present. Most items on the checklist are consistently demonstrated. The performance is confident and expressive.

❑ More Practice Needed The student has difficulty performing evenly and in time. Hesitations and errors are clearly evident. Only some of the checklist items are demonstrated. The performance does not convey the expressive intent of the piece performed.

Assessment

Name ______________________ Class ____________

Assessment: Performance Skills

Moving and Improvising

Checklist for Moving

- ❑ Weight of the body is balanced and secure.
- ❑ Limbs move easily and without unnecessary tension.
- ❑ Movements depict the style of music (for example, rhythm, articulation).
- ❑ Movements are coordinated with the pulse of the music (if applicable).
- ❑ Changes in movements appropriately mirror changes in the music.
- ❑ Sizes and distances of movements are appropriate for the occasion and location (for example, on a dance floor, in a circle with classmates, or seated in a chair).

Checklist for Improvising

- ❑ Notes are grouped in discernible phrases.
- ❑ Repetition of melodic motives is used to extend and elaborate phrases.
- ❑ Individual phrases are unified by consistency and continuity.
- ❑ Phrases are organized with clear, balanced antecedents and consequents.
- ❑ Harmonic motion (when harmony is present) is logical.
- ❑ Dynamic and rhythmic variations are used to create expressive effects.
- ❑ Musical effects are consistent with the improviser's intent.

Rubric for Moving and Improvising

❑ **Fluent** The student moves or improvises with fluency and ease. There are few errors. All items on the checklist are consistently demonstrated. The performance is confident, beautiful, and expressive.

❑ **Competent** The student moves or improvises with relative ease, but several errors or hesitations are present. Most items on the checklist are consistently demonstrated. The performance is confident and expressive.

❑ **More Practice Needed** The student has difficulty performing evenly and in time. Hesitations and errors are clearly evident. Only some of the checklist items are demonstrated. The performance does not convey the expressive intent of the piece performed.

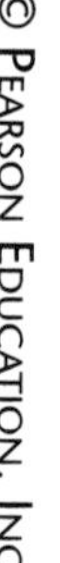

Name ______________________ Class ______________________

Assessment: Non-Performance Skills

Composing/Arranging/Notating

Checklist for Composing/Arranging/Notating

- ❑ Instrument timbres and voice parts are combined effectively.
- ❑ Notes are grouped in phrases.
- ❑ Repetition of melodic motives is used to extend and elaborate phrases.
- ❑ Individual phrases are unified by consistency and continuity.
- ❑ Phrases are organized with clear, balanced antecedents and consequents.
- ❑ Harmonic motion (when harmony is present) is logical.
- ❑ Part-writing (if applicable) follows the conventions of the style of composition.
- ❑ Dynamic and rhythmic variations are used to create expressive effects.
- ❑ Musical effects are consistent with the intent of the composer or arranger.
- ❑ Musical sounds are accurately transcribed using formal, informal, or invented notation.
- ❑ Notation is clear and readable by others.

Rubric for Composing/Arranging/Notating

❑ **Fluent** The composition or arrangement is expressive, beautiful, and consistent with the intent of the composer or arranger. All items on the checklist are consistently demonstrated.

❑ **Competent** The composition or arrangement is well organized and consistent with the intent of the composer or arranger. Most items on the checklist are consistently demonstrated.

❑ **More Practice Needed** The composition or arrangement is somewhat organized and may not be consistent with the intent of the composer or arranger. Only some of the checklist items are demonstrated.

Name ______________________ Class ______________

Assessment: Non-Performance Skills

Listening

Checklist for Listening

The first four items on this checklist pertain to behavior while listening; the remaining four pertain to auditory discriminations explained after listening.

- ❑ Remains quiet (when appropriate) while listening to live or recorded music.
- ❑ Remains stationary (when appropriate) while listening to live or recorded music.
- ❑ Moves appropriately while listening to music (for example, tapping to the beat, dancing) in social settings where movement is appropriate.
- ❑ Acknowledges performers with applause (when appropriate).
- ❑ Describes the timbres of musical tones and labels instruments and voice parts.
- ❑ Describes the formal organization of sounds (for example, the use of repetition, melodic contour, motivic development).
- ❑ Describes the emotional effects that the music elicits from self and others.
- ❑ Describes possible functions of the music in cultural contexts.

Rubric for Listening Discrimination

❑ **Fluent** All aspects of the music are accurately described, and the observations about the music are informative and interesting. All items on the checklist are consistently demonstrated.

❑ **Competent** Most aspects of the music are accurately described, and the observations about the music are informative. Most items on the checklist are consistently demonstrated.

❑ **More Practice Needed** Aspects of the music are described, but some important information is inaccurate or omitted. Only some of the checklist items are demonstrated.

Assessment Answer Key

Unit 1

What Do You Know?

1. **a.** tempo
   b. dynamics
   c. dynamics
   d. tempo
2. There are four downbeats.
   The pickup is the first two eighth notes of the rhythm.
   There is one pickup.

What Do You Hear? 1A

1. **b.** women's "barbershop" chorus
2. **e.** men's and women's chorus of Tahiti
3. **f.** sacred harp singing
4. **d.** English boy's choir
5. **c.** Tibetan monks of Central Asia
6. **a.** opera chorus

What Do You Hear? 1B

Form: c. ABAB (Verse, Refrain, Verse, Refrain)

Unit 2

What Do You Know?

1. **a.** *mezza forte*—moderately loud; ***mf***
   b. *piano*—soft; ***p***
   c. *pianissimo*—very soft; ***pp***
   d. *forte*—loud; ***f***
   e. *mezzo piano*—moderately soft; ***mp***
   f. *fortissimo*—very loud; ***ff***
2. **a.** *"Adiós, amigos"*—Major (F); *do* = F
   b. *"El condor pasa"*—Minor (A); *do* = C
   c. *"La mariposa"*—Minor (B); *do* = D
   d. "Farewell to Tarwathie"—Major (G); *do* = G

What Do You Hear? 2A

1. **a.** theme 1 (in minor)
2. **c.** themes 1 and 2
3. **a.** theme 1 (in canon)
4. **b.** theme 2

What Do You Hear? 2B

1. **a.** smooth violins
   f. mellow drums
   g. clear voice(s)
   h. children's voices
2. **b.** piano
   d. soft guitar
   e. buzzy voice
   f. mellow drums

The word that best describes the timbre of Louis Armstrong's voice is *buzzy.*

What You Can Do

Move to Show Form: The form for *"El condor pasa"* is aaba.

Unit 3

What Do You Know?

1. **a.** *crescendo*—gradually getting louder; <
   b. *sforzando*—suddenly loud; ***sfz***
   c. *descrescendo*—gradually getting softer; >
   d. motive—a short musical idea
2. **a.** middle column
   b. middle column
3. **a.** right column
   b. middle column

What Do You Hear? 3

1. bowing *(arco)*
2. bowing *(arco),* plucking *(pizzacato),* and tremolo
3. strumming, plucking *(pizzacato),* and tremolo
4. bowing *(arco)*

What You Can Do

Show Form with Movement

The form of "Bridges" is aaba (by phrase).

Unit 4

What Do You Know?

1. **b.** simple meter
2. **a.** C
3. **d.** ¢
4. **c.** compound meter

What Do You Hear? 4A

1. **c.** round
2. **d.** canon
3. **a.** verse form (ballad form)
4. **b.** fugue

What Do You Hear? 4B

1. **b.** concert band
2. **b.** concert band
3. **a.** big band
4. **c.** polka band

What You Can Do

Sing with Expression

slow = *adagio*
fast = *allegro*

Sing Sequences

The melodic sequence in the 2nd line of *"Alleluia"* is descending.

Assessment

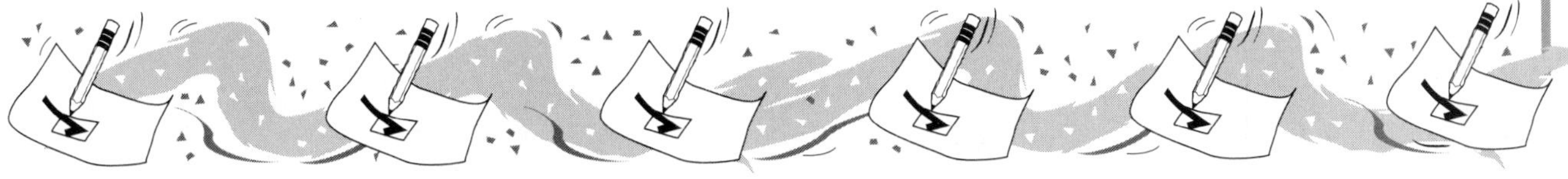

Assessment Answer Key (continued)

Unit 5

What Do You Know?

1. The rhythms that contain syncopation are **a, b,** and **f.**
2. **a.** third
   b. octave
   c. fifth
   d. fourth
   e. second

What Do You Hear? 5A

1. **c.** solo vocal and three-part harmony
2. **a.** folk-like vocal timbre
3. **d.** voice imitates instruments
4. **b.** solo vocal, three-part response

What Do You Hear? 5B

1. **e.** theme with just a little ornamentation
2. **a.** fast descending notes
3. **d.** many fast notes
4. **c.** melody as low notes, plus high notes
5. **b.** main theme; *legato*

Unit 6

What Do You Know?

1. **a.** fifth
   b. fourth
   c. fourth
   d. fifth
   e. fourth
   f. fifth
2. **a.** musical piece in which sections do not repeat
   b. vocal music performed without instrumental accompaniment
   c. a change in tempo; music pushes ahead, or slightly pulls back
   d. musical texture in which two or more melodic parts occur at same time

What Do You Hear? 6A

1. **c.** ABA form
2. **e.** round
3. **d.** AB form
4. **b.** chance music
5. **a.** through-composed

What Do You Hear? 6B

1. **b.** chorus and orchestra
2. **c.** *a cappella* chorus
3. **a.** African chorus
4. **b.** chorus and orchestra

What You Can Do

Analyzing Texture

Responsory: Alleluia = polyphonic

Overture to Candide = homophonic, polyphonic

Perform with Expression

Rubato, the slight push and pull of tempo, allows music to be more expressive and free flowing.

Graphic Organizers

Table of Contents

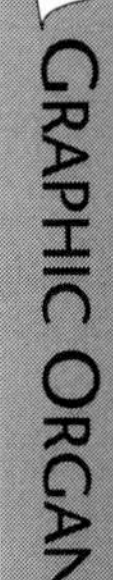

Name ______________________ Class ______________

GRAPHIC ORGANIZER 1

Comparison

Alike	Different

Name ______________________ Class ______________________

GRAPHIC ORGANIZER 2

Information Organizer Chart

Name ______________________ Class ______________

GRAPHIC ORGANIZER 3

KWHL Chart

What I know	
What I want to know	
How I will learn this	
What I learned	

Name ______________________ Class ______________________

GRAPHIC ORGANIZER 4

Semantic Feature Analysis

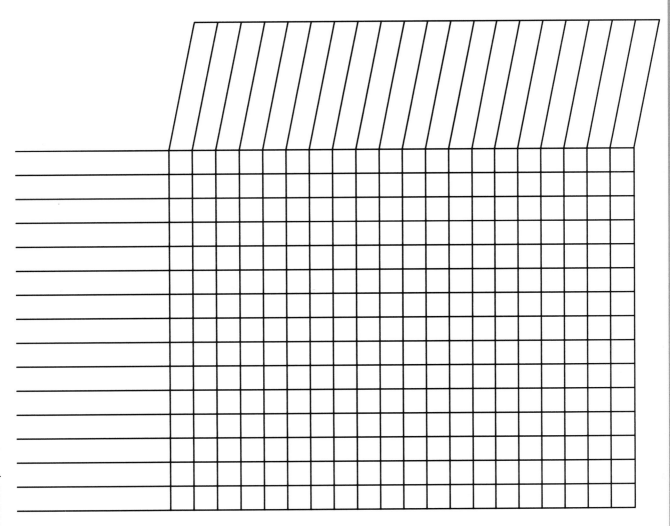

Name ______________________ Class ____________

GRAPHIC ORGANIZER 5

Semantic Map

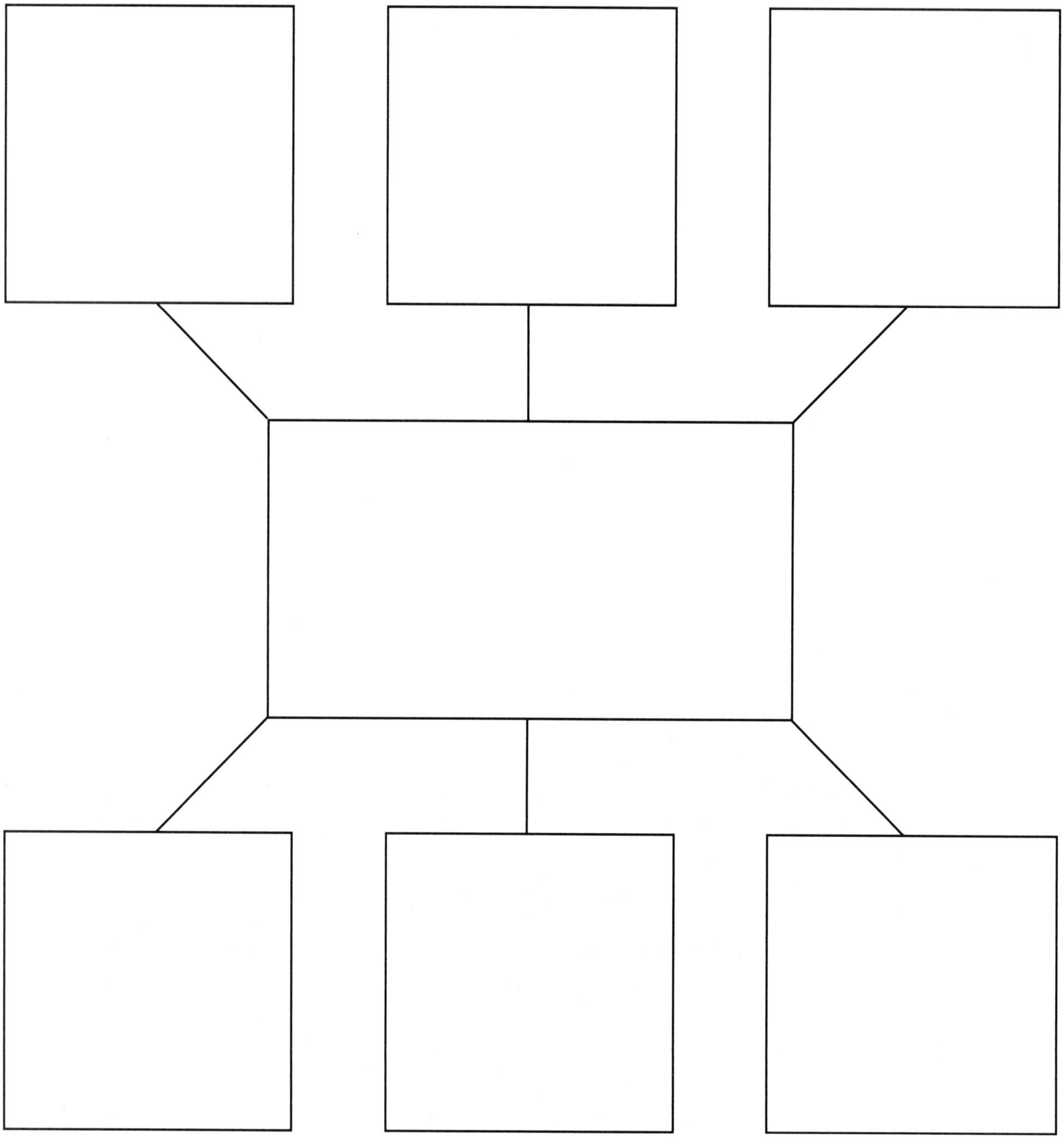

Name ______________________ Class ______________________

Graphic Organizer 6

Story Map

Title: ______________________

Setting
Characters:
Place:
Time:

▼

Problem:

Events Leading to Resolution

→ [ ]

▼

→ [ ]

▼

→ [ ]

▼

→ [ ]

▼

Resolution:

Graphic Organizer

Name ______________________ Class ______________

GRAPHIC ORGANIZER 7

Venn Diagram

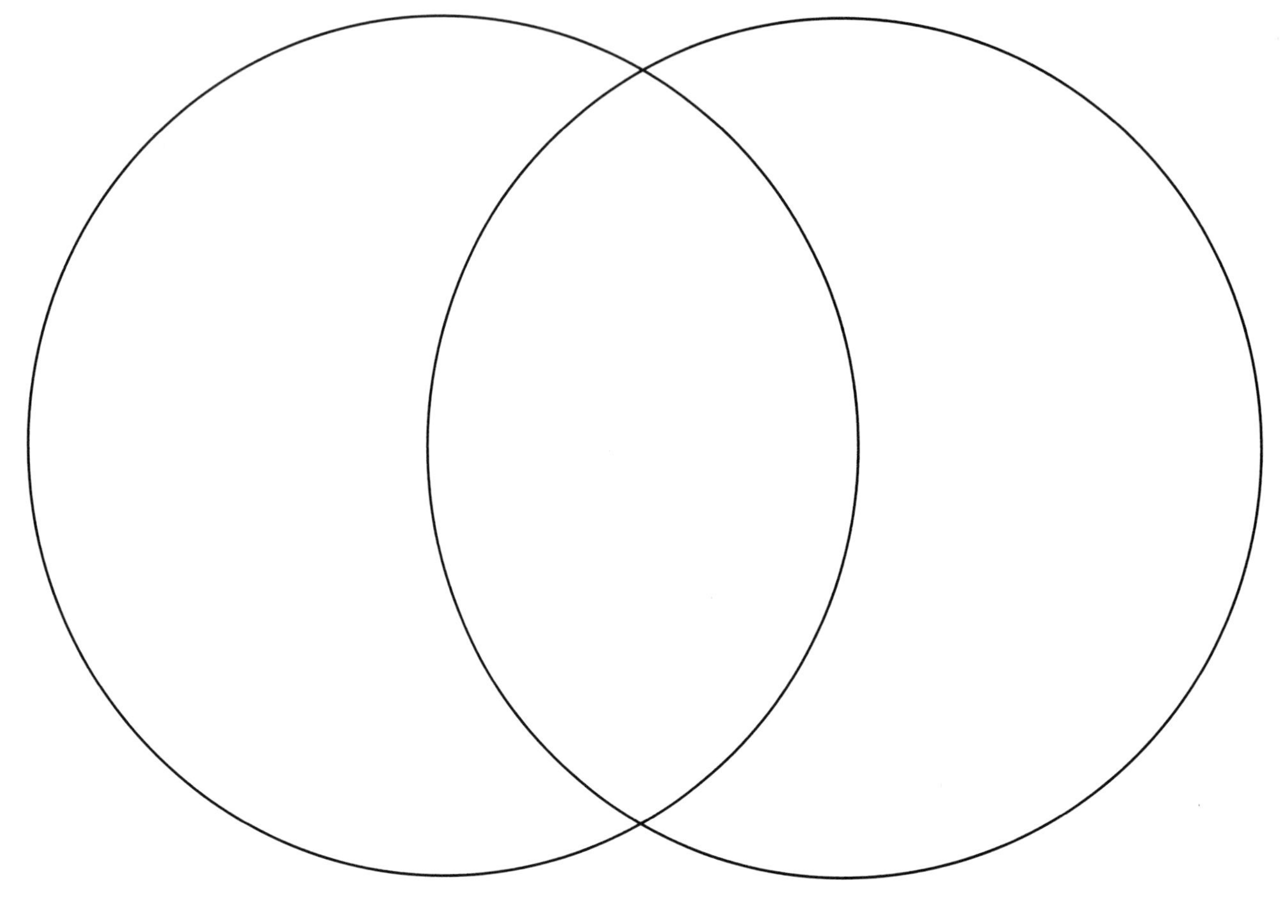

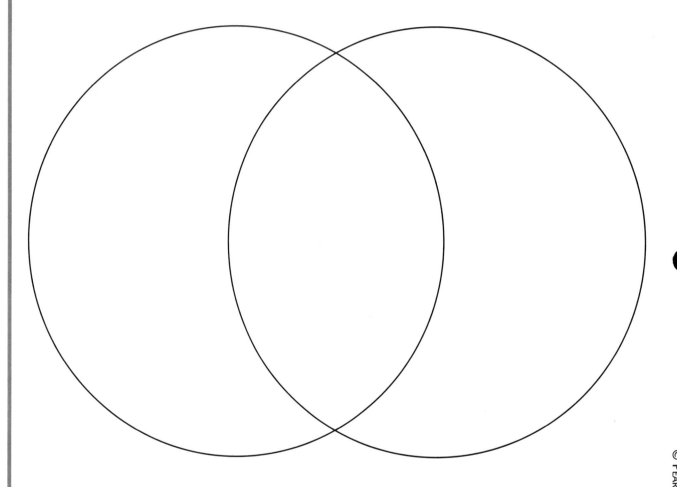

Music Reading Worksheets

Table of Contents

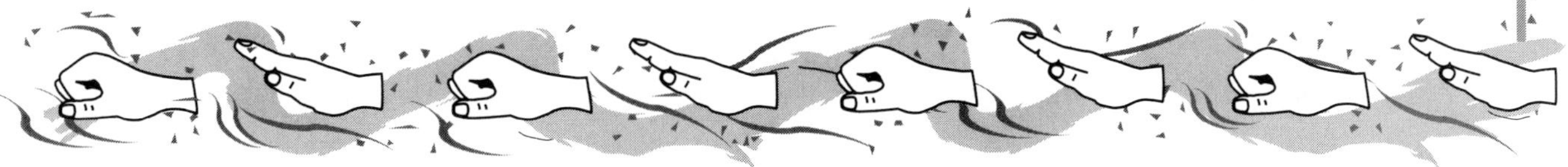

Name ______________________ Class ______________

Music Reading Worksheet 1

Lonesome Cowboy Rhythms

Red River Valley

Cowboy Song from the United States

1. Conduct the $\frac{4}{4}$ pattern.

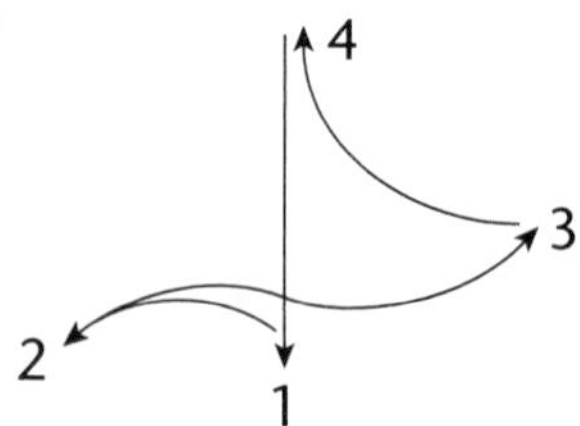

2. Practice tied notes and pickups (anacrusis) by saying the rhythm syllables as you conduct these rhythms.

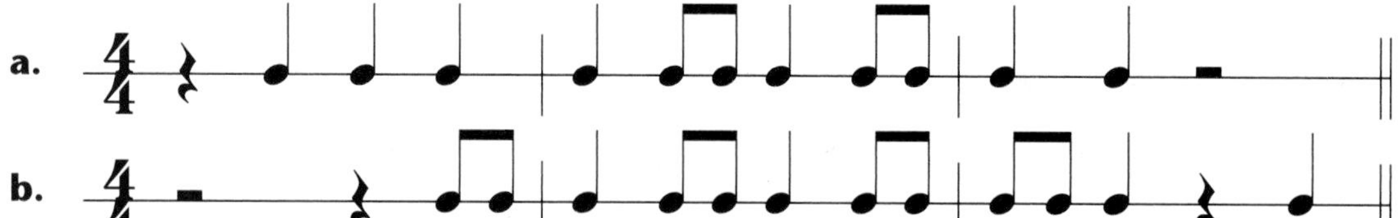

3. Create a pickup (anacrusis) for each of these rhythm patterns. How do you know how many beats the anacrusis should have?

Name ______________________________ Class ______________________

Music Reading Worksheet 2

Listen to the Le Le Bird

Bắt kim thang (Setting Up the Golden Ladder)

Traditional Song from Vietnam

1. Fill in the bar lines to show a one-beat pickup (anacrusis).

2. Fill in the bar lines to show the stronger-weaker arrangement of beats. Remember that bar lines are placed before the stronger beats.

3. Use either a *do re mi so la* or *so*, *la*, *do re mi* pitch set to notate a pentatonic melody for this rhythm. Play it on recorder or mallet instrument.

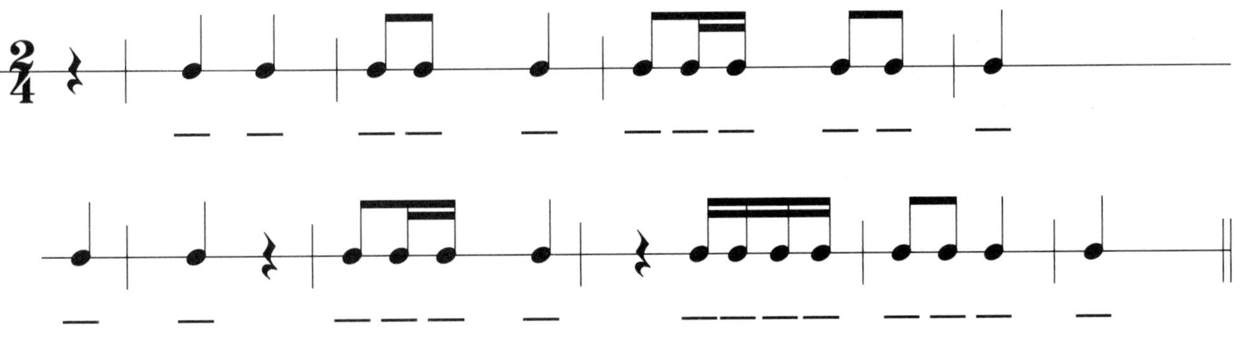

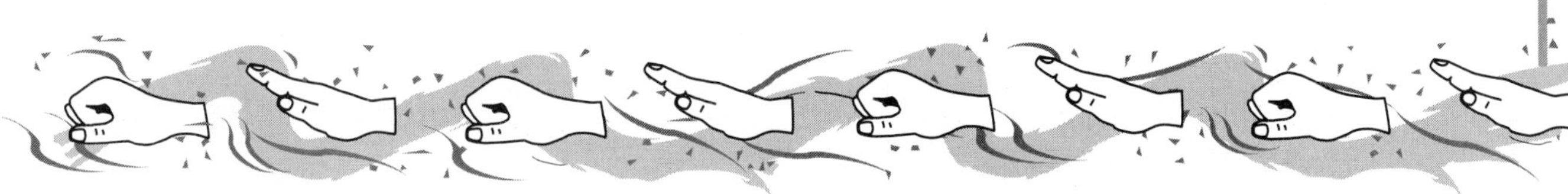

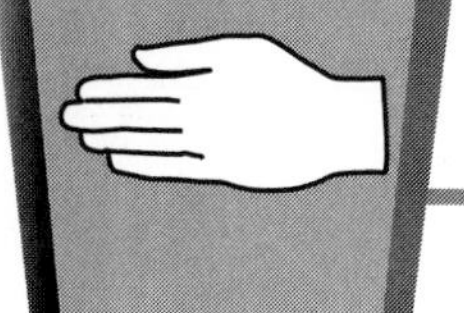

Name ______________________ Class ______________

MUSIC READING WORKSHEET 3

Melodic Roundup

Bury Me Not on the Lone Prairie

Cowboy Song from the United States

1. Sing the *F-do* pentatonic scale.

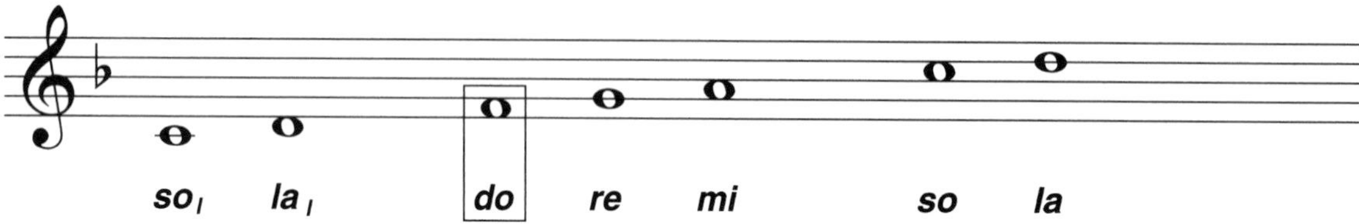

2. Write a *G-do* pentatonic scale.

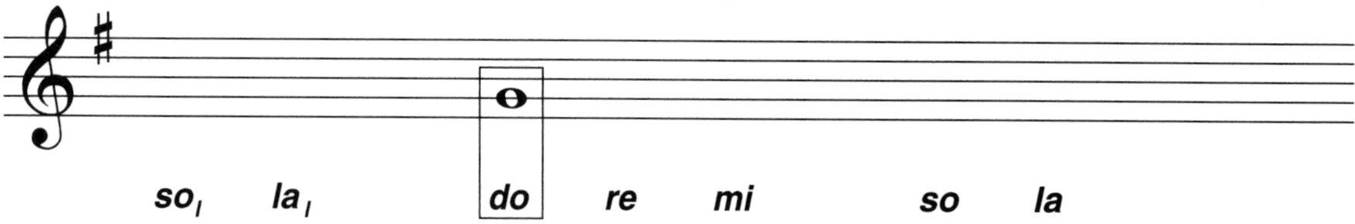

3. Sing the *F-do* diatonic scale.

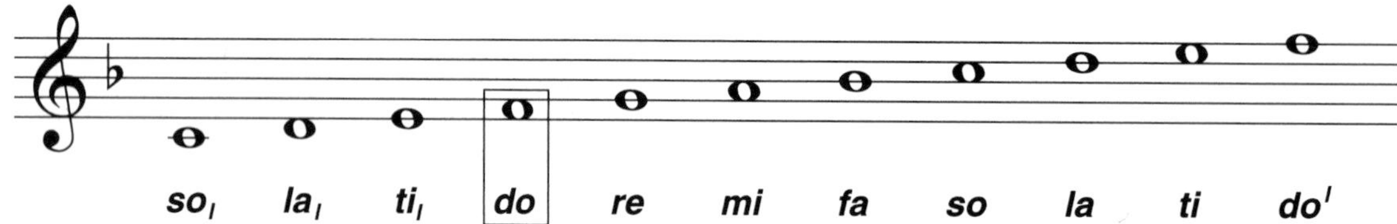

4. Write a *G-do* diatonic scale.

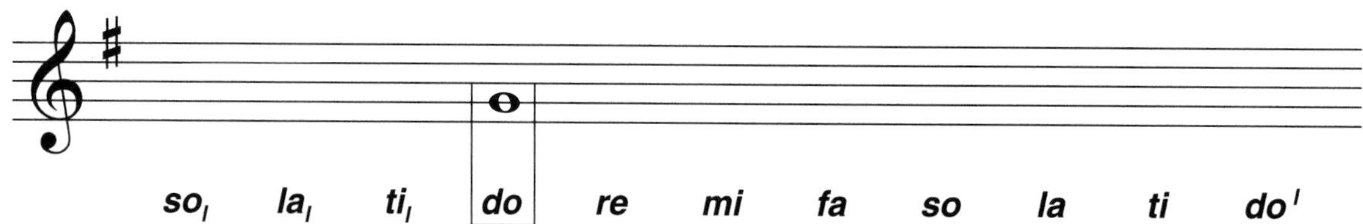

Name ______________________ Class ______________________

MUSIC READING WORKSHEET 4

Reach for the Sky!

Gonna Build a Mountain

Words and Music by Leslie Bricusse and Anthony Newley

1. Use hand signs and pitch syllables to sing this diatonic song.

2. Use pitch syllables to compose a melody that follows the shape of the melodic contour. The rhythm as well as the first and last pitches are provided for you.

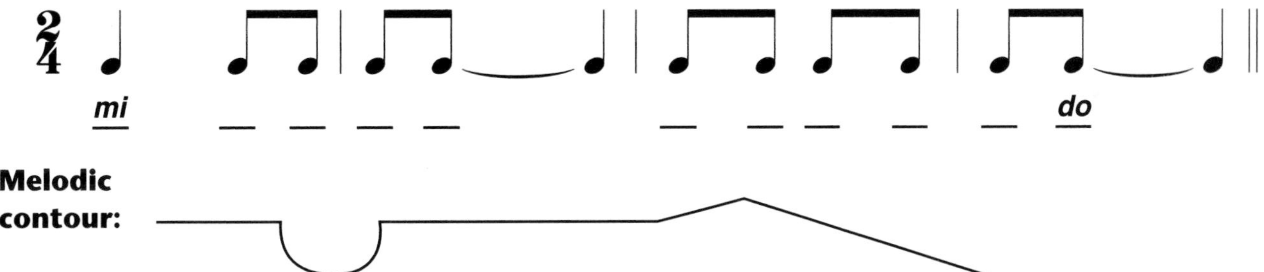

3. Compose a melody to match the melodic contour. Use a *so, la, ti, do re mi* pitch set.

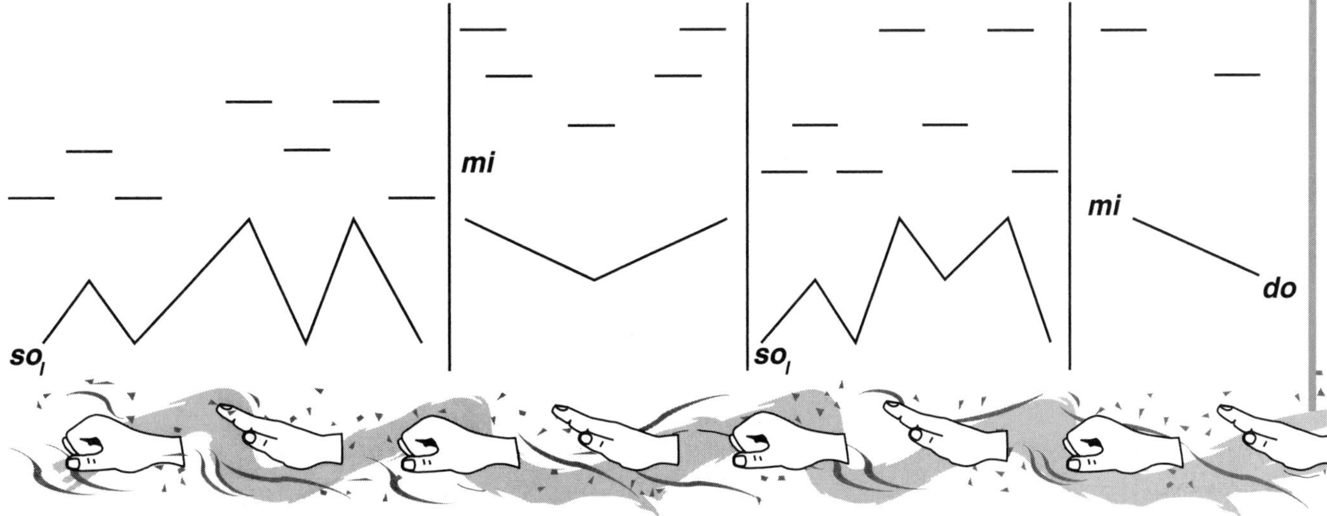

Name ______________________________ Class ______________

MUSIC READING WORKSHEET 5

Signs of Time

Farewell to Tarwathie

Folk Song from Scotland

1. Write the measure numbers in which these rhythms are found in the notation of "Farewell to Tarwathie."

a. ______ ______ ______ ______ ______ ______ ______

b. ______ ______ ______ ______

c. ______

d. ______

2. Conduct and say rhythm syllables for these rhythms. How are the rhythms alike? How are they different?

a.

b.

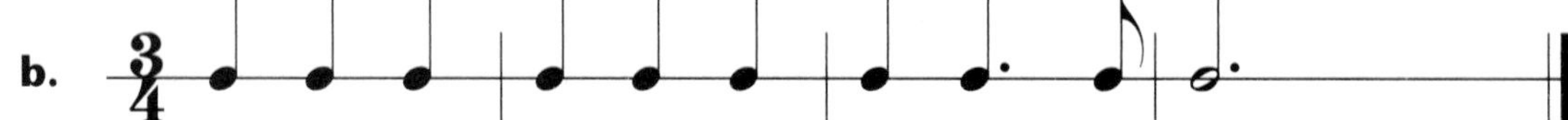

c.

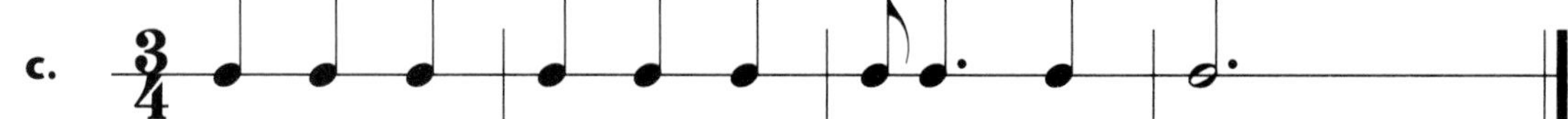

3. Conduct and say these rhythms that begin with a pickup (anacrusis).

a.

b.

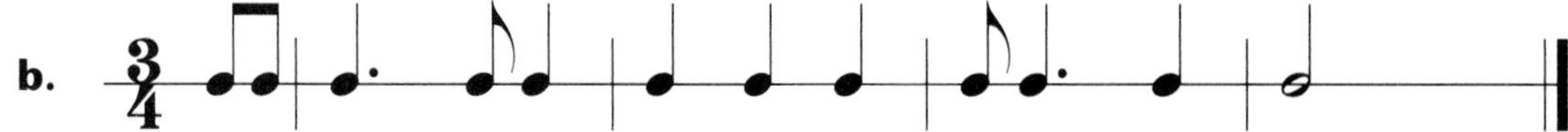

c.

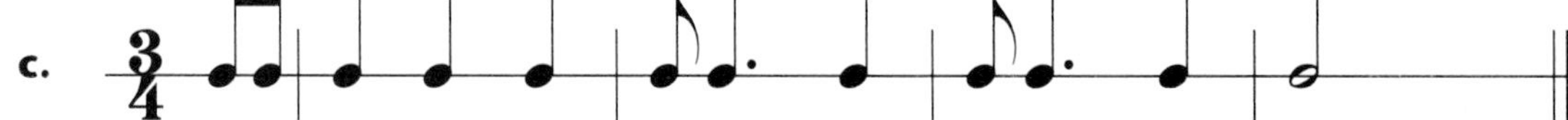

Name ______________________ Class ______________________

Music Reading Worksheet 6

Ballad Rhythms

Barb'ry Allen

Folk Song from The British Isles

1. Write the measure numbers in which these rhythms are found in the notation.

a. 

b. 

c. 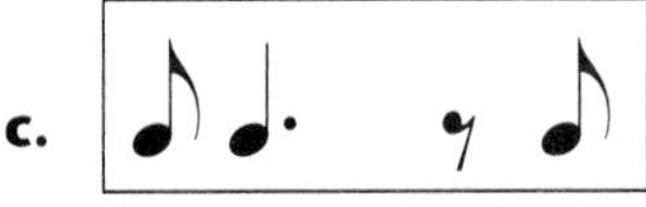

______________ ______________ ______________

2. Listen as your teacher claps the rhythms below, using ♩. ♪ ♩ or ♪ ♩. ♩ in the blank measures. Write in the rhythm you hear.

a. 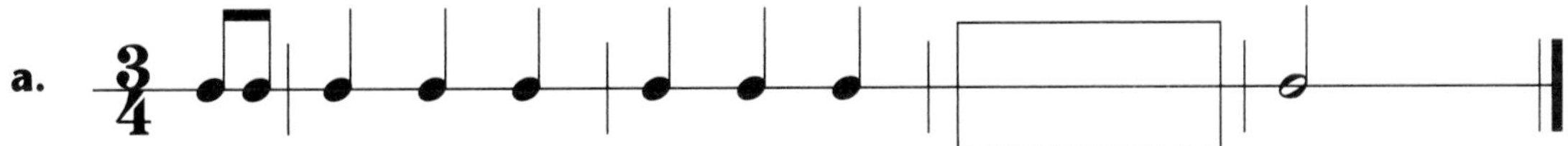

b. 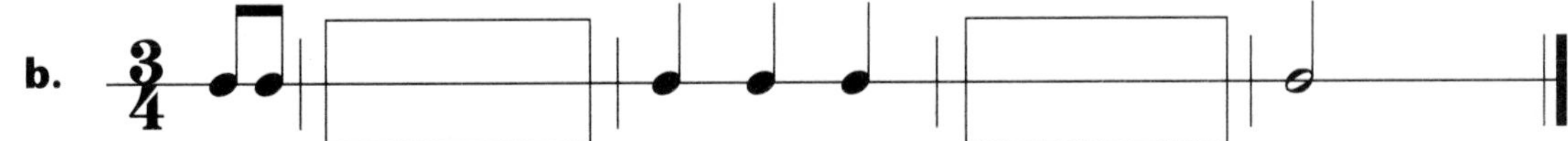

3. Use the ♩. ♪ ♩ and ♪ ♩. ♩ rhythmic patterns in combination with 𝅗𝅥., 𝅗𝅥, ♩, ♪, 𝄾, and 𝄽 to complete a rhythm composition. Make sure each measure has the correct number of beats.

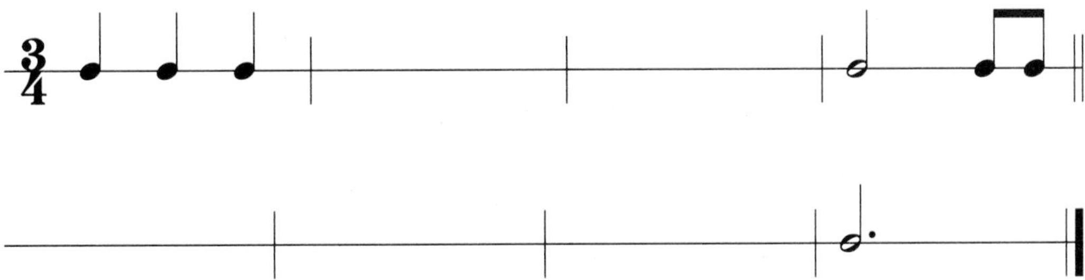

4. Now compose a melody for your rhythm by writing pitch syllables below the rhythm. Decide if you want the melody to be pentatonic or diatonic. Sing it using pitch syllables or play it on a mallet instrument or recorder.

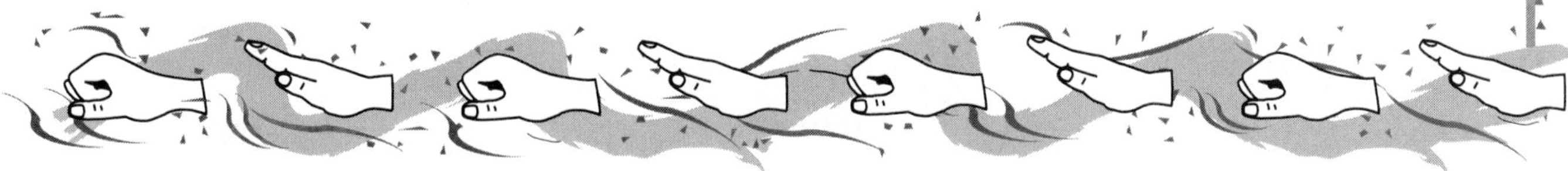

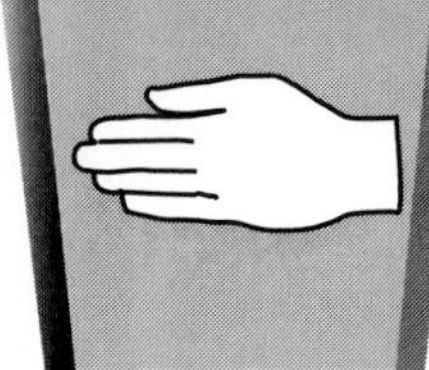

Name ______________________ Class ______________

Music Reading Worksheet 7

A Singing "Tonic"

Adiós, amigos (Goodbye, My Friends)

Folk Song from New Mexico

1. Use pitch syllables and hand signs to sing the *do* pentachord.

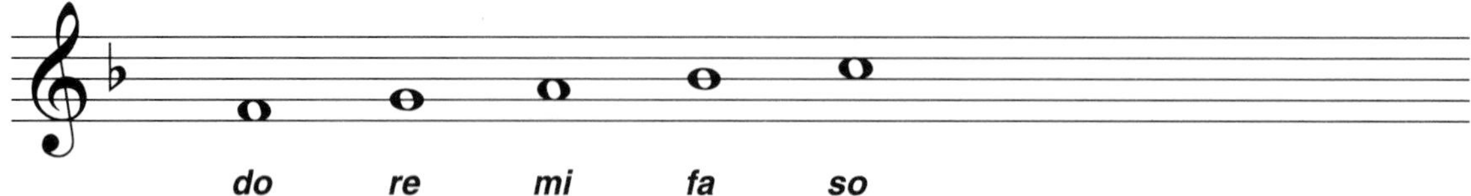

2. Use pitch syllables and hand signs to sing the *do* hexachord.

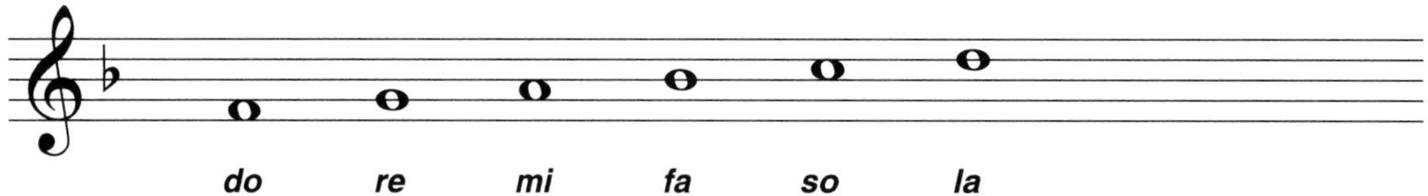

3. Sing the extended major scale in two different keys.

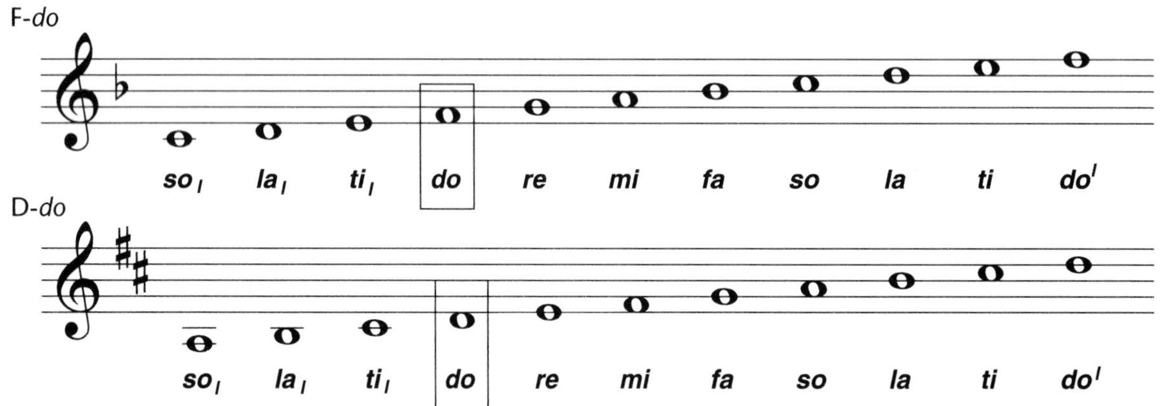

4. Using the major key signatures below, notate the tonic note on each staff. Write the name of the key below the staff.

MAJOR (*do*) tonic

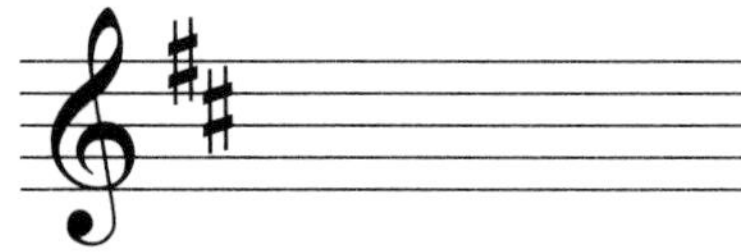

____

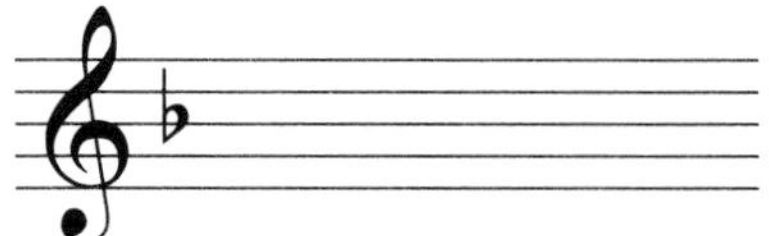

____

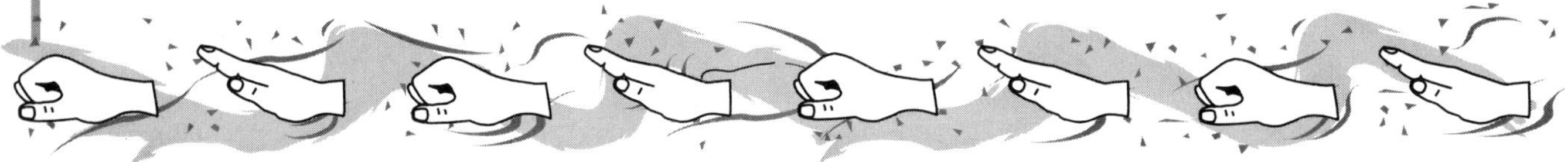

Name ______________________ Class ______________________

MUSIC READING WORKSHEET 8

Migrate to Minor

La mariposa (The Butterfly)

Folk Song from Bolivia

1. Sing the *la* pentachord.

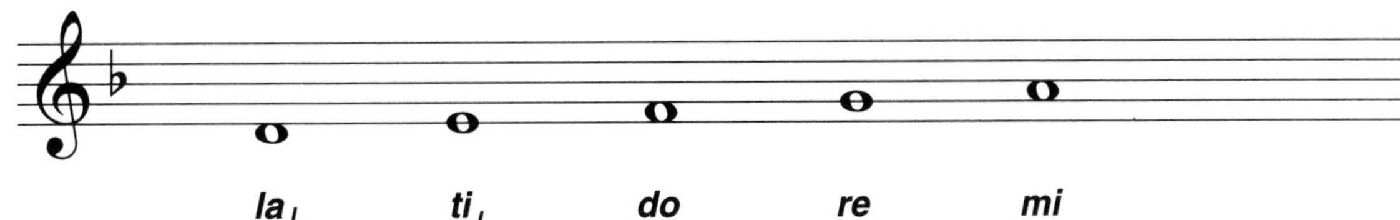

2. Sing the *la* hexachord.

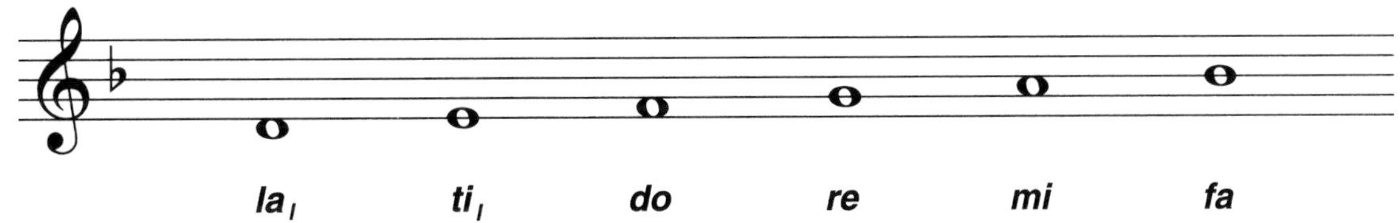

3. Sing the minor scale in two different keys.

D-*la*

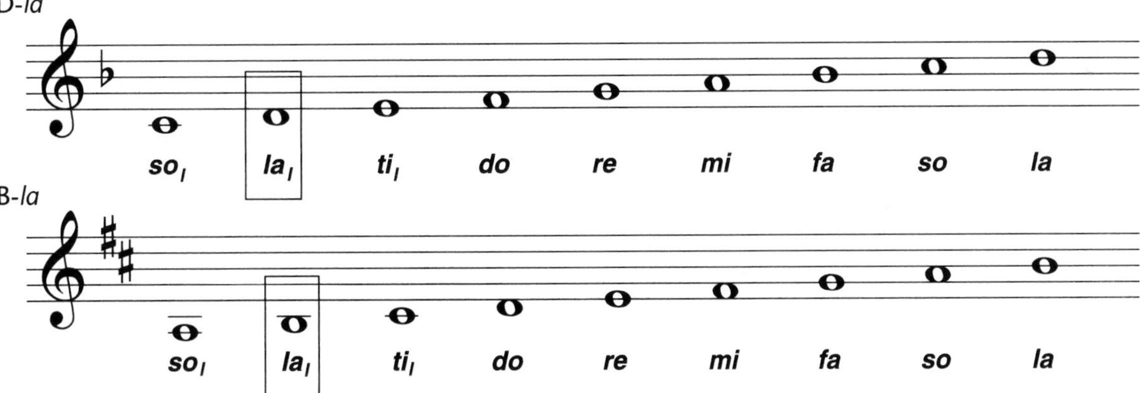

4. Using the minor key signatures below, notate the tonic note on each staff. Write the name of the key below the staff.

Minor (*la*) tonic

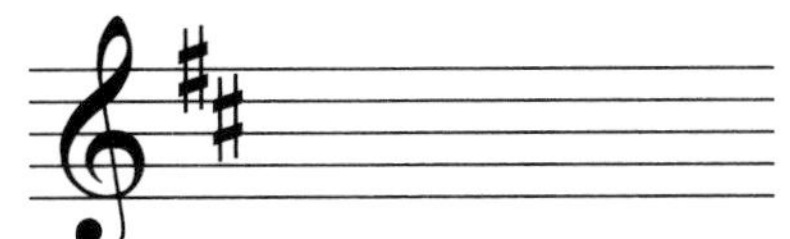

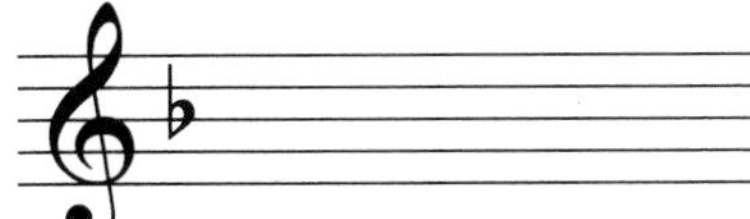

______________ ______________

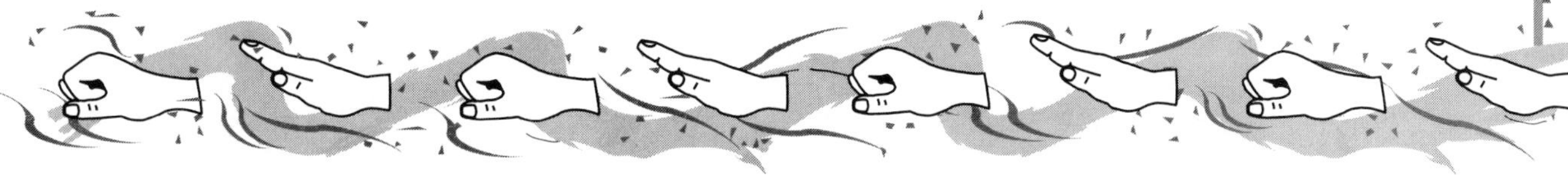

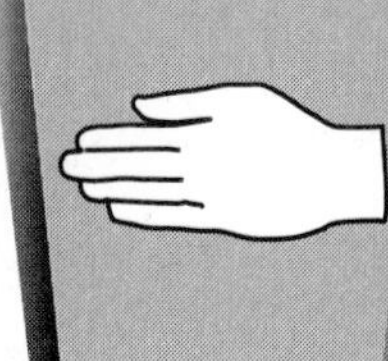

Name ______________________ Class ____________

Music Reading Worksheet 9

Playing for Time

Do, Re, Mi, Fa

The School Round Book, 1852

1. Tap the beat as you sing, *"Do, Re, Mi, Fa."* How many measures are in the song?

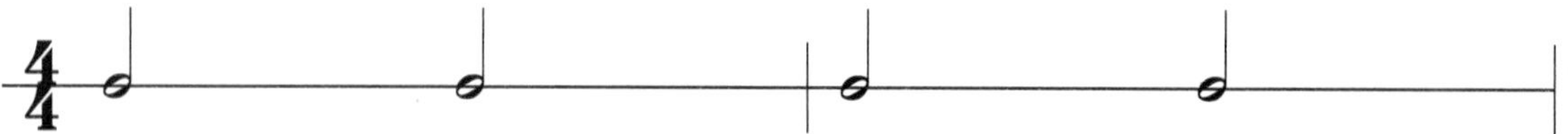

2. Notate *"Do, Re, Mi, Fa"* in augmentation. How many measures are in the song now?

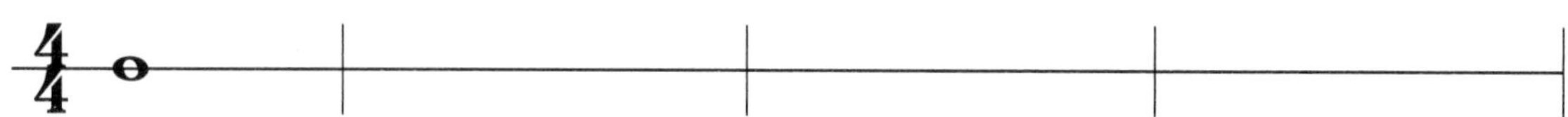

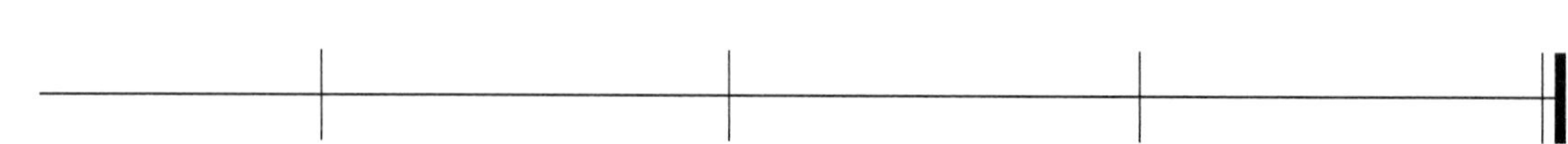

3. Notate *"Do, Re, Mi, Fa"* in diminution. How many measures will you use?

Name ______________________ Class ______________________

MUSIC READING WORKSHEET 10

Joyful Rhythms

Hava nashira (Sing and Be Joyful)

Round from Israel

1. Notate an augmentation and diminution of the third phrase of "*Hava nashira.*"

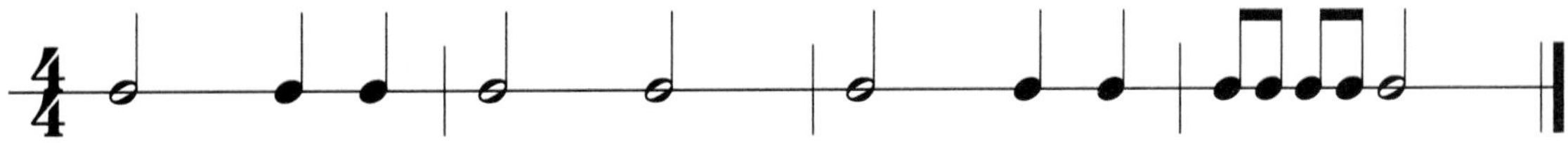

Augmentation

Diminution

4/4

2. Notate an augmentation and diminution of the following phrase.

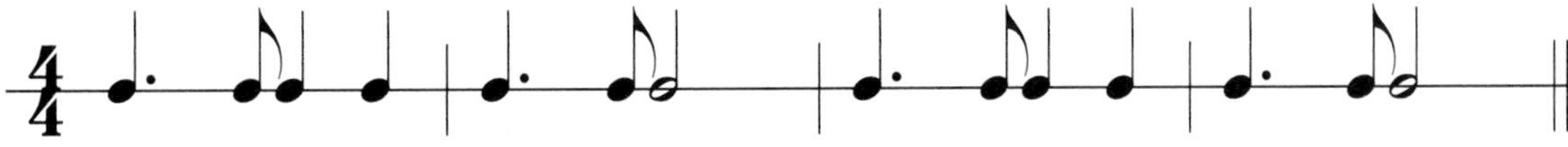

Augmentation

Diminution

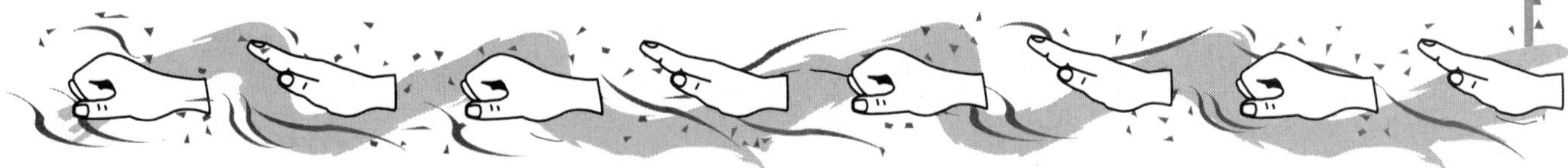

Name ______________________ Class ______________

Music Reading Worksheet 11

Scales à la mode

Scarborough Fair

Folk Song from England

1. Use C as your starting pitch to sing the major scale using hand signs and pitch syllables. Where are the half steps?

Major scale	***do***	***re***	***mi‿fa***	***so***	***la***	***ti‿do'***

2. Now sing the dorian mode using hand signs and pitch syllables. Start on D *(re).*

Dorian mode	***re***	***mi‿fa***	***so***	***la***	***ti‿do'***	***re'***

3. Songs usually end on *do* or *la.* Sing the minor scale (also called the aeolian mode) using hand signs and pitch syllables. How can the scale be altered so it sounds like the dorian mode?

Minor scale (aeolian mode)	***la,***	***ti,‿do***	***re***	***mi‿fa***	***so***	***la***
Aeolian mode with *fi*	***la,***	***ti,‿do***	***re***	***mi***	***fi‿so***	***la***

fa hand sign

fi hand sign

4. Notate the dorian mode on the staff. How can *fa* be raised a half step to *fi*?

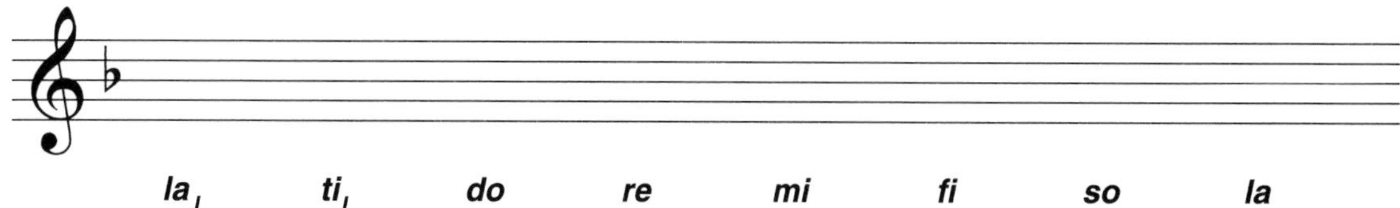

la, ***ti,*** ***do*** ***re*** ***mi*** ***fi*** ***so*** ***la***

Name ______________________________ Class ______________________

Music Reading Worksheet 11 (continued)

5. Practice reading *fi* using hand signs and pitch syllables.

6. Create a dorian melody for this rhythm. Use *fi* at least five times.

3/4

la,

mi *mi*

so

la,

Name ______________________ Class ______________

Music Reading Worksheet 12

Make it Modal

Harrison Town

Folk Song from the Ozarks

1. Sing the ionian (major scale) and mixolydian modes with hand signs and pitch syllables. Where are the half steps located in each scale?

Ionian mode (major scale)	***do***	***re***	***mi‿fa***	***so***	***la***	***ti‿do'***
Mixolydian mode	***do***	***re***	***mi‿fa***	***so***	***la‿ta***	***do'***

ti hand sign

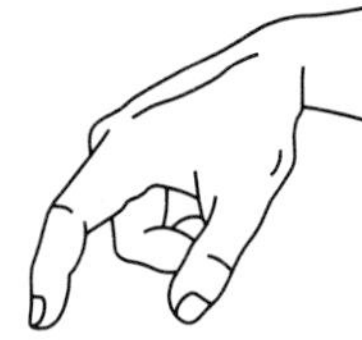

ta hand sign

2. Notate the ionian and mixolydian modes on the staff. Sing each mode first using pitch syllables and hand signs. Then sing the letter names. Sing each mode in canon, with the second voice entering when the first voice reaches *mi.* Mark the half steps with a curved line.

Ionian mode (major scale)

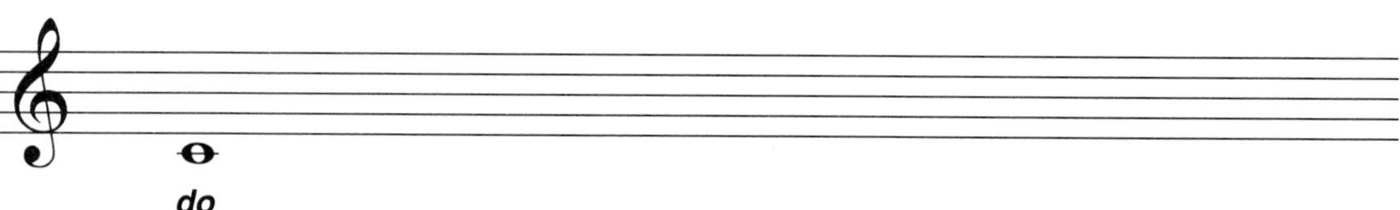

Mixolydian mode

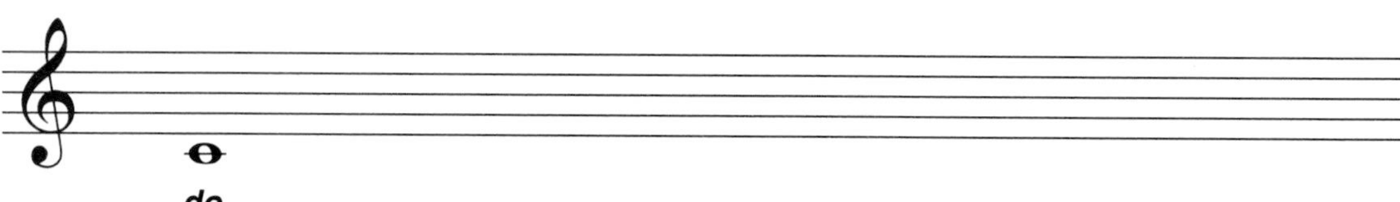

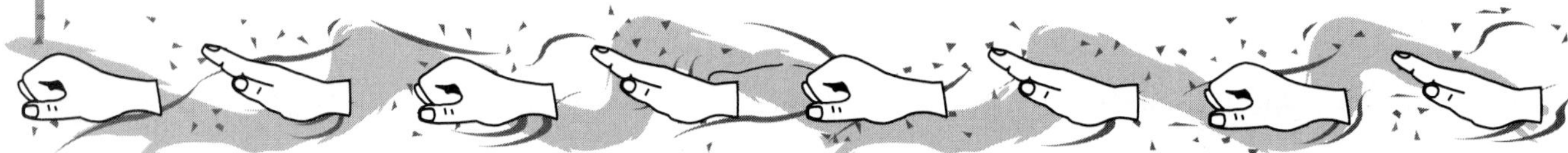

Name ______________________________ Class ______________________

Music Reading Worksheet 12 (continued)

3. Sing each of the modes below using hand signs and pitch syllables. Listen as your teacher sings or plays one of the modes and identify which mode it is.

Ionian	**Mixolydian**	**Aeolian**	**Dorian**
do^{l}	do^{l}	*la*	*la*
ti			
	ta	*so*	*so*
la	*la*		*fi*
		fa	
so	*so*	*mi*	*mi*
fa	*fa*	*re*	*re*
mi	*mi*		
		do	*do*
re	*re*	ti_{l}	ti_{l}
do	*do*	la_{l}	la_{l}

4. For each scale below, mark all of the half steps with a curved line. Use the same starting pitch to sing each mode. Use pitch syllables and hand signs, then sing the letter names.

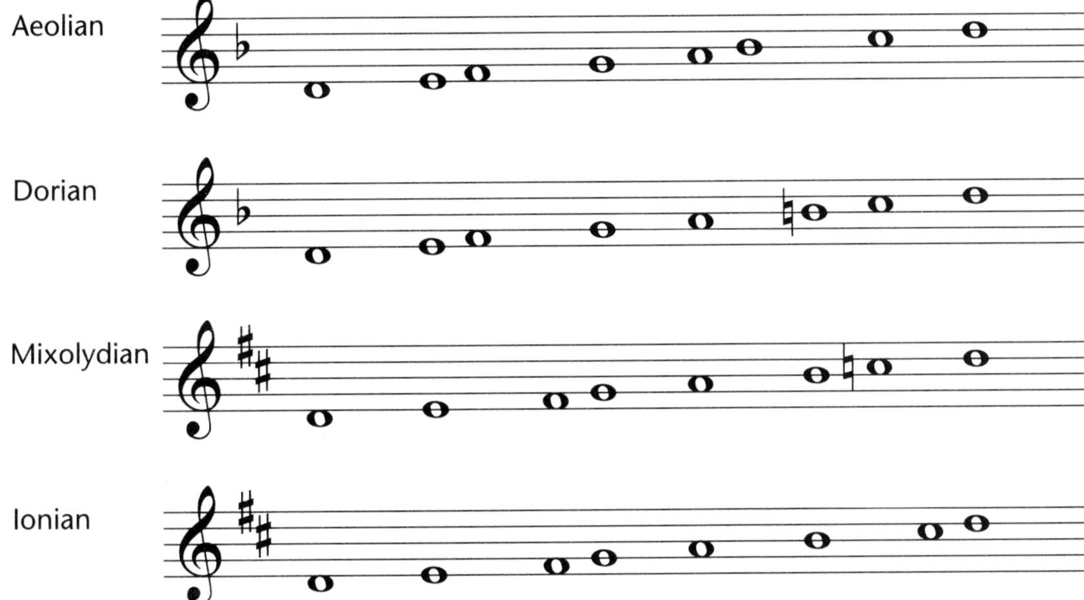

Name ______________________ Class ____________

Music Reading Worksheet 13

Meter—The Foundation of Music

Swanee

Music by George Gershwin

1. Conduct each pattern below. Listen to "Swanee" and determine which pattern best fits the song.

a. _____ _____ =

b. _____ _____ _____ =

c. _____ _____ _____ _____ =

2. Set the metronome to the marking indicated for each example. Conduct and say the rhythms.

Ex. a ♩ = 132

Ex. b ♩ = 66

Ex. c 𝅗𝅥 = 66

Name ______________________ Class ______________________

Music Reading Worksheet 14

A Springtime Meter

One Morning in May

Folk Song from the Appalachian Mountains

1. Conduct the beat note as you say rhythm syllables. Compose a *do*-pentatonic melody.

Notate your *do*-pentatonic melody on the staff.

2. Conduct the beat note as you say rhythm syllables. Compose a major diatonic melody.

Notate your major diatonic melody on manuscript paper. (See Resource Book p. J-16.)

Name ______________________ Class ______________

Music Reading Worksheet 15

Building Intervals

Lo yisa (Vine and Fig Tree)

Music by Shalom Altman

1. Show hand signs and use pitch syllables to sing the harmonic-minor scale. Where are the minor seconds (half steps) located?

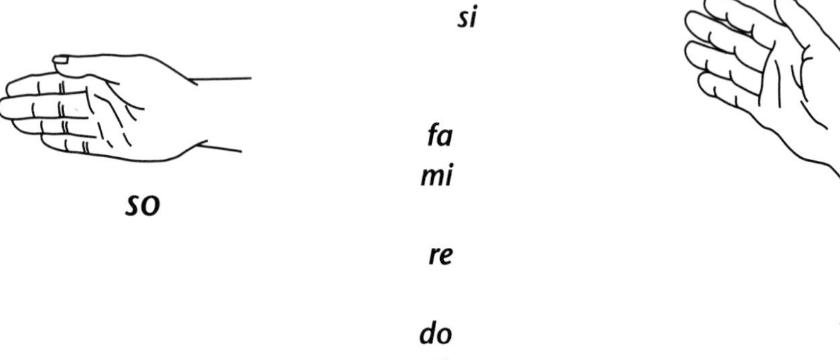

2. Sing the harmonic-minor scale.

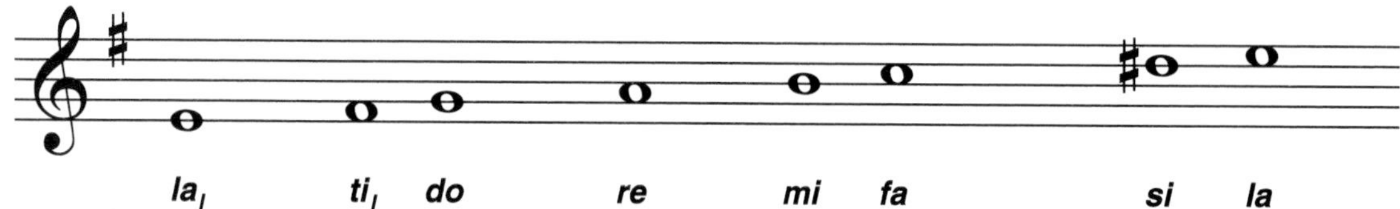

3. Sing the pitch set for "*Lo yisa.*"

Name ______________________________ Class ____________________

Music Reading Worksheet 16

Moving Motives

Alleluia

Music by Wolfgang Amadeus Mozart

1. Notate the B-flat diatonic scale on the staff below. Write the pitch syllables below the notes.

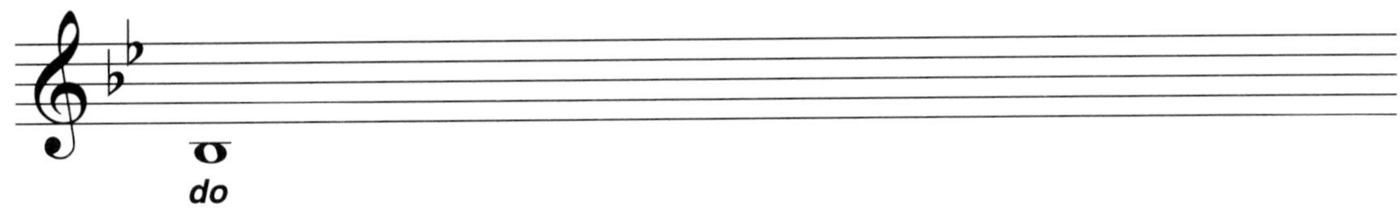

2. Write ascending and descending melodic sequences for these patterns.

a. Ascending melodic sequence in B-flat-*do*

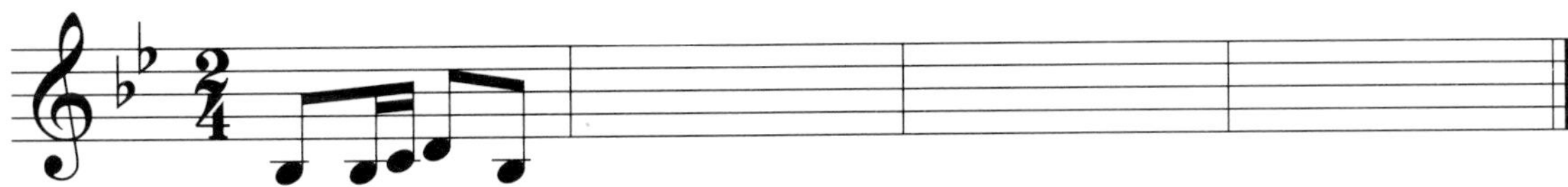

b. Descending melodic sequence in F-*do*

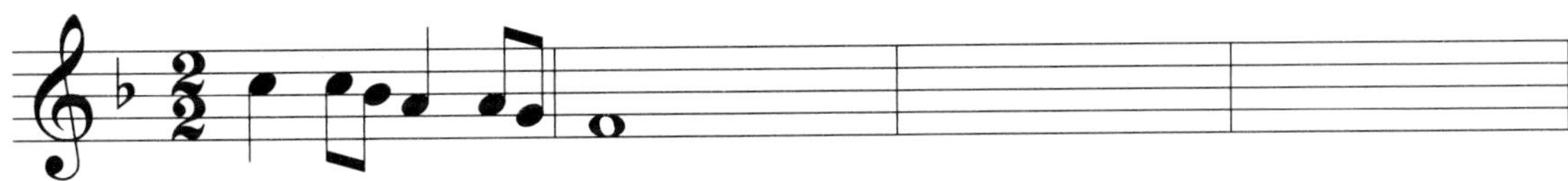

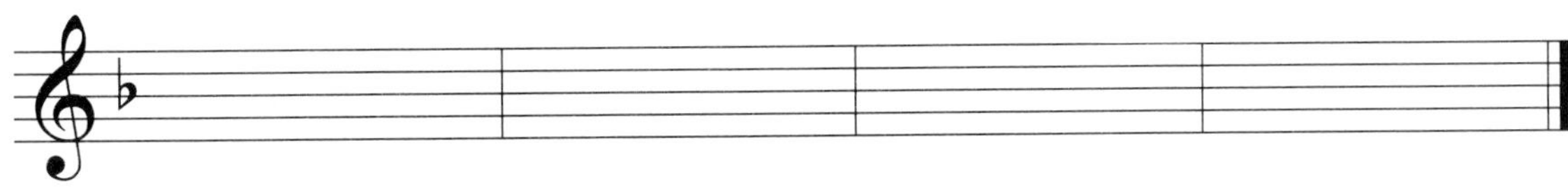

c. Descending melodic sequence in D-*do*

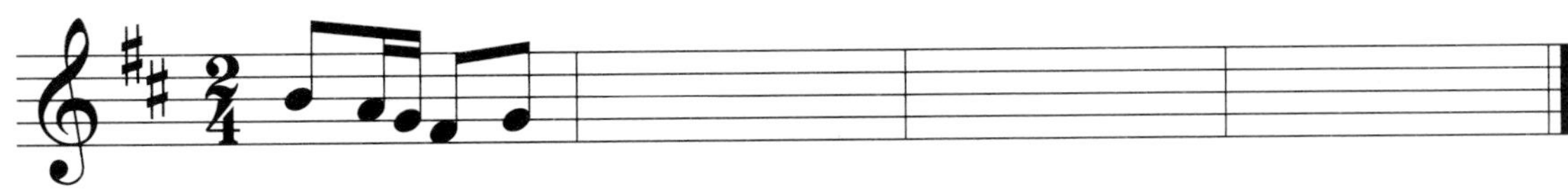

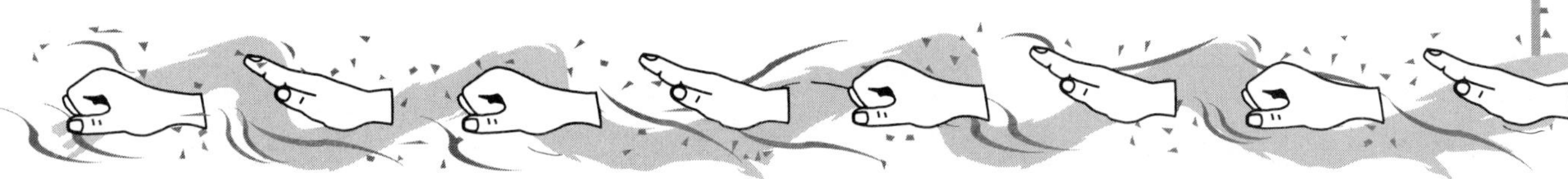

Name ______________________ Class ____________

Music Reading Worksheet 17

Syncopated Rhythms

Let Us Sing Together

Traditional Czech Folk Melody

1. Clap the rhythm as you sing this motive from "Let Us Sing Together." Which eighth notes must be tied to follow the rhythm of the words in the second measure? Draw the tie and clap the rhythm.

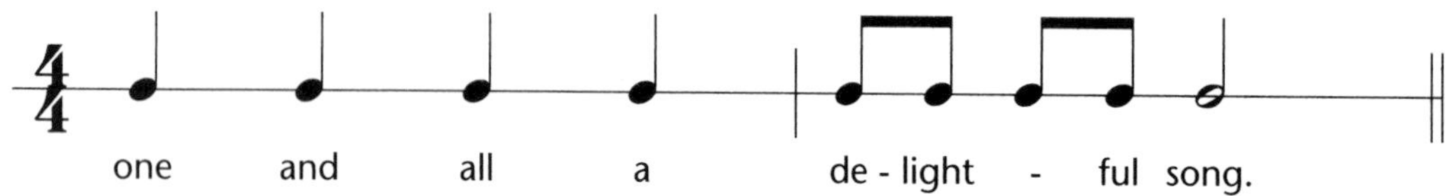
one and all a de - light - ful song.

2. Tap the beat and say rhythm syllables for the examples below. Then tap the beat with your foot and clap the rhythms.

a.

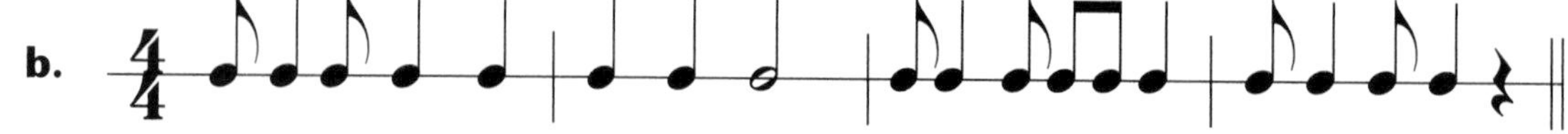
b.

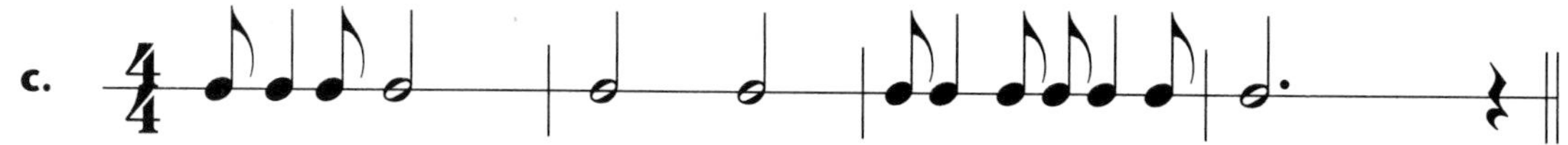
c.

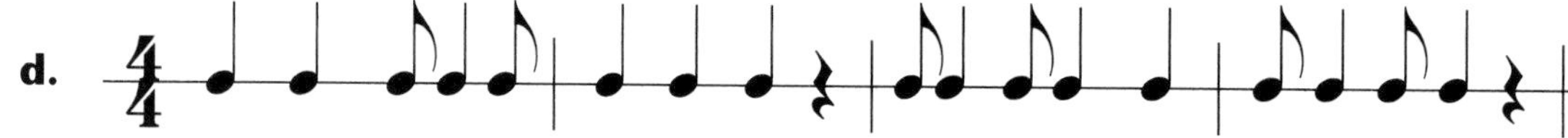
d.

Name ______________________ Class ______________

Music Reading Worksheet 18

Double the Speed

Lost My Gold Ring

Singing Game from Jamaica

1. Tap the beat lightly with your foot as you clap these syncopated rhythms.

For an added challenge, divide into two groups; group 1 claps 1a while group 2 claps 1b. Make sure you begin at the same time.

2. Compose and notate an eight-beat syncopated rhythm. Perform it on a nonpitched percussion instrument of your choice.

3. Super challenge! Compose a melody for the rhythm you composed. Use all the notes of the scale in any mode you choose: ionian, mixolydian, aeolian, or dorian.

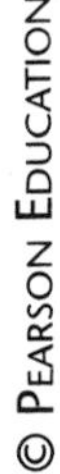

Name ______________________ Class ____________

MUSIC READING WORKSHEET 19

Melodic Distances

O lê lê O Bahía (O Le O La)

Folk Song from Brazil

1. Sing the pitch syllables for these patterns sung by the chorus in *"O lê lê O Bahía."* Which patterns are repeated in the song?"

a. **b.** **c.** **d.**

2. This chart shows the *major* seconds, marked with a carat, and the *minor* seconds, marked with a curved line, in the *do*-diatonic scale.

3. Mark the major seconds with a carat (∨) and the minor seconds with a curved line (‿).

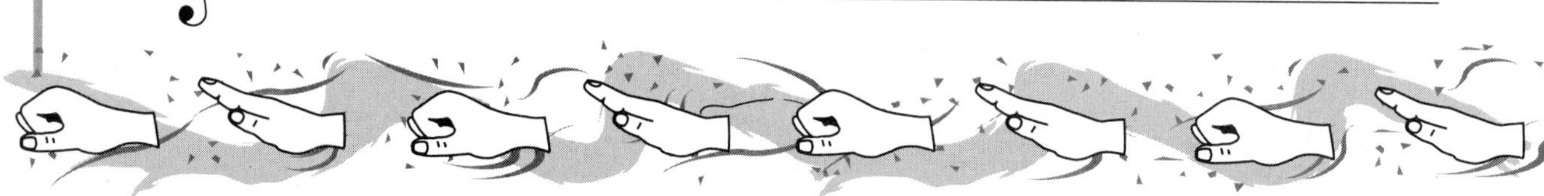

Name ______________________________ Class ______________________

Music Reading Worksheet 20

Distance = Intervals

Like a Bird

Music by Luigi Cherubini

1. Here is a chart showing all of the thirds, fourths, and fifths between *so,* and *do'*. Smaller (minor) thirds are marked with a bracket; larger (major) thirds are marked with carat. All fourths are of equal size, as are fifths.

Thirds:

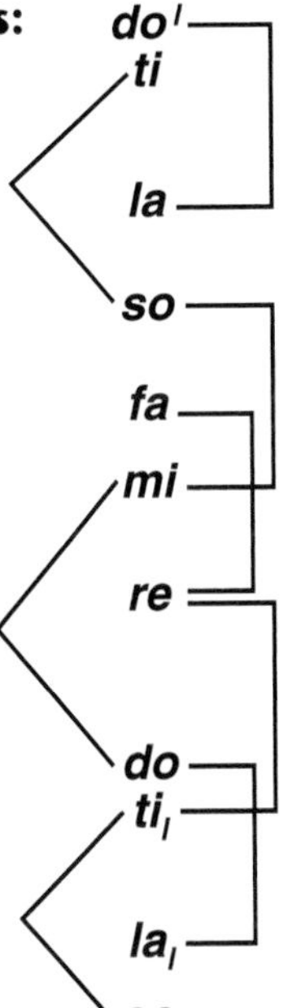

Fourths:

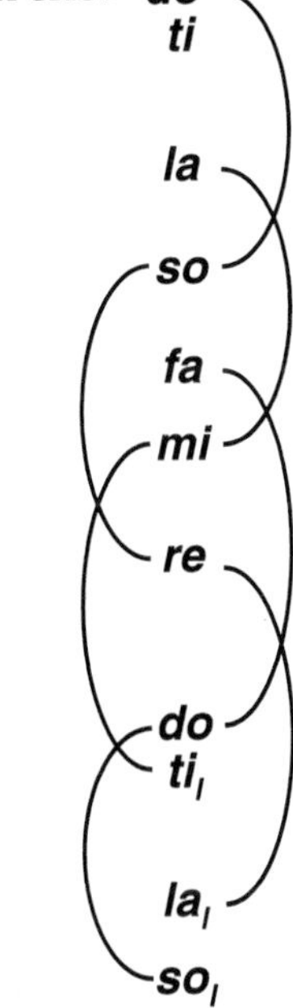

Fifths:

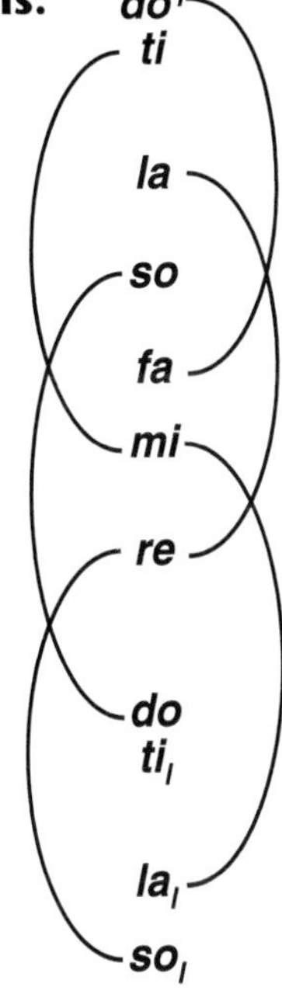

2. Write the pitch syllables below each notehead. Write the interval name above each measure.

1. ____________ **2.** ____________ **3.** ____________ **4.** ____________

3. Sing the pitch syllables for each interval. Write the interval name above each measure. Write the noteheads on the staff.

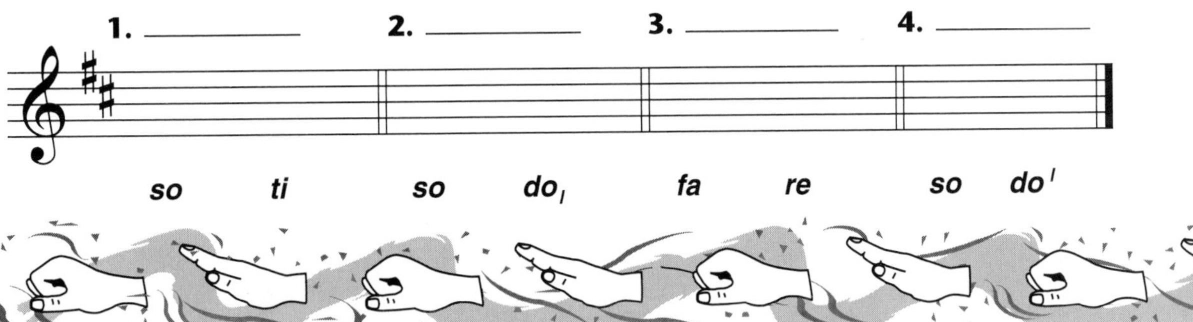

Name ______________________________ Class ______________

Music Reading Worksheet 21

Adjust the Accents

Paths of Victory

Words and Music by Bob Dylan

1. Clap or tap the rhythm of the upper line in each of these exercises. Then add the lower line. Note that in the first measure of exercise a, the upper line outlines the syncopation in the lower line.

a.

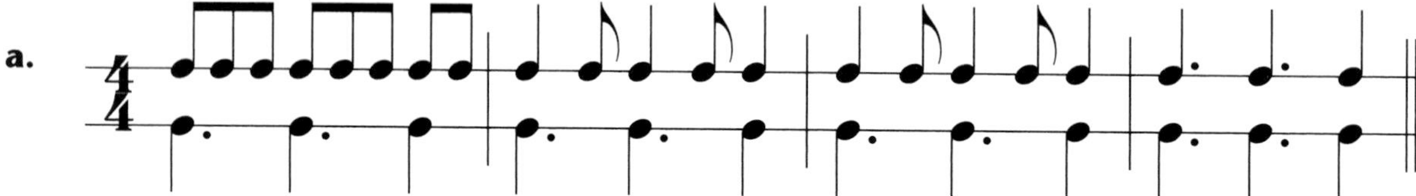

b.

2. Perform the above rhythm in quartet. Two players tap the lower rhythm while two other players clap the upper rhythm.

Name ____________________ Class ____________________

Music Reading Worksheet 22

Meters Move

New Hungarian Folk Song

Words and Music by Béla Bartók

Study the rhythm score below. Which phrases are exactly alike? Which phrases are similar? Tap the beat as you say the following rhythm. Conduct the beat and say the rhythm.

Name ______________________ Class ____________

Music Reading Worksheet 23

Lumberjack Intervals

Blue Mountain Lake

Lumberjack Song from New York

1a. This pitch ladder shows the pitch set for "Blue Mountain Lake." Mark all of the fourths with a curved line (‿) and all fifths with a carat (∨). Two are marked for you.

la
so
mi
re
do
ti,
la,

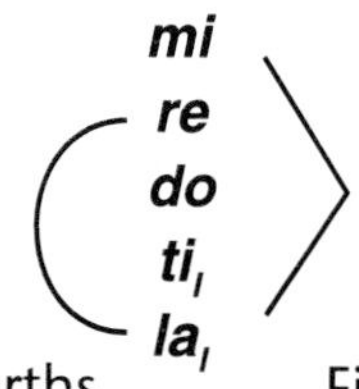

Fourths Fifths

1b. Write the pitch set for "Blue Mountain Lake" on the staff.

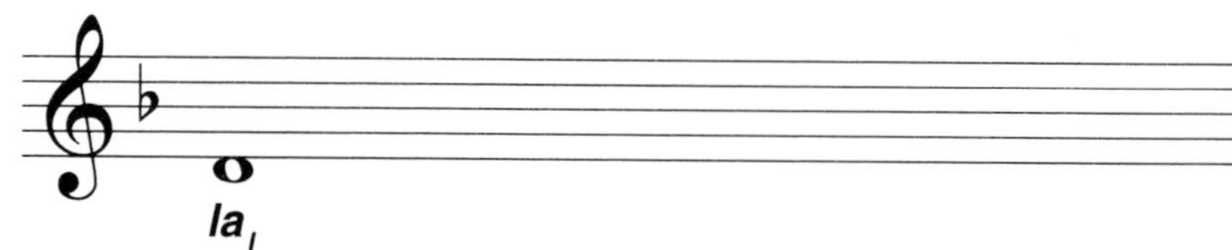

2. Write the pitch syllables and interval name. Then sing the intervals.

a. ____ ____ : ____

b.

____ ____ : ____

c.

____ ____ : ____

d.

____ ____ : ____

e.

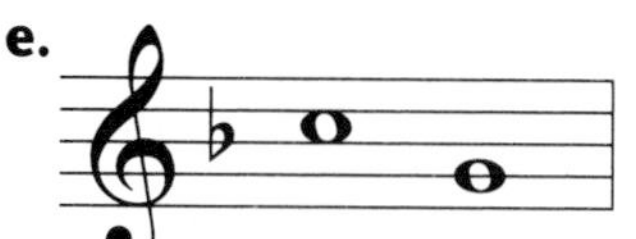

____ ____ : ____

f.

____ ____ : ____

3. Sing the pitch syllables, then write the interval name. Write the noteheads on the staff.

a.

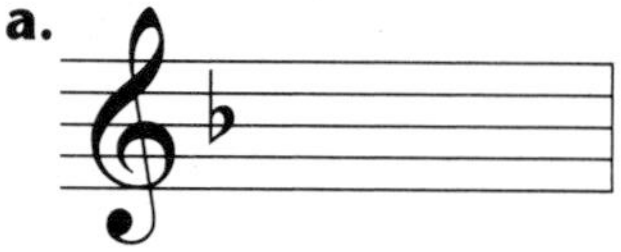

do-re : ____

b.

c.

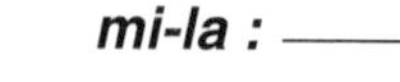

d.

so-re : ____

e.

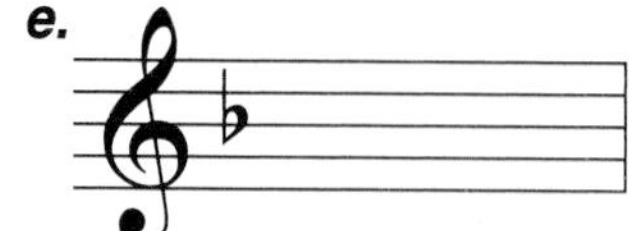

re-ti, : ____

f.

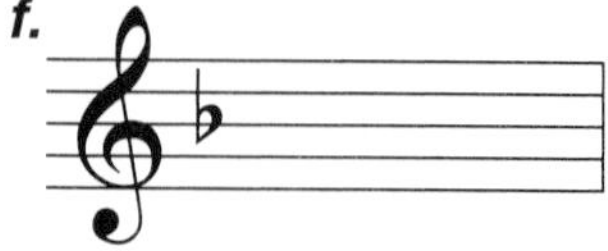

mi-la, : ____

Name ______________________ Class ______________________

Music Reading Worksheet 24

'Round a Melody

Kyrie

Round from Suriname

1. Sing each of the rounds below in unison, using pitch syllables. Sing round a in two parts. Then sing round b in two parts.

a.

b.

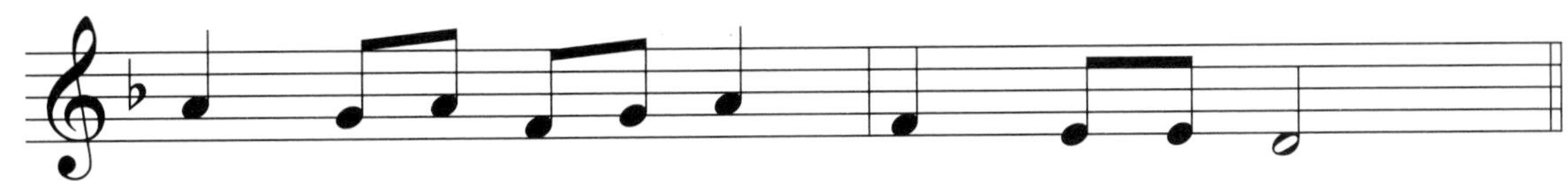

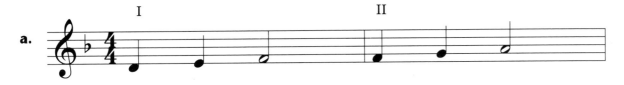

2. Divide the class into four groups. Sing the two rounds at the same time.

Name ______________________ Class ______________

Music Reading Worksheet 25

Curwen Hand Signs

do'

ti

ta

la

si

so

fi

fa

mi

re

do

Music Reading Practice

Recordings of the Reading Sequence exercises in this section are provided in the CD package.

Table of Contents

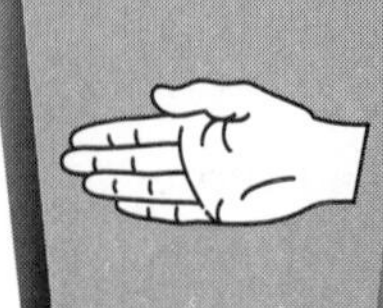

Name ______________________ Class ____________

MUSIC READING PRACTICE: SEQUENCE 1

Rhythm: Review ♩, ♫, 𝅗𝅥, and Ties

As you conduct in meter in 4, use rhythm syllables to **read** and **perform** this counter-rhythm. Note how the ties change the rhythm.

Red River Valley

Cowboy Song from the United States

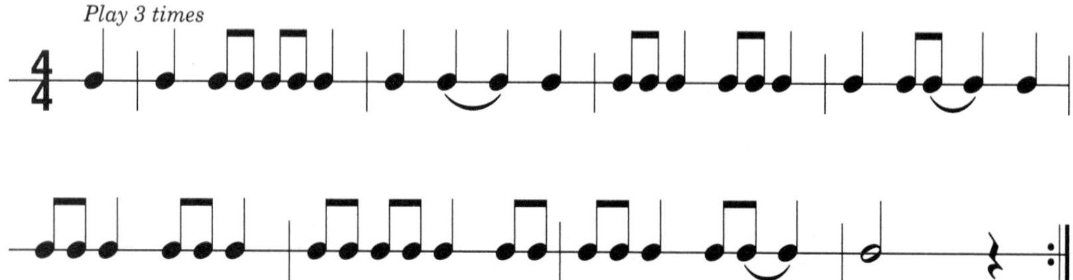

Name ______________________________ Class ______________

Music Reading Practice: Sequence 2

Rhythm: Review ♬♬, ♪♬, ♪. ♬, and Upbeats

Read and **perform** this counter-rhythm, using rhythm syllables.

Bắt kim thang (Setting Up the Golden Ladder)

Traditional Song from Vietnam

Reading Practice

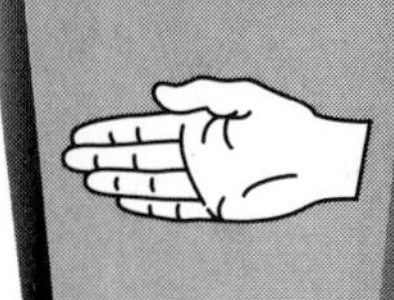

Name ________________________________ Class ________________

Music Reading Practice: Sequence 3

Melody: Reading Melodic Patterns

Using pitch syllables, **read** and **sing** this countermelody.

Bury Me Not on the Lone Prairie

Cowboy Song from the United States

Name ______________________ Class ____________

Music Reading Practice: Sequence 4

Melody: Reading Melodic Contour

Read and **sing** this countermelody, using pitch syllables.

Gonna Build a Mountain

Words and Music by
Leslie Bricusse and Anthony Newley

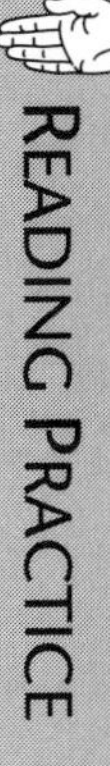

Reading Practice

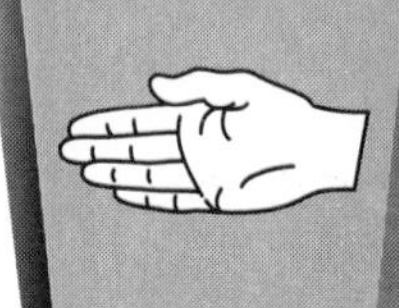

Name ______________________ Class ______________

Music Reading Practice: Sequence 5

Rhythm: Reading Rhythms in $\frac{3}{4}$

Find the dotted-rhythm patterns below. As you conduct a three-beat pattern, use rhythm syllables to **read** the rhythms. Then **perform** them as an accompaniment.

Farewell to Tarwathie

Folk Song from Scotland

Name ______________________________ Class ______________

Music Reading Practice: Sequence 6

Rhythm: Reading Rhythms in $\frac{3}{4}$

Using rhythm syllables, **read** and **perform** these rhythms.

Barb'ry Allen

Folk Song from the British Isles

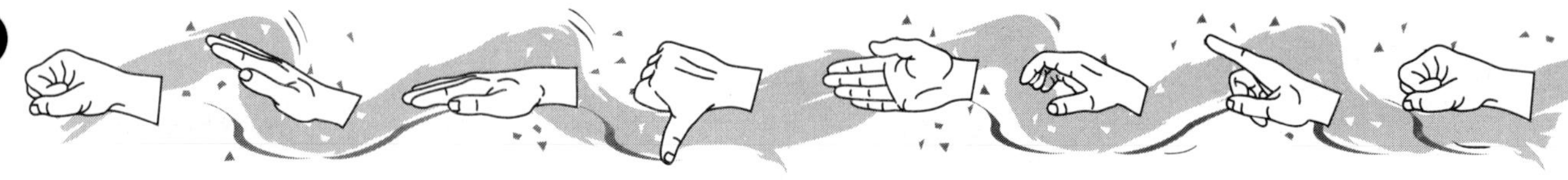

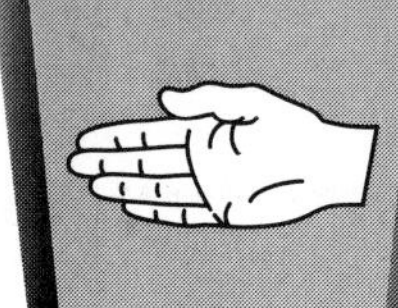

Name ______________________ Class ______________

Music Reading Practice: Sequence 7

Melody: Reading a Major Scale

Using pitch syllables and hand signs, **read** and **sing** this countermelody.

Adiós, amigos (Goodbye, My Friends)

Folk Song from New Mexico

Name ____________________ Class ____________

Music Reading Practice: Sequence 8

Melody: Reading a Minor Scale

As you tap a steady beat, use pitch syllables to silently **read** and **sing** this countermelody. This will help develop your inner hearing.

La mariposa (The Butterfly)

Folk Song from Bolivia

re mi la, re mi la

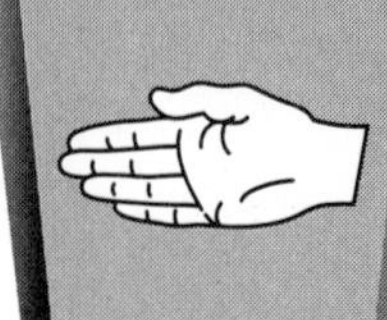

Name ____________________ Class ____________

Music Reading Practice: Sequence 9

Rhythm: Reading Augmentation and Diminution

Using rhythm syllables, **read** and **perform** this three-part rhythm accompaniment.

Do, Re, Mi, Fa

The School Round Book, 1852

1 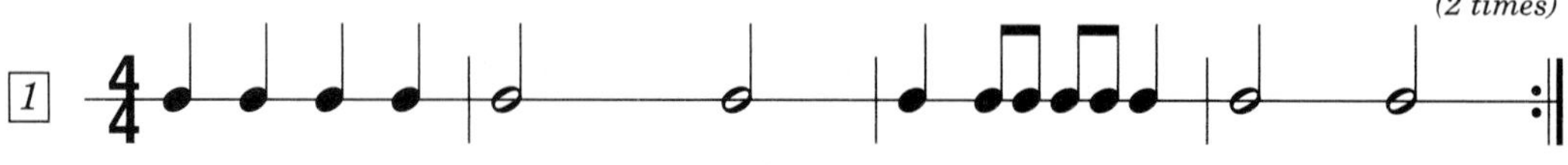

2 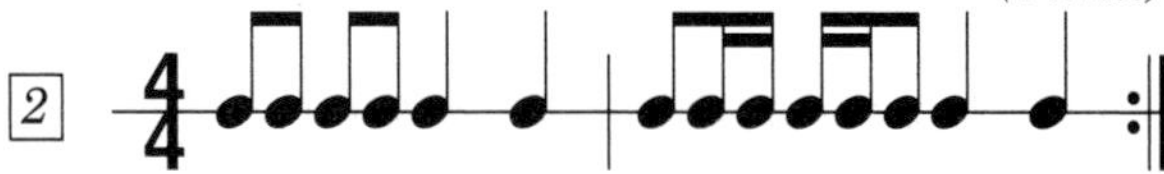

3 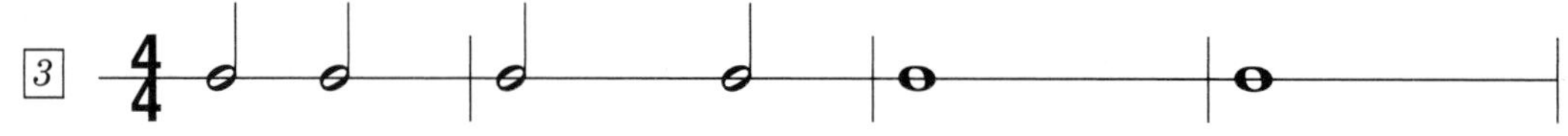

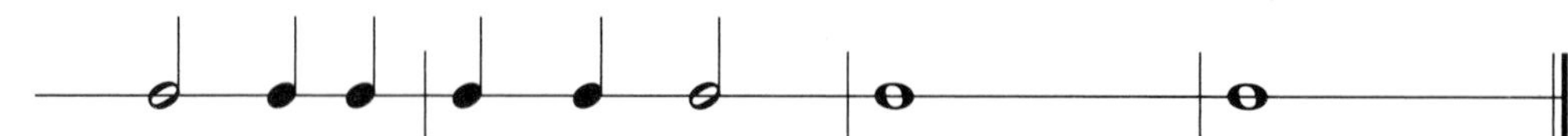

Name ______________________________ Class ______________

Music Reading Practice: Sequence 10

Rhythm: Reading Augmentation and Diminution

As you lightly tap the beat, use rhythm syllables to **read** and **perform** this two-part rhythm accompaniment.

Hava nashira (Sing and Be Joyful)

Round from Israel

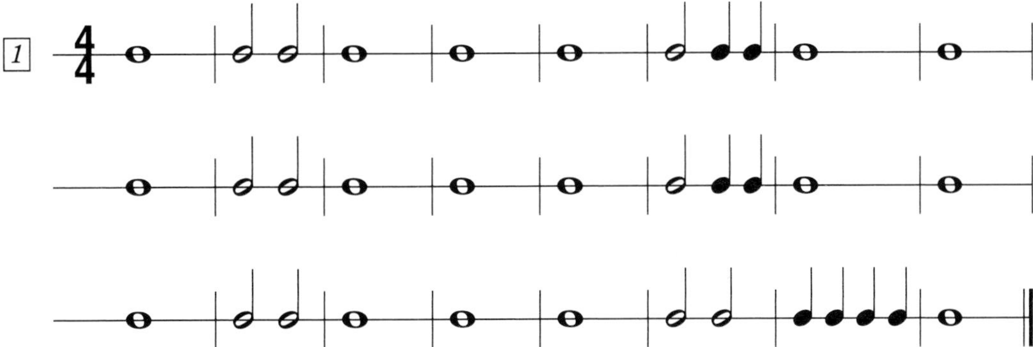

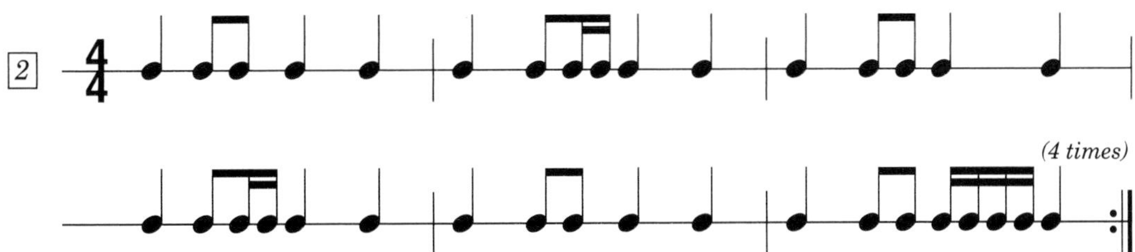

Reading Practice

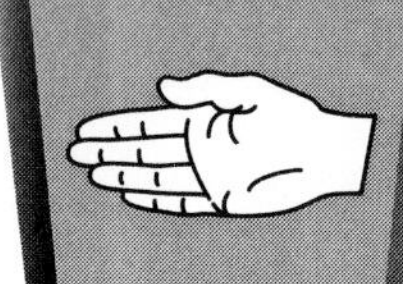

Name ______________________________ Class ______________

Music Reading Practice: Sequence 11

Melody: Reading in Dorian Mode

Using pitch syllables and hand signs, **read** and **sing** this countermelody, which is in dorian mode.

Scarborough Fair

Folk Song from England

Name ______________________ Class ______________

Music Reading Practice: Sequence 12

Melody: Reading in Mixolydian Mode

Locate the measures that are identical in each phrase. How are the last two measures of each phrase alike, or different? Then, use pitch syllables to **read** and **sing** this countermelody.

Harrison Town

Folk Song from the Ozarks
Adapted by Jill Trinka

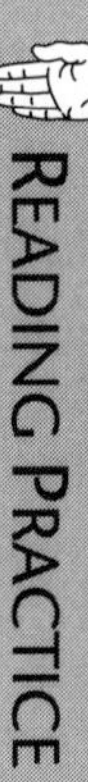

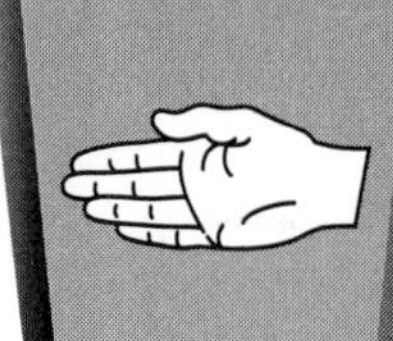

Name ______________________ Class ______________

MUSIC READING PRACTICE: SEQUENCE 13

Rhythm: Reading Rhythms in $\frac{2}{2}$

As you conduct in meter in 2, use rhythm syllables to **read** and **perform** this counter-rhythm.

Swanee

Music by George Gershwin
Words by Irving Caesar

Name ______________________________ Class ______________

Music Reading Practice: Sequence 14

Rhythm: Reading Rhythms in $\frac{3}{8}$

Using rhythm syllables, **read** and **perform** this two-part rhythm accompaniment.

One Morning in May

Folk Song from the Appalachian Mountains

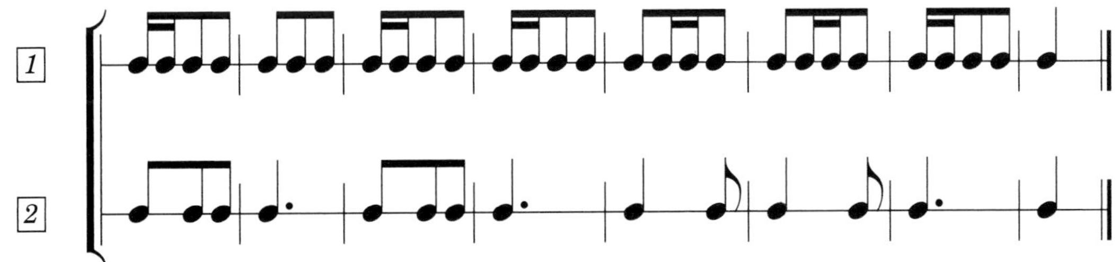

Reading Practice

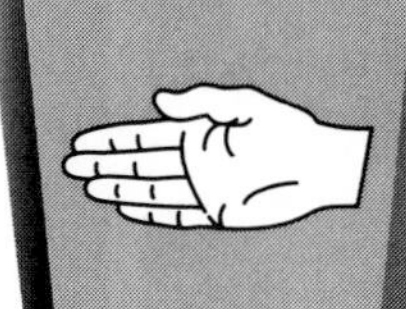

Name ______________________ Class ____________

Music Reading Practice: Sequence 15

Melody: Reading in Harmonic Minor

Read and **sing** this countermelody, using hand signs and pitch syllables.

Music by Shalom Altman
Hebrew Words from the Book of Isaiah
English Version by Leah Jaffa and Fran Minkoff

Lo yisa (Vine and Fig Tree)

Name ______________________ Class ____________

Music Reading Practice: Sequence 16

Melody: Reading Melodic Sequences

Identify the melodic sequence in this countermelody for "Alleluia." Then, **read** and **sing** it using pitch syllables.

Alleluia

Music by Wolfgang Amadeus Mozart

Reading Practice

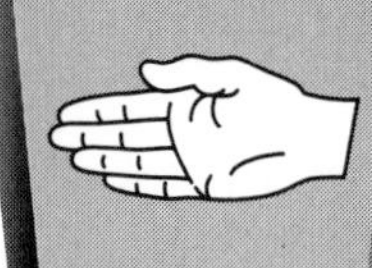

Name ______________________ Class ______________

Music Reading Practice: Sequence 17

Rhythm: Reading ♪♩ ♪ Syncopation

Using rhythm syllables, **read** and **perform** this counter-rhythm. As you do so, tap a steady beat with your foot.

Let Us Sing Together

Traditional Czech Folk Melody

Name ______________________________ Class ______________

Music Reading Practice: Sequence 18

Rhythm: Reading ♪♩♪ Syncopation

Tap a steady beat with your foot. Using rhythm syllables, **read** and **perform** this three-part rhythm accompaniment.

Lost My Gold Ring

Singing Game from Jamaica

Reading Practice

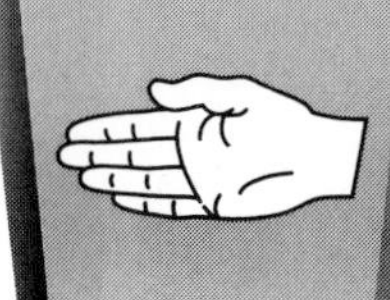

Name ______________________________ Class ______________

Music Reading Practice: Sequence 19

Melody: Reading Intervals (Seconds and Thirds)

Using hand signs and pitch syllables, **read** and **sing** this countermelody.

O lê lê O Bahía (O Le O La)

Folk Song from Brazil

Name ______________________ Class ____________

Music Reading Practice: Sequence 20

Melody: Reading Intervals (Major)

Locate and sing the intervals of a third, a fourth, a fifth, and an octave in this exercise. Then, using pitch syllables, **read** and **sing** it as a countermelody.

Like a Bird

Music by Luigi Cherubini
Words by E. Bolkovac

Reading Practice

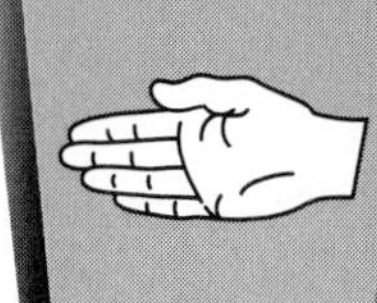

Name ______________________________ Class ______________

Music Reading Practice: Sequence 21

Rhythm: Reading Syncopation

Using rhythm syllables, **read** and **perform** this syncopated counter-rhythm. Conduct in meter in 4 as you say the syllables.

Paths of Victory

Words and Music by Bob Dylan

Name ______________________________ Class ______________

Music Reading Practice: Sequence 22

Rhythm: Reading Mixed Meter

Using rhythm syllables, **read** and **perform** this counter-rhythm. Then, conduct it, paying close attention to the meter changes.

New Hungarian Folk Song

English Words by Jean Sinor
Words and Music by Béla Bartok

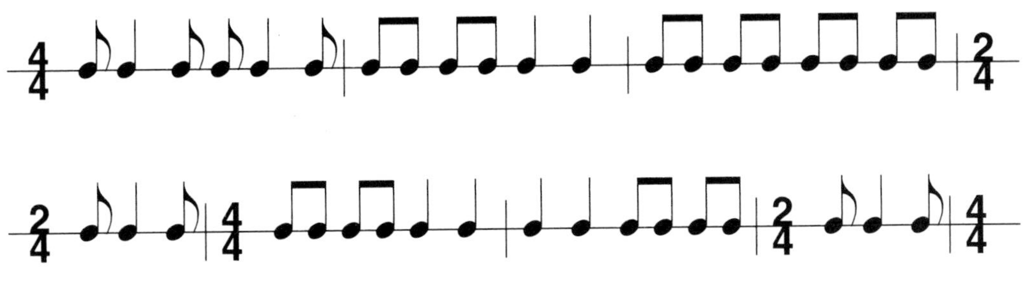

Reading Practice

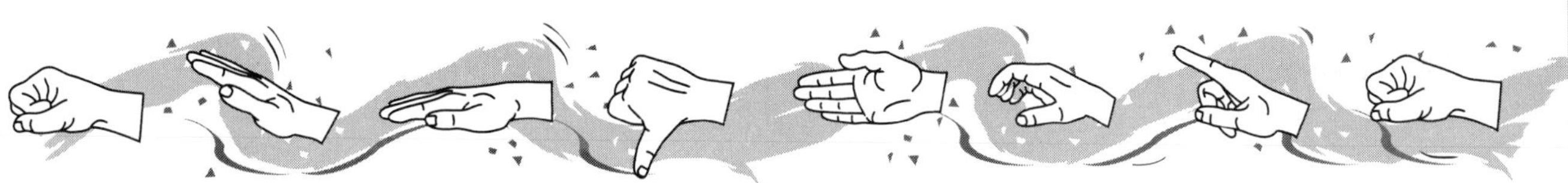

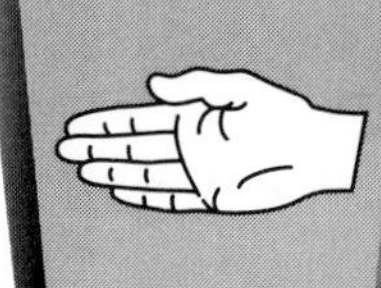

Name ______________________ Class ____________

MUSIC READING PRACTICE: SEQUENCE 23

Melody: Reading Intervals (Fourths and Fifths)

Using hand signs and pitch syllables, **read** and **sing** this melody. **Identify** and **sing** the intervals of fourths and fifths.

Blue Mountain Lake

Adapted by Susan Brumfield
Lumberjack Song from New York

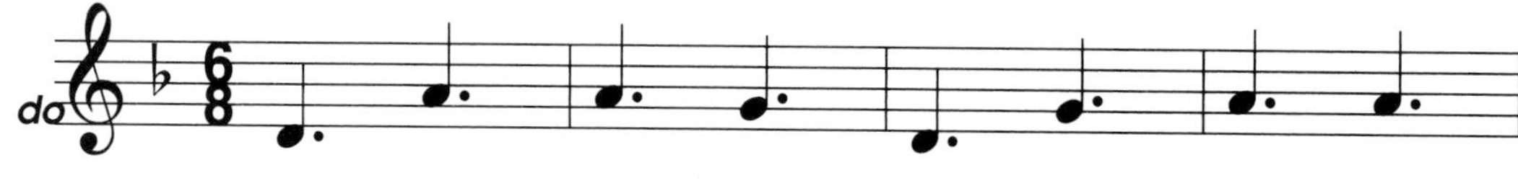

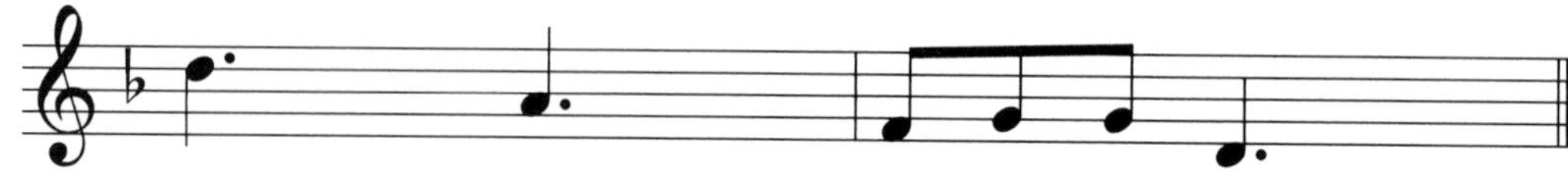

Name ______________________ Class ______________

Music Reading Practice: Sequence 24

Melody: Reading Intervals (Harmonic Minor)

Using pitch syllables and hand signs, **read** and **sing** this countermelody.

Kyrie

Round from Suriname

Reading Practice

Teacher Notes

Orff

Table of Contents

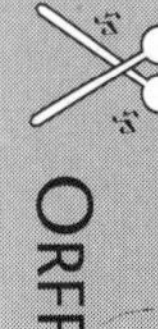

Orff

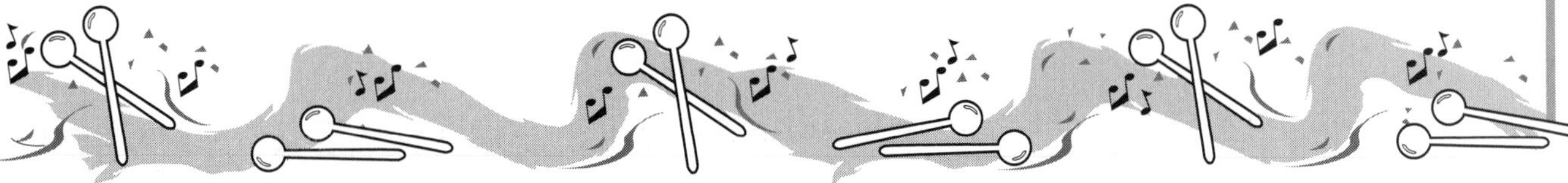

Name ______________________ Class ____________

Orff 1

Bury Me Not on the Lone Prairie

Cowboy Song from the United States
Arranged by Konnie Saliba

*For abbreviations of instruments, see Instrumentarium on page F-37.

Name ______________________ Class ______________________

Orff 2

Hey, Ho! Nobody Home

Old English Round
Arranged by Konnie Saliba

Name ______________________ Class ____________

Orff 3

Farewell to Tarwathie

Folk Song from Scotland
Arranged by Konnie Saliba

Name ______________________ Class ______________________

Orff 4

Barb'ry Allen

Folk Song from the British Isles
Arranged by Konnie Saliba

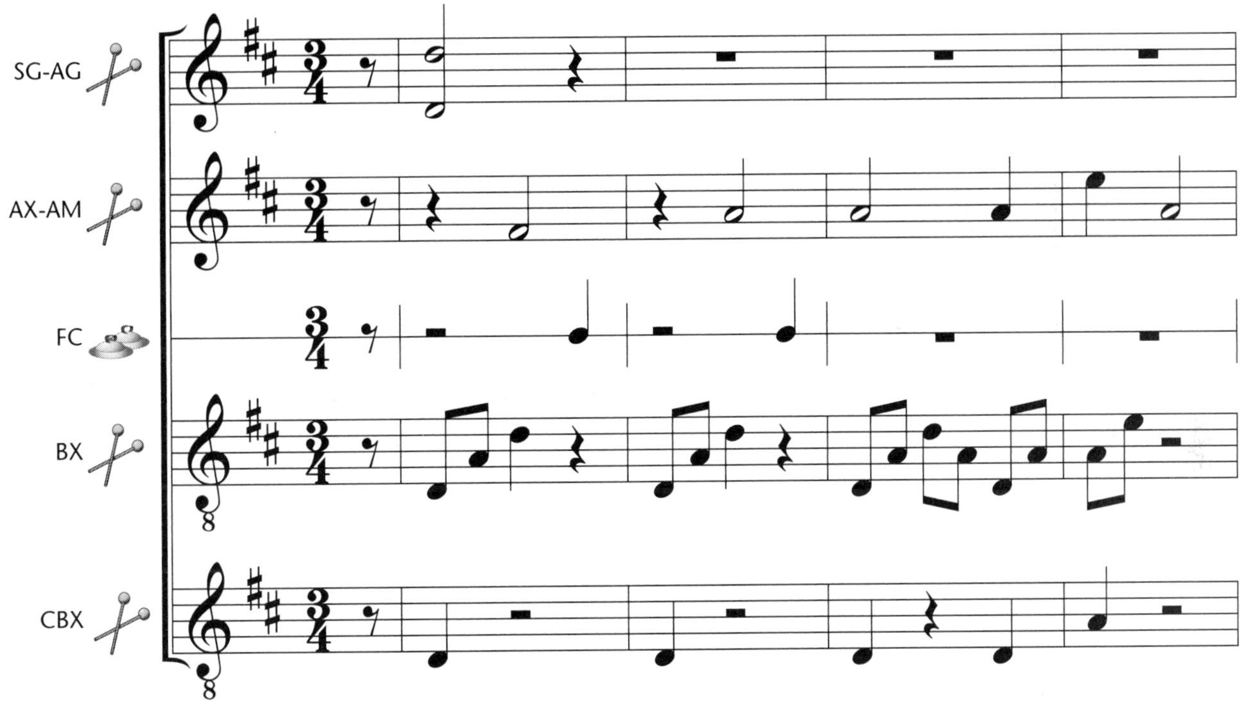

SG-AG

AX-AM

FC

BX

CBX

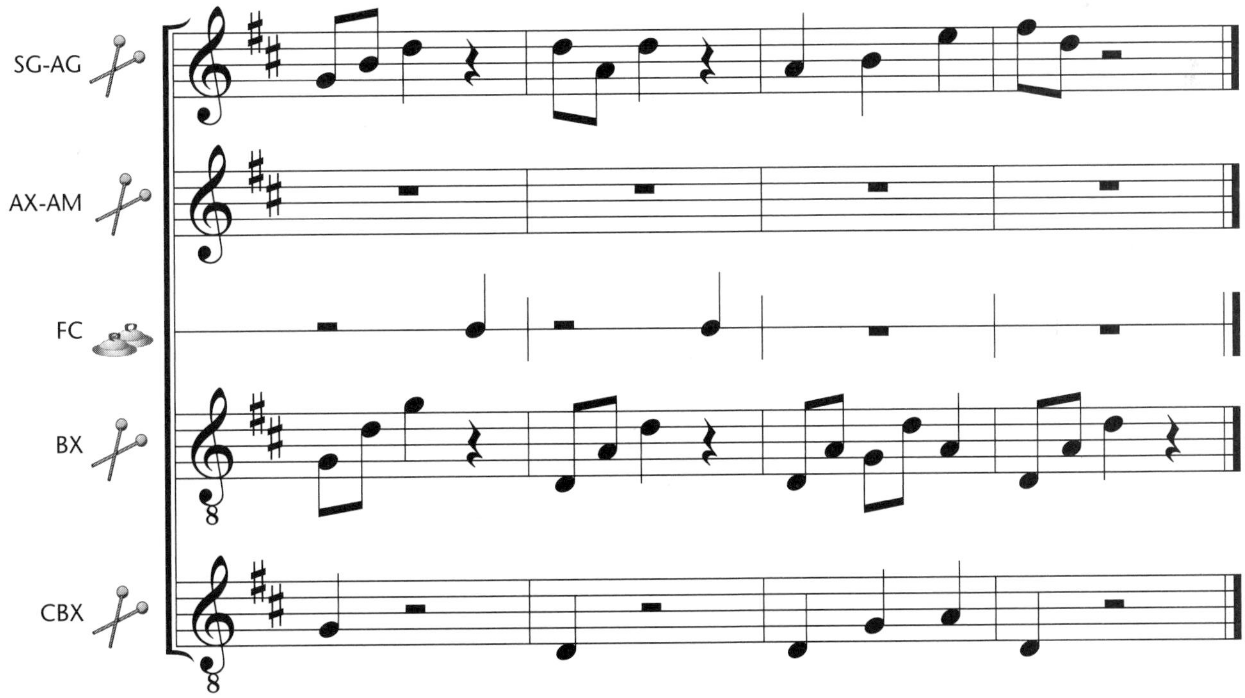

SG-AG

AX-AM

FC

BX

CBX

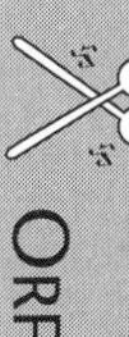

Name ______________________ Class ____________

Orff 5

El condor pasa

Music by Daniel Almonica Robles
Arranged by Konnie Saliba

Name ______________________ Class ______________________

ORFF 5 (CONTINUED)

Perform this percussion ostinato with *El condor pasa.*

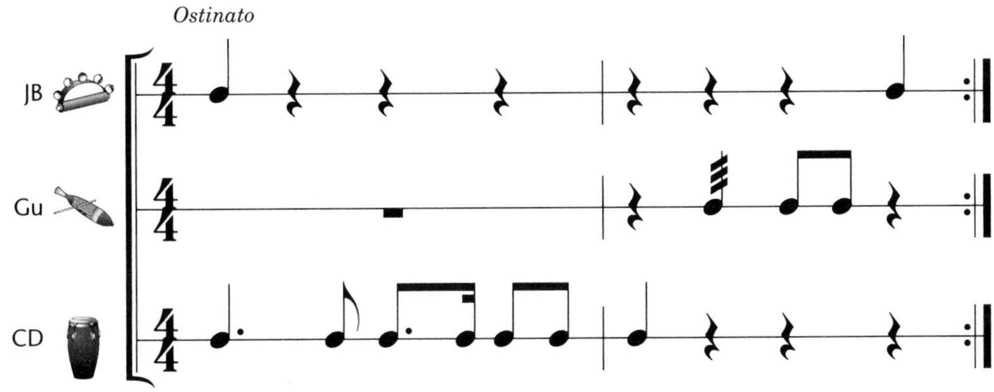

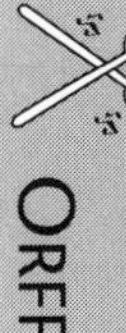

ORFF

Name ________________________ Class ____________

Orff 6

La paloma se fué (The Dove that Flew Away)

Folk Song from Puerto Rico
Arranged by Konnie Saliba

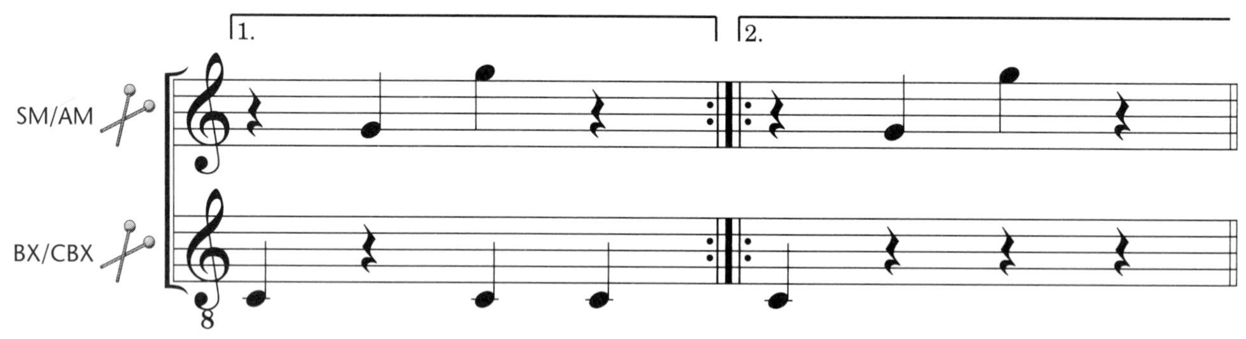

Name ______________________ Class ______________________

ORFF 6 (CONTINUED)

1. Perform this rhythm accompaniment to *"La paloma se fué."* Perform the rhythms in different sections of the song to create contrast.

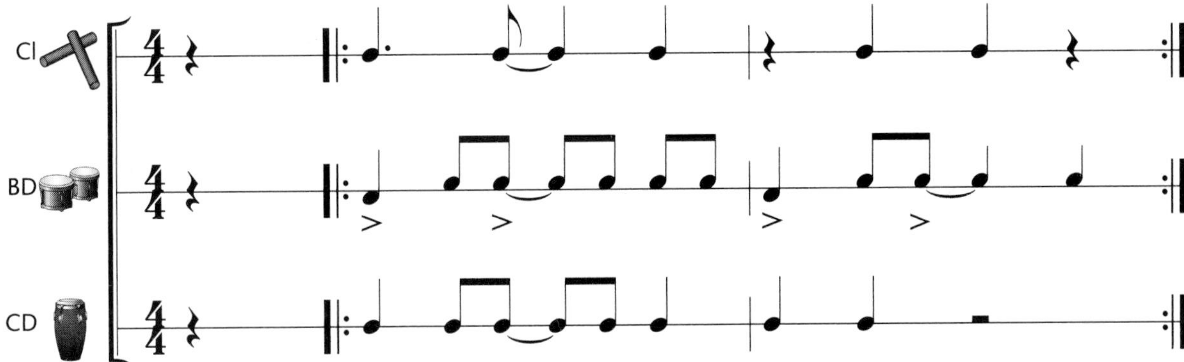

2. Create a new rhythm accompaniment to *"La paloma se fué,"* using nonpitched percussion instruments of your choice. Then perform your accompaniment with the song.

ORFF

Name ______________________ Class ______________

ORFF 7

Scarborough Fair

Folk Song from England
Arranged by Danai Gagne

Name ______________________ Class ______________________

Orff 7 (continued)

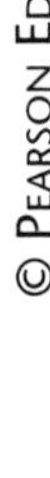

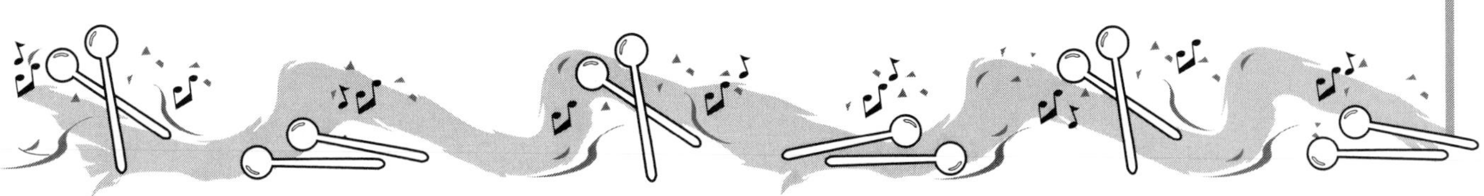

Orff

Name ______________________ Class ______________

ORFF 7 (CONTINUED)

Name ______________________ Class ______________________

Orff 8

One Morning in May

Folk Song from the Appalachian Mountains
Arranged by Konnie Saliba

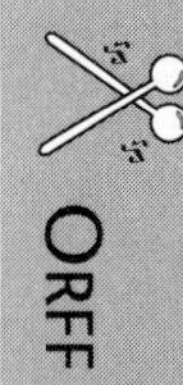

Name ______________________ Class ______________

Orff 9

Lo yisa (Vine and Fig Tree)

Music by Shalom Altman
Arranged by Konnie Saliba

Name ______________________ Class ______________________

ORFF 9 (CONTINUED)

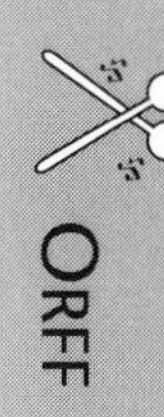

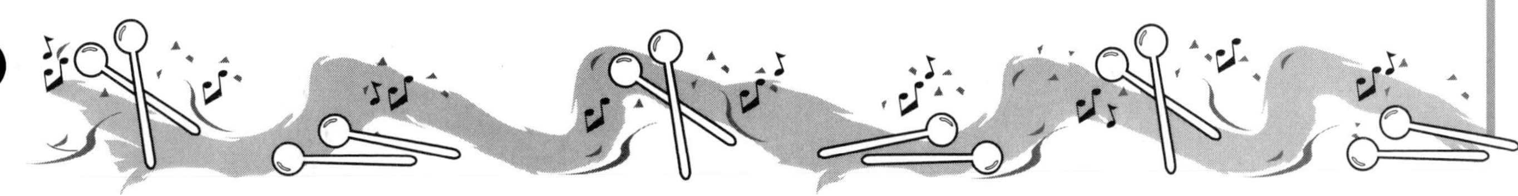

Name ______________________ Class ______________

ORFF 10

El payo (The Cowpoke)

Folk Song from Mexico
Arranged by Konnie Saliba

Name ______________________ Class ______________________

ORFF 10 (CONTINUED)

Perform this percussion ostinato with *El payo.*

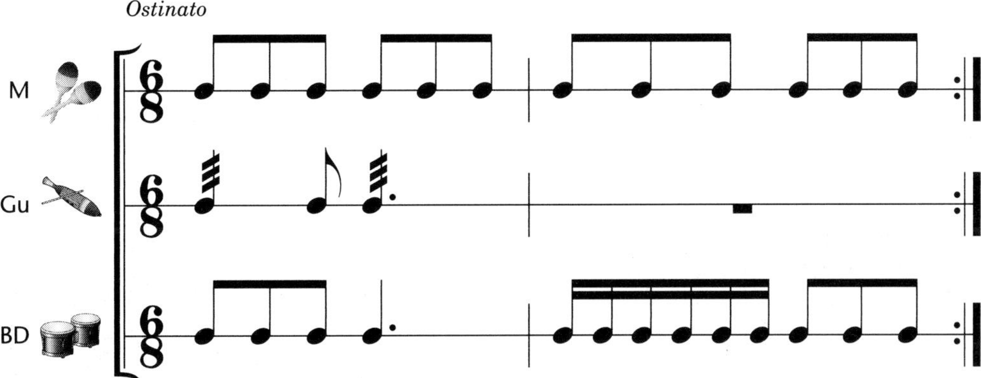

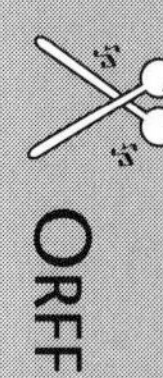

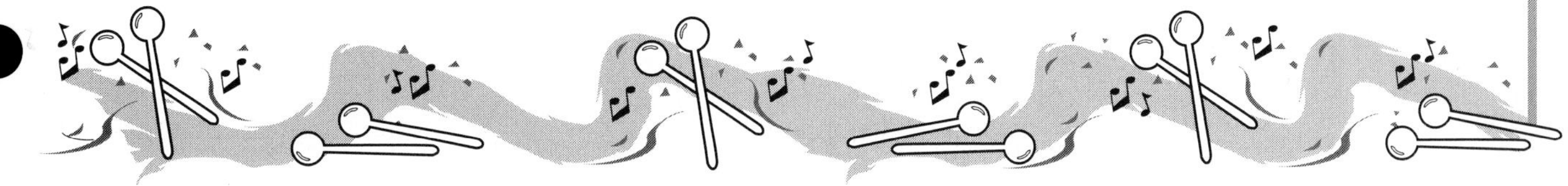

Name ______________________ Class ____________

Orff 11

Lost My Gold Ring

Singing Game from Jamaica
Arranged by Konnie Saliba

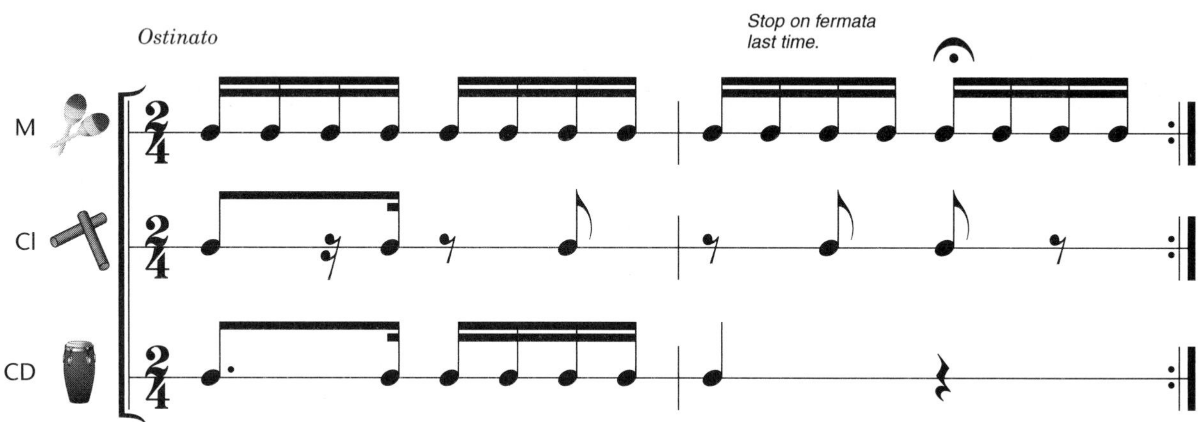

Name ______________________ Class ______________________

ORFF 12

Paths of Victory

Words and Music by Bob Dylan
Arranged by Konnie Saliba

CBX part may be doubled on guitar.

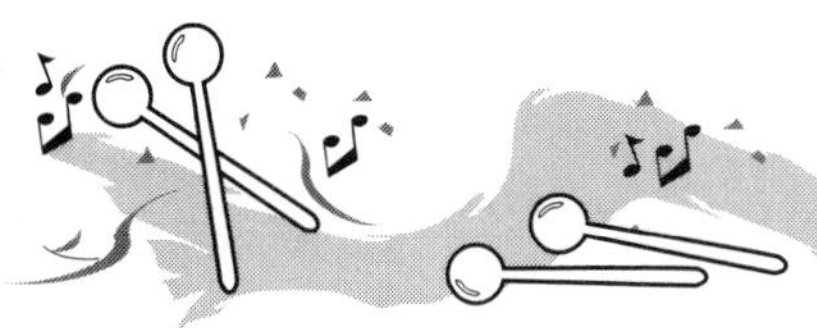

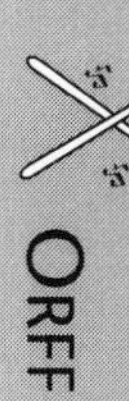

ORFF

Name ______________________ Class ____________

ORFF 12 (CONTINUED)

Name ______________________ Class ______________________

Orff 13

Siyahamba

Traditional Freedom Song
from South Africa
Arranged by Konnie Saliba

Orff

Name ______________________ Class ______________

Orff 14

The Water Is Wide

Folk Song from England
Arranged by Konnie Saliba

Name ______________________________ Class ____________________

Orff 14 (continued)

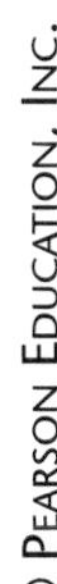

Orff

Name ______________________ Class ______________

Orff 15

You Are My Sunshine

Words and Music by
Jimmie Davis and Charles Mitchell
Arranged by Konnie Saliba

Name ______________________ Class ______________________

Orff 15 (continued)

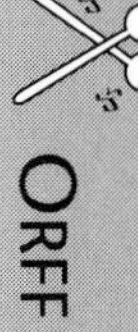

Orff

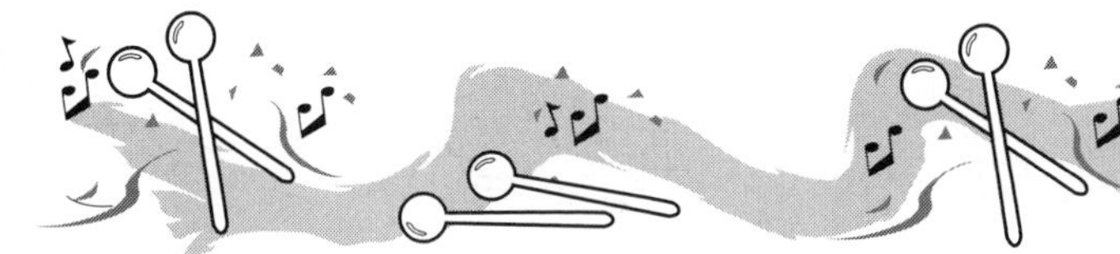

Name ______________________ Class ______________

Orff 16

Take Time in Life

Folk Song from Liberia
Arranged by Konnie Saliba

Name ______________________ Class ______________________

ORFF 16 (CONTINUED)

ORFF

Name ______________________ Class ______________

Orff 17

Everybody Loves Saturday Night

Folk Song from West Africa
Arranged by Konnie Saliba

Name ______________________ Class ______________________

Orff 18

Water Come a Me Eye

Folk Song from Trinidad
Arranged by Konnie Saliba

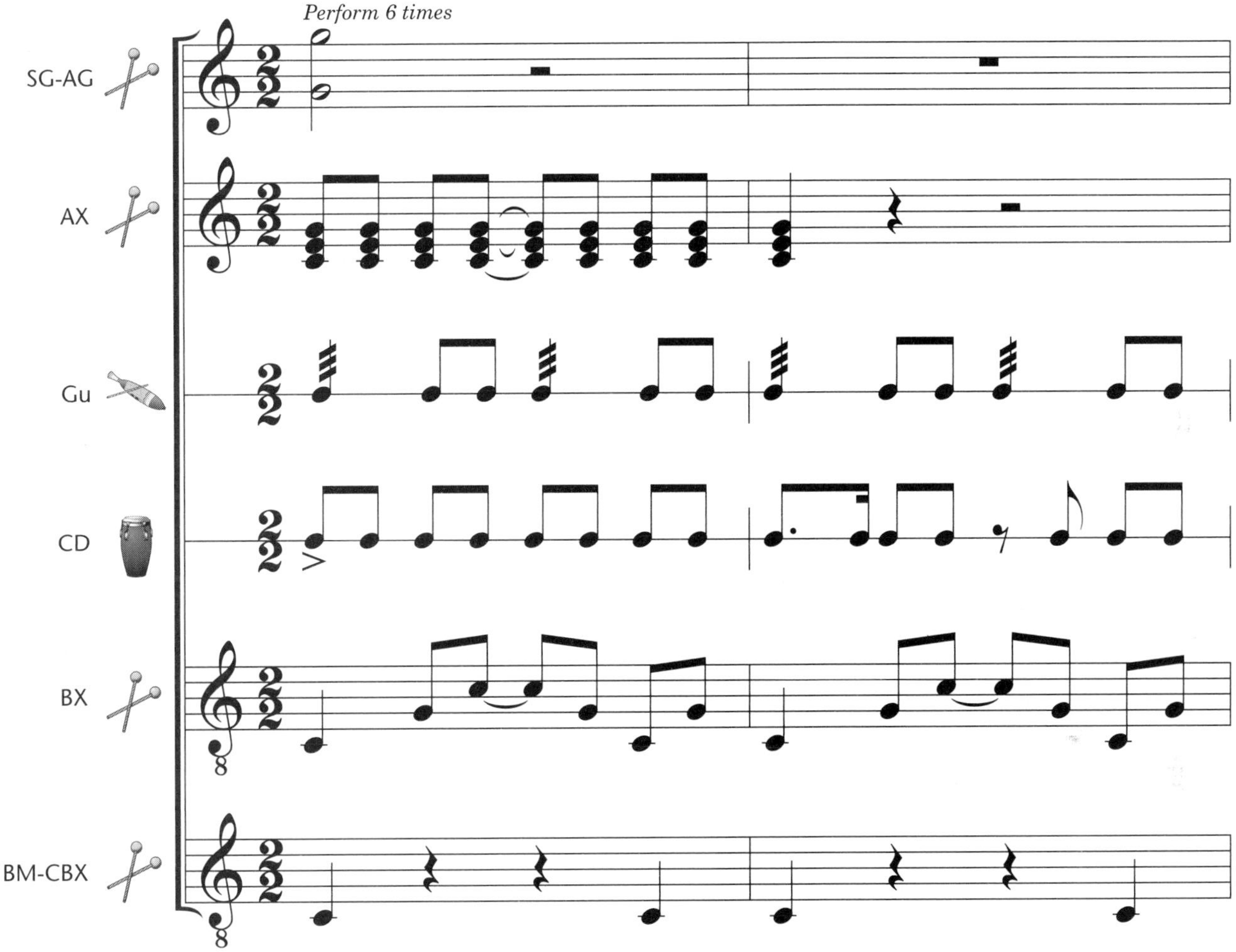

Perform 6 times

SG-AG

AX

Gu

CD

BX

BM-CBX

Begin SG-AG and AX at measure 9.

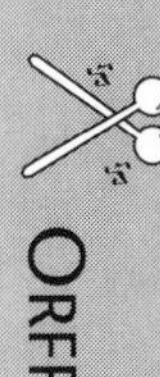

Name ______________________ Class ______________

ORFF 18 (CONTINUED)

SG-AG

AX

Gu

CD

BX

BM-CBX

Name ______________________ Class ______________

ORFF 19

Asadoya

Folk Song from Okinawa
Arranged by Konnie Saliba

(Transposed from E Major.)

Play SM and AM with wooden mallets.

ORFF

Name ____________________ Class ____________

Orff 20

Worried Man Blues

Traditional Blues
Arranged by Konnie Saliba

CBX part may be doubled on guitar.

Name ______________________ Class ______________________

ORFF 20 (CONTINUED)

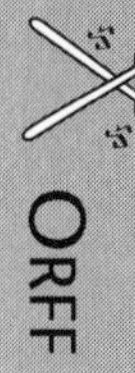

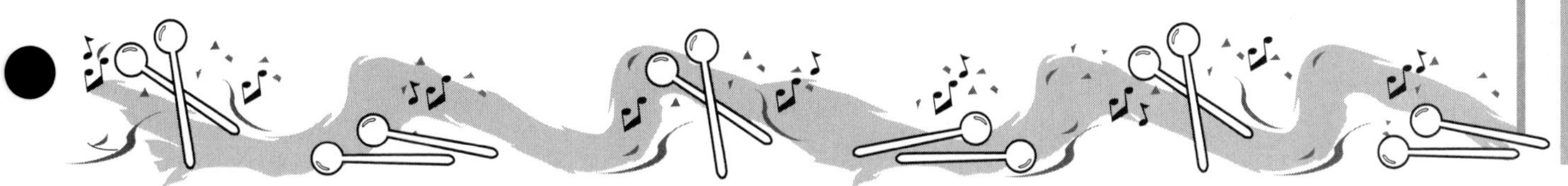

Name ______________________ Class ______________

Orff 21

Tom Dooley

Folk Song from the United States
Arranged by Konnie Saliba

CBX part may be doubled on guitar.

Name ______________________ Class ______________________

Orff 21 (continued)

Orff

Name ______________________ Class ______________

Orff 22

Play this percussion ostinato with the Orff accompaniment on page 483 of the student text.

El Carnavalito humahuaqueño (The Little Humahuacan Carnival)

Folk Song from Argentina
Arranged by Konnie Saliba

Name ______________________ Class ______________________

ORFF 23

INSTRUMENTARIUM

Abbreviations of Instruments on a Score

Winds

SoR Sopranino Recorder
SR Soprano Recorder
AR Alto Recorder
TR Tenor Recorder
BR Bass Recorder

Mallet Instruments

SG Soprano Glockenspiel
AG Alto Glockenspiel
SX Soprano Xylophone
AX Alto Xylophone
BX Bass Xylophone
CBX Contrabass Xylophone
SM Soprano Metallophone
AM Alto Metallophone
BM Bass Metallophone

Percussion—Metals

Tr Triangle
FC Finger Cymbals
JB Jingle Bells
BT Bell Tree
AB Agogo Bells
CB Cow Bell
Cym Cymbals
W Slide Whistle

Percussion—Woods

WB Wood Block
ToB Tone Block
C Castanets
Sh Shakers
M Maracas
Cb Cabasa
R Ratchet
Rt Rattles
TeB Temple Blocks
VS Vibra Slap
Cl Claves
Gu Guiro
LD Log Drum
SB Sand Blocks
Af Afuchi

Percussion—Membranes or Skins

HD Hand Drum
Tam Tambourine
BD Bongo Drums
CD Conga Drum
SD Snare Drum

Large Percussion

HC Hanging Cymbal
G Gong
BD Bass Drum

Tuned Instruments

G Guitar
P Piano
Tp Timpani
DB Double Bass

Name ______________________ Class ______________

ORFF 24

Instrumentarium Diagram

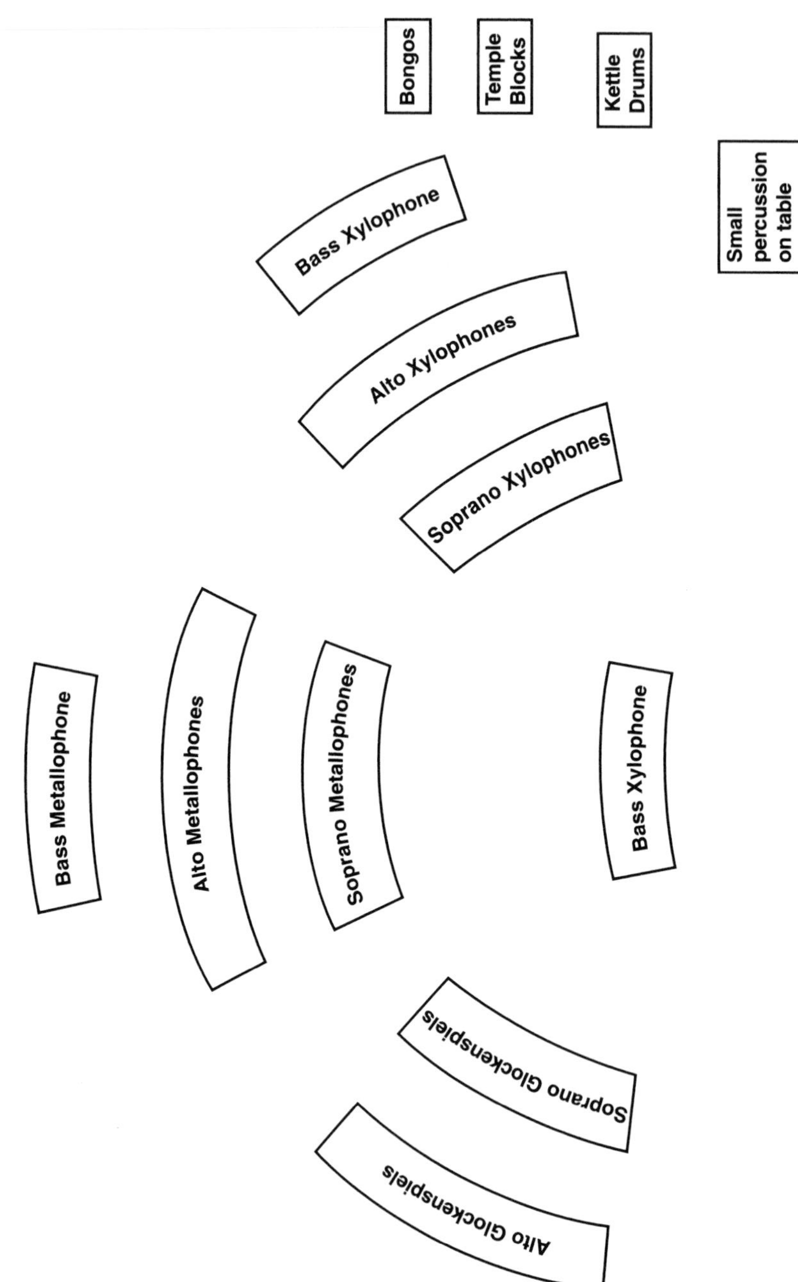

SIGNING

Table of Contents

Name ______________________ Class ____________

Signing 1

Lean On Me

Words and Music by Bill Withers

REFRAIN

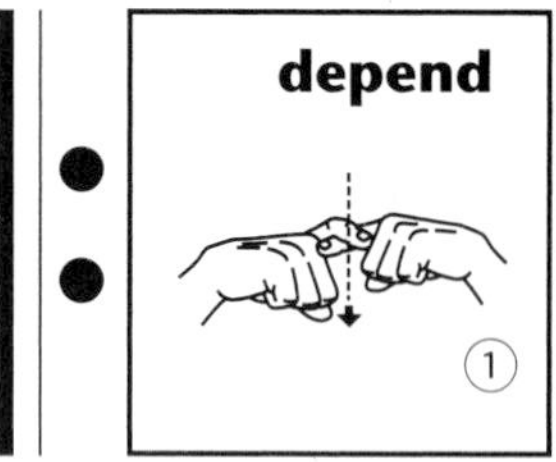

Lean on me

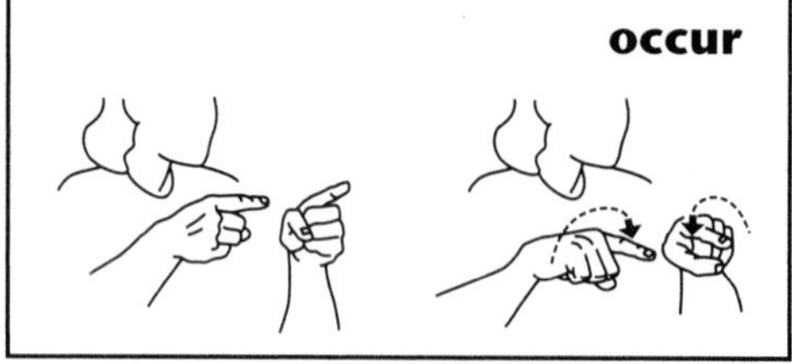

when

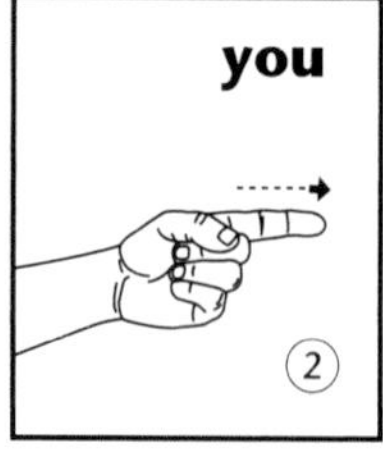

you're

not

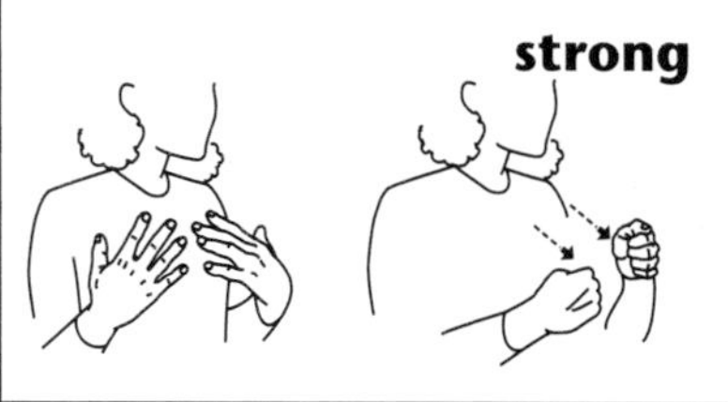

strong

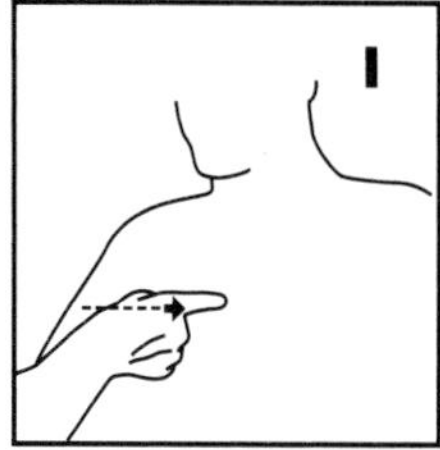

and I'll

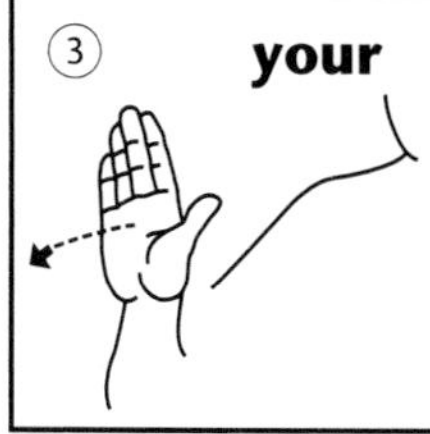

be your

friend,

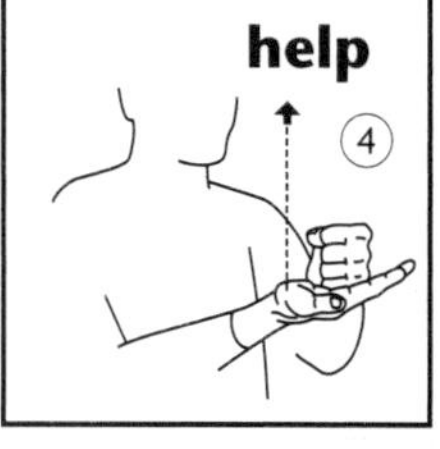

I'll help

you carry on,

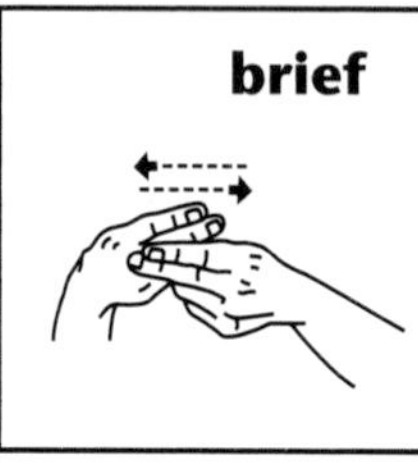

For it won't be long

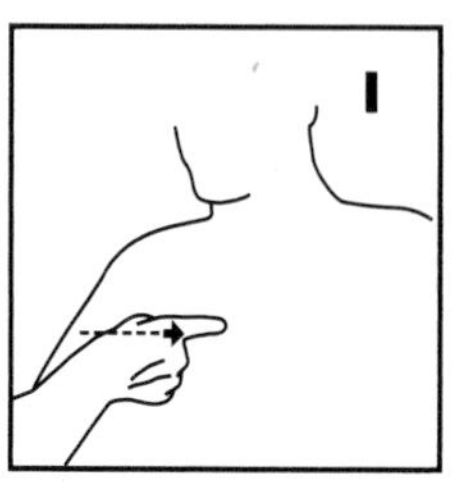

'till I'm

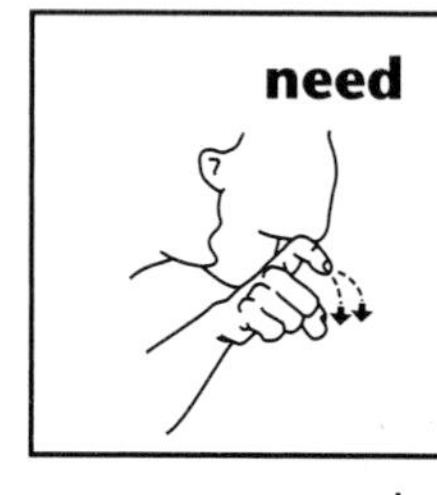

gonna need

somebody to

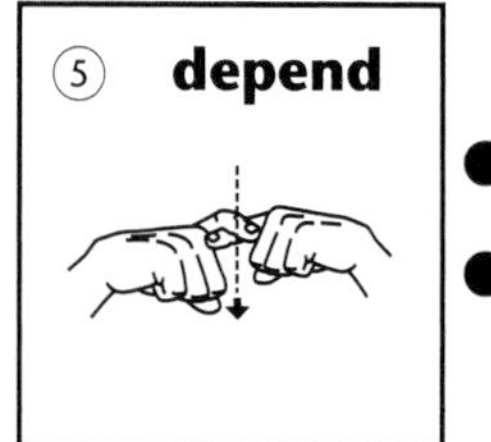

lean on.

"Lean on" and "help" are both directional signs. For the phrase "lean on me," the fingers should be pointed toward the signer. In general use, the fingers are pointed out. The sign for "help" should always move in the direction of whomever is being helped. In general use, the sign should move up slightly.

1. tips of fingers directed toward body of signer—denotes person being leaned or depended on ("me")
2. point out or to specific person
3. palm out or to specific person
4. move from body out
5. tips of fingers pointed out

Name ______________________ Class ______________________

Signing 1 (continued)

(after second ending)

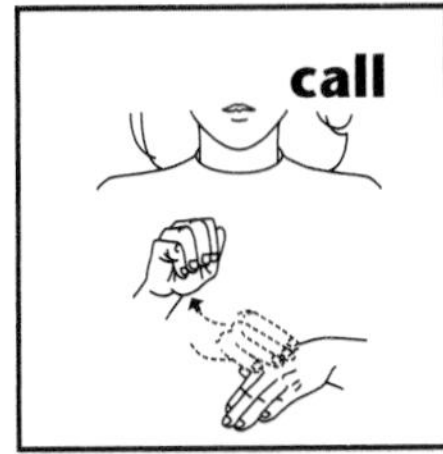

Just call on me,

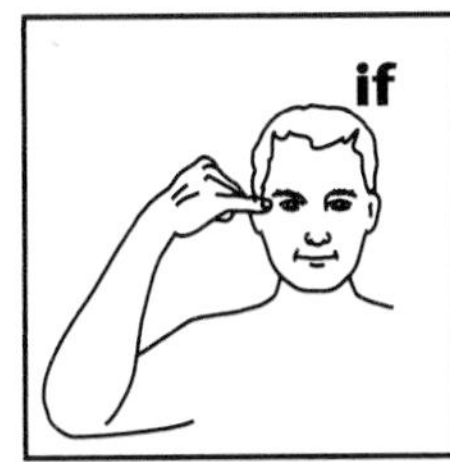

brother,

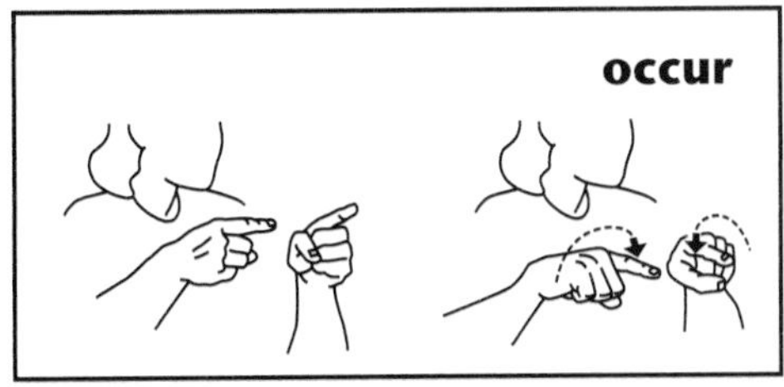

when

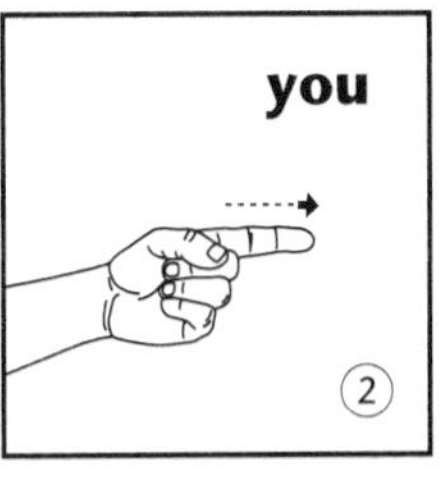

you

need

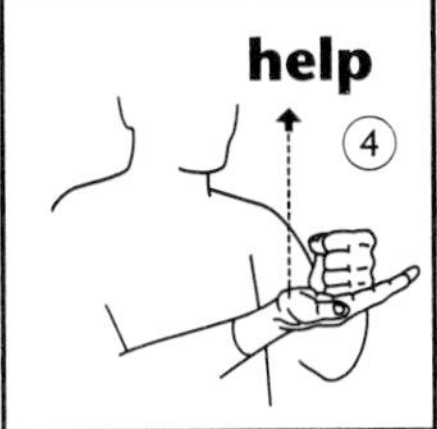

a hand.

We all need

somebody

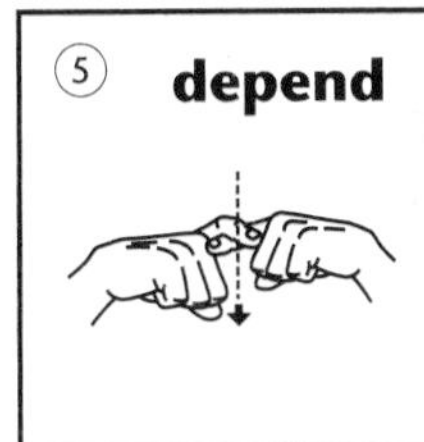

to lean on.

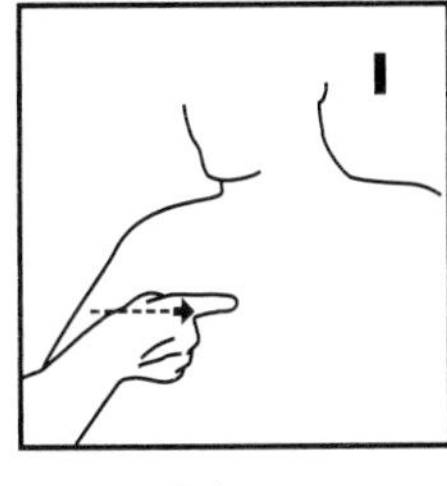

I just

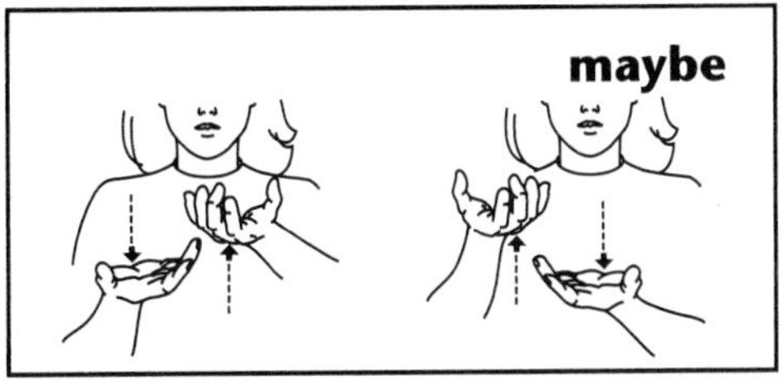

might

have a

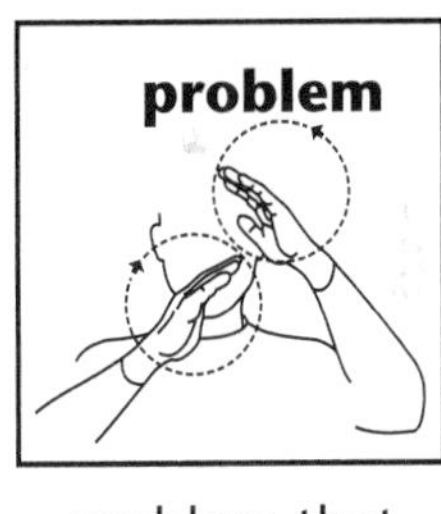

problem that

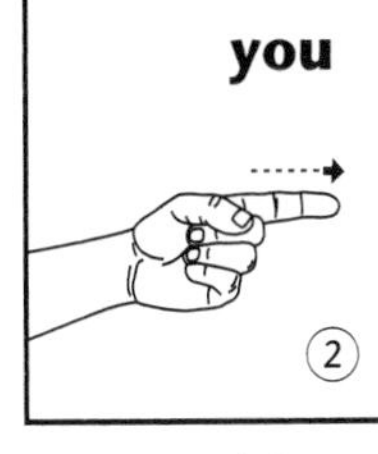

you'd

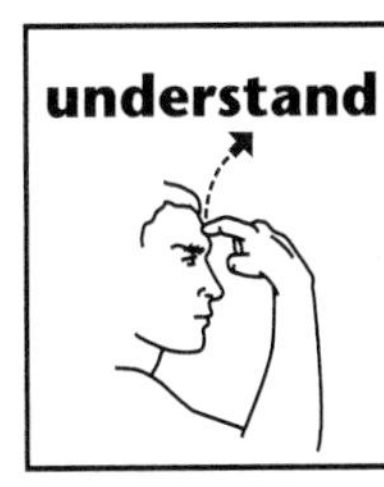

understand.

We all need

somebody to

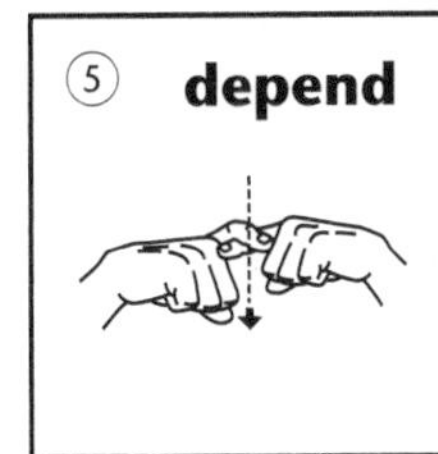

lean on.

② point out or to specific person

④ move from body out

⑤ tips of fingers pointed out

Name ______________________________ Class ______________

SIGNING 2

Hey, Ho! Nobody Home

Old English Round

Hey,

ho,

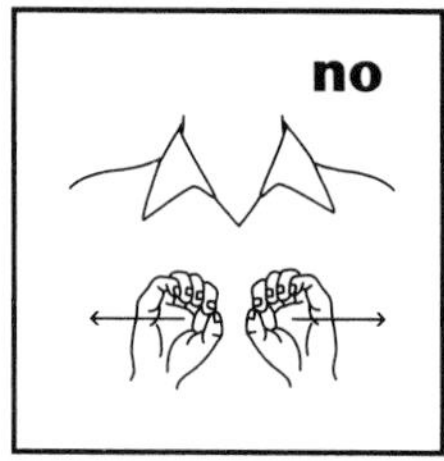

no-

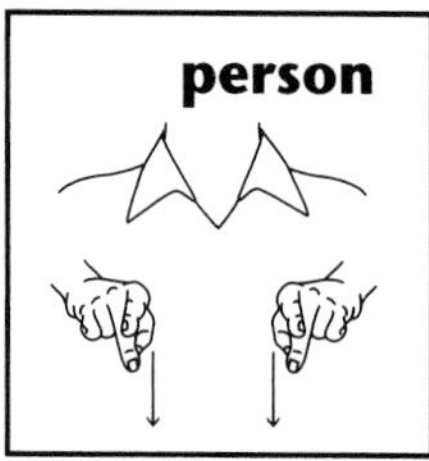

body

home,

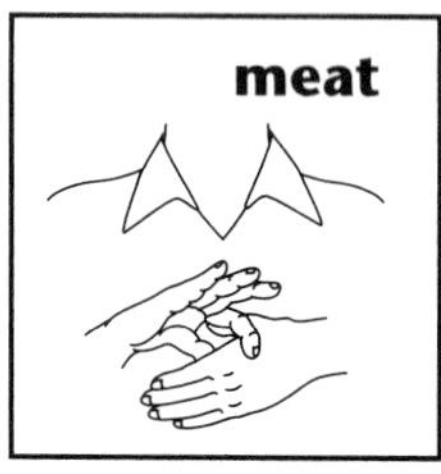

Meat

nor drink

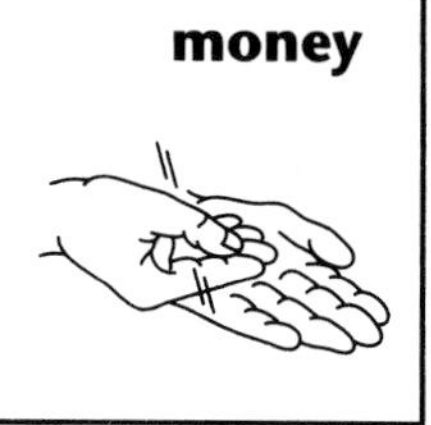

nor money

have I

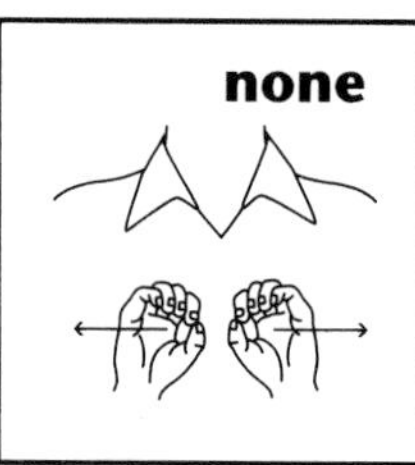

none.

Name ______________________ Class ______________________

SIGNING 2 (CONTINUED)

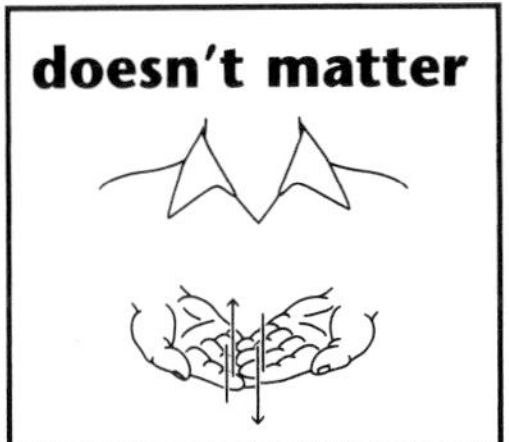

Yet

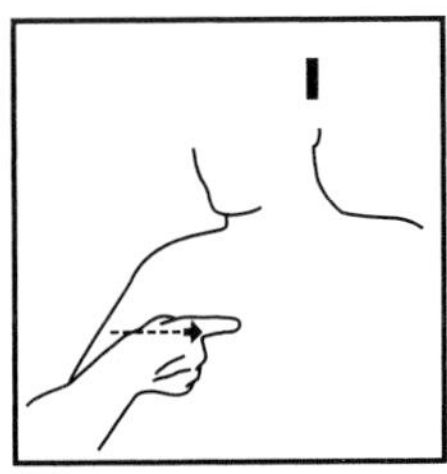

I will

be merry,

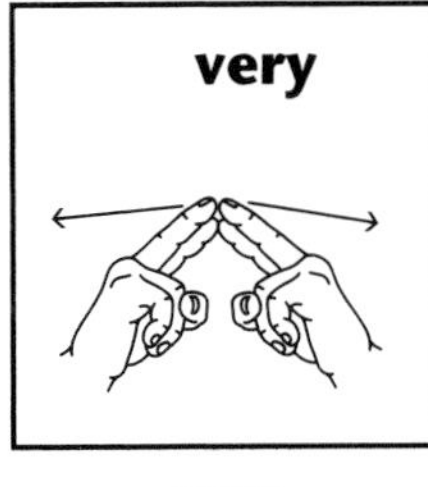

very

merry.

Hey,

ho,

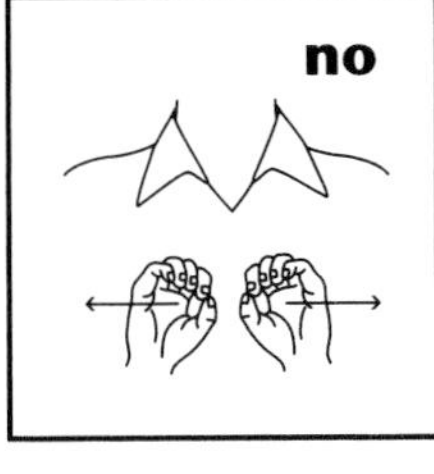

no-

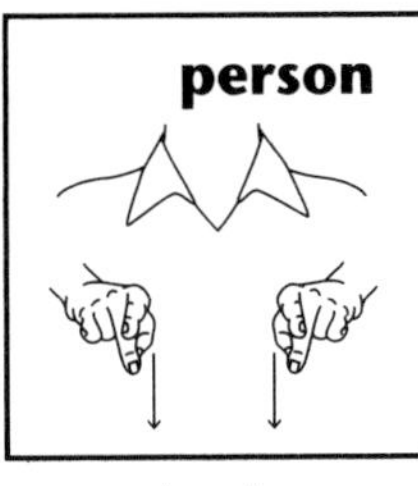

body

home.

① often signed with both hands

Name ______________________________ Class ______________

Signing 2 (continued)

Ostinato 1

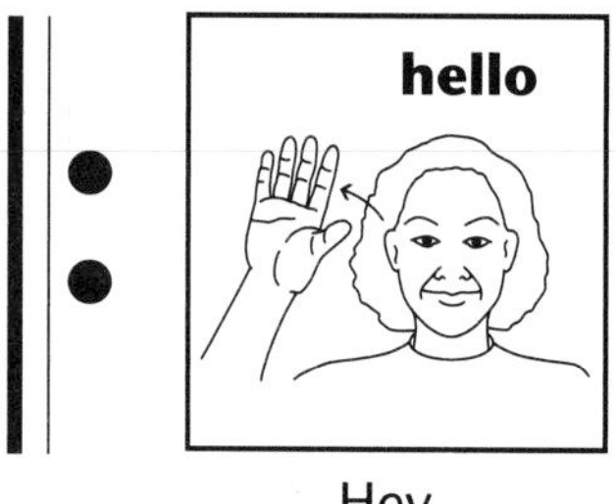

Hey,

ho,

Hey,

ho,

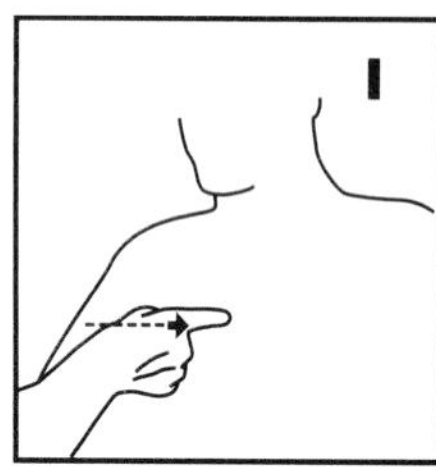

I

said,

Ostinatos 2 and 3

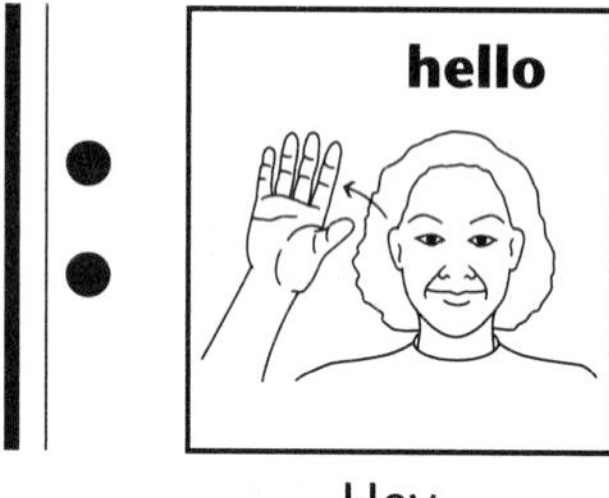

Hey,

ho,

Hey,

ho.

Name ______________________ Class ______________

SIGNING

SIGNING 3

Adiós, amigos (Goodbye, My Friends)

Folk Song from New Mexico
English words by Donald Scafuri

Goodbye,

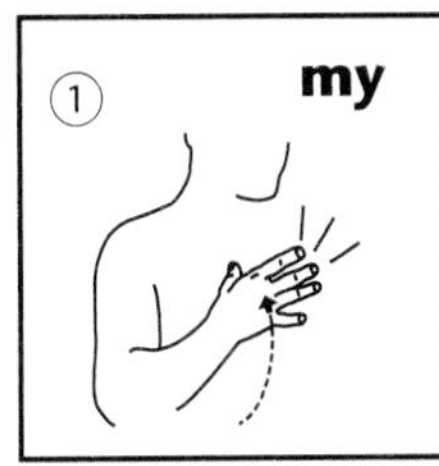

my

good friends,

Sleep well,

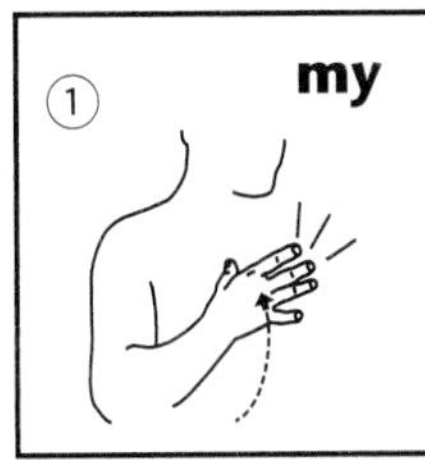

my

good friends,

May

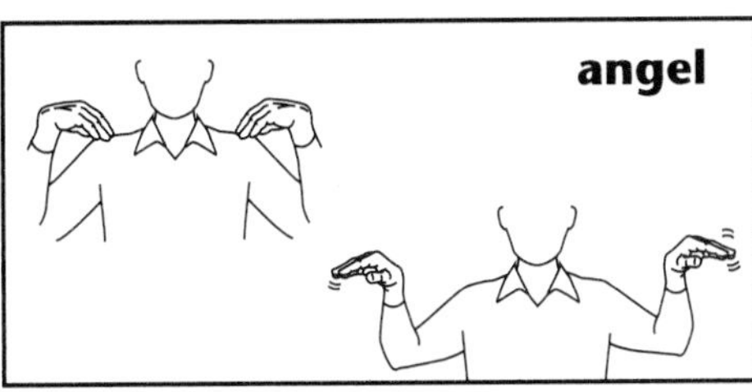

angels

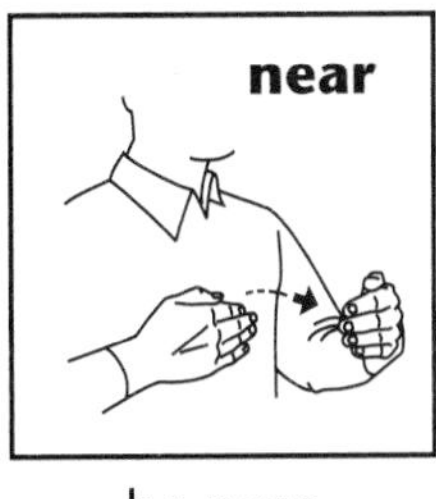

be near

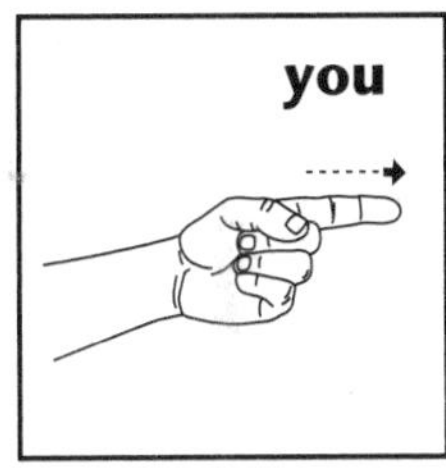

you

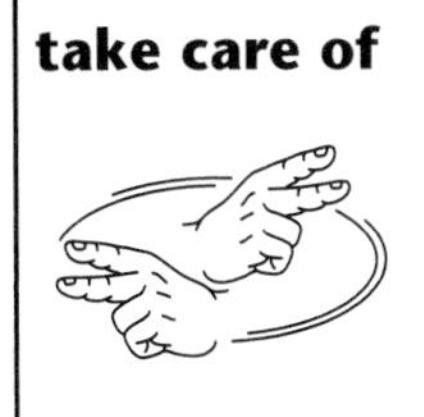

to keep

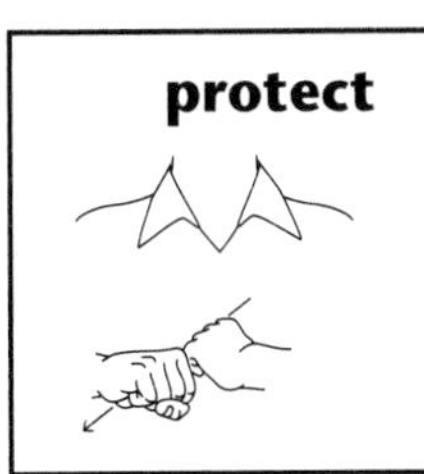

you from

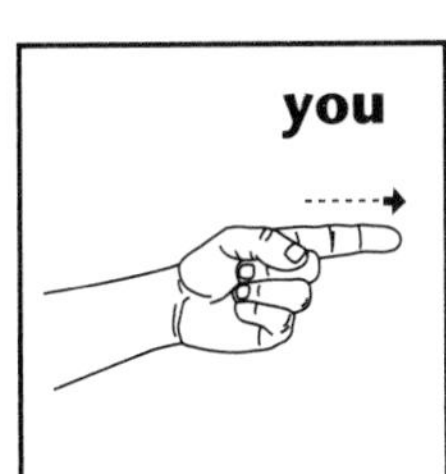

harm.

① palm flat against chest

Name ______________________ Class ______________

Signing 3 (continued)

Goodbye,

goodbye,

goodbye,

goodbye.

Name ______________________________ Class ____________________

SIGNING 4

Ain't Gonna Let Nobody Turn Me 'Round

African American Civil Rights Song

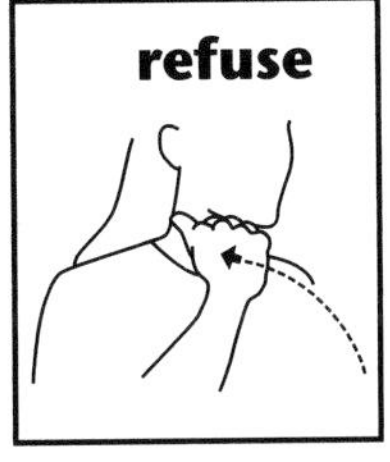

Ain't

gonna let

nobody

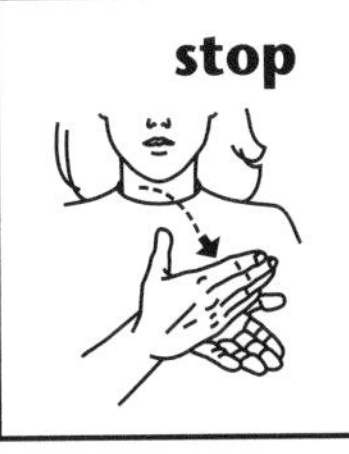

turn me

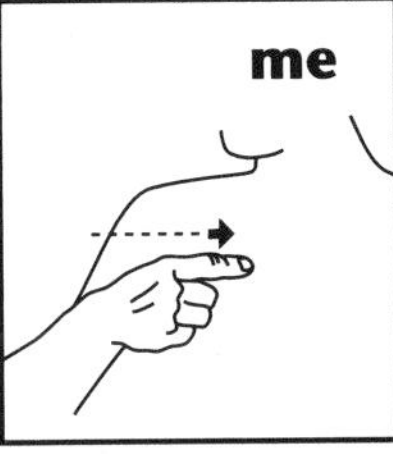

'round,

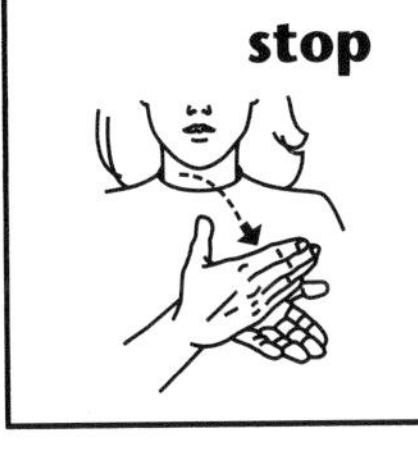

turn me

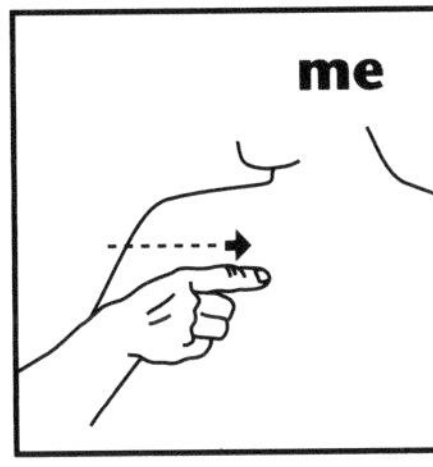

'round,

turn me

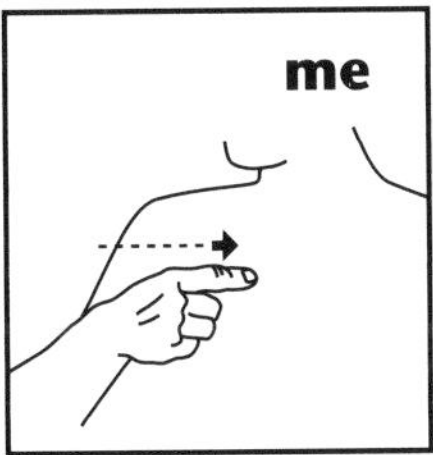

'round.

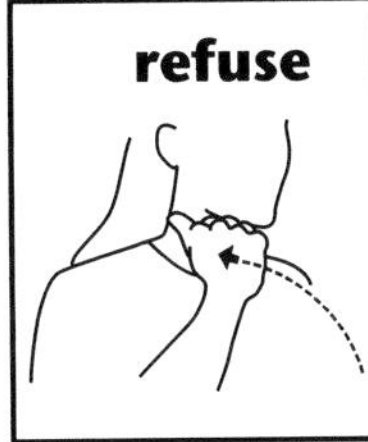

Ain't

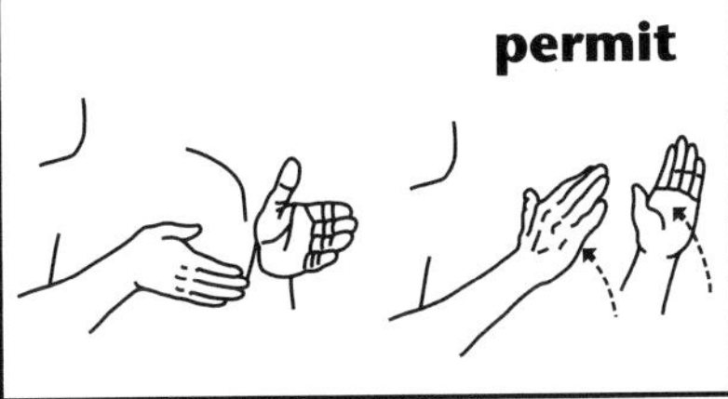

gonna let

nobody

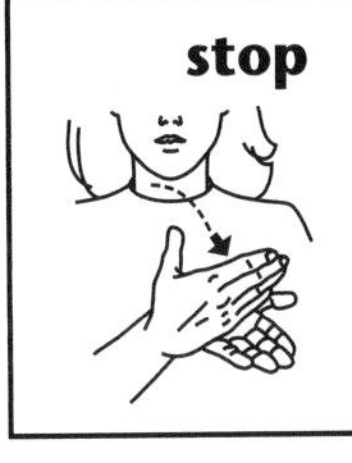

turn me

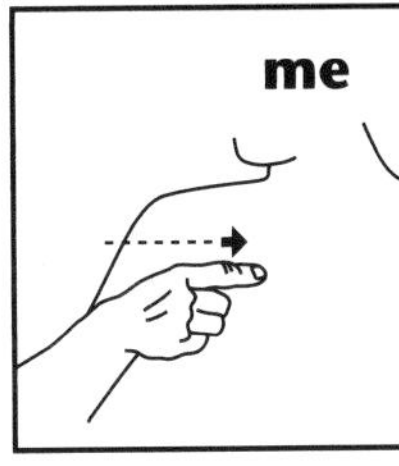

'round,

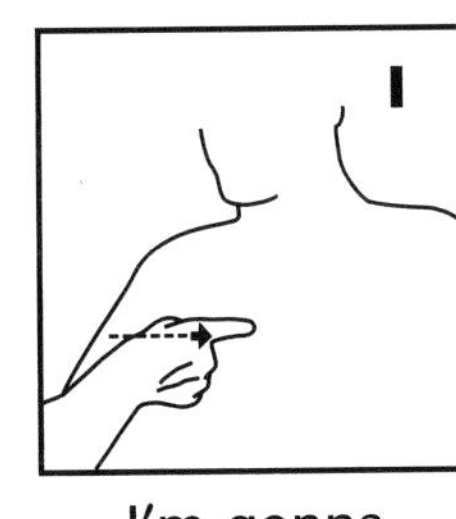

I'm gonna

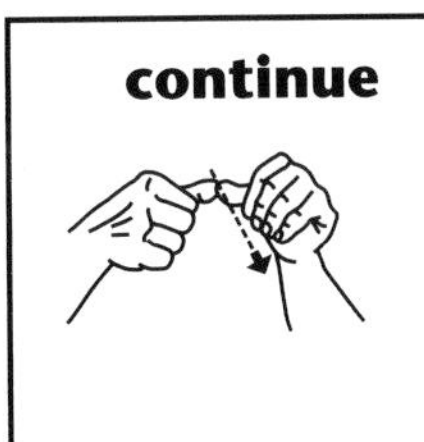

keep on

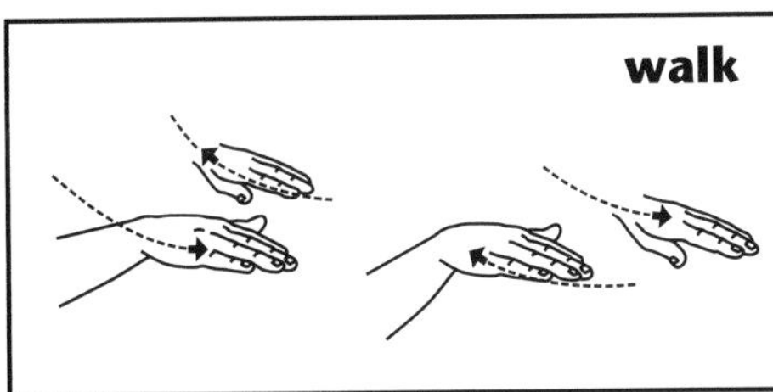

a-walkin',

keep on

Name ______________________ Class ______________

Signing 4 (continued)

a-talkin',

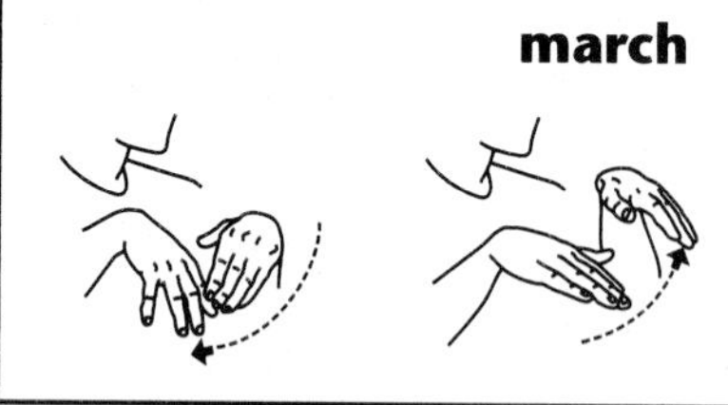

Marchin'

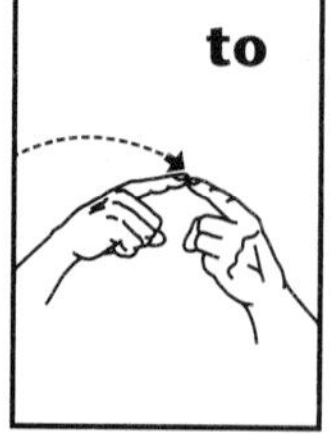

to

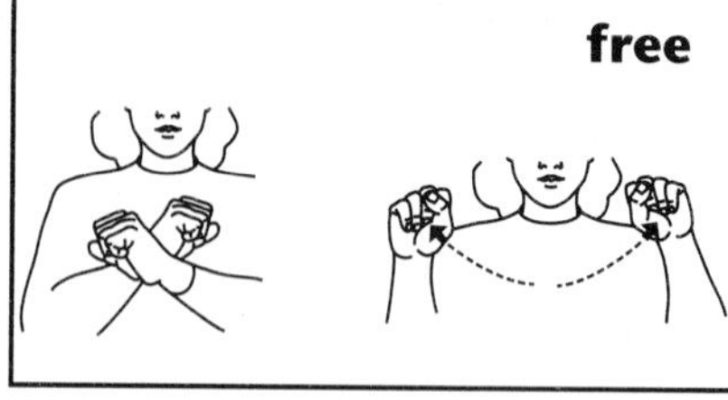

the freedom

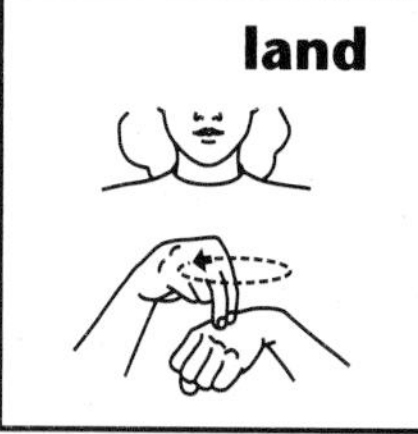

land.

The sign for "march" represents the movement of many feet. The sign for "freedom" represents wrists being untied and freed. The sign for "walkin'" represents the movement of two feet walking.

Name ____________________ Class ____________________

SIGNING 5

Peace Like a River

African American Spiritual

VERSE 1

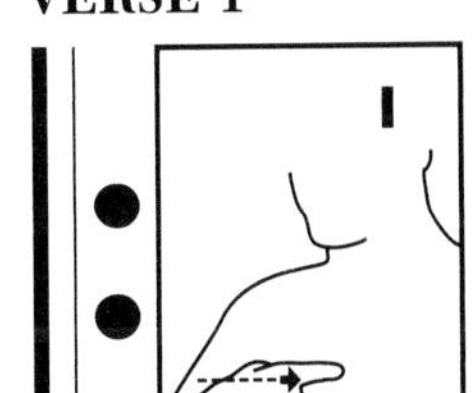

I've

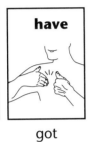

have

got

peace

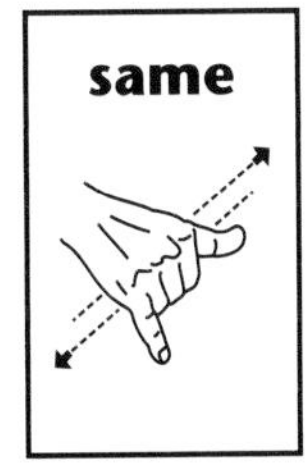

like a

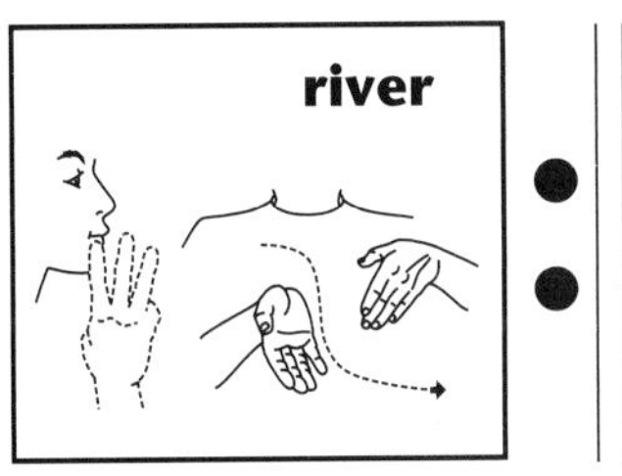

river,

3 times

in

in

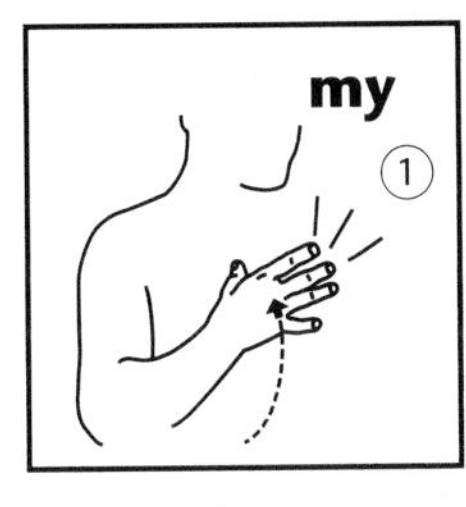

my

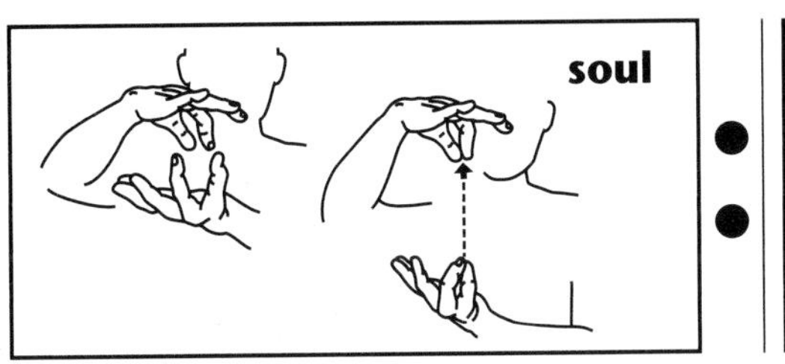

soul.

VERSE 2

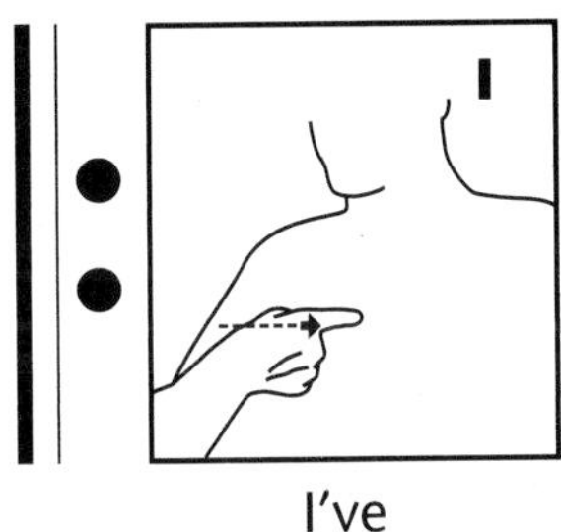

I've

got

joy

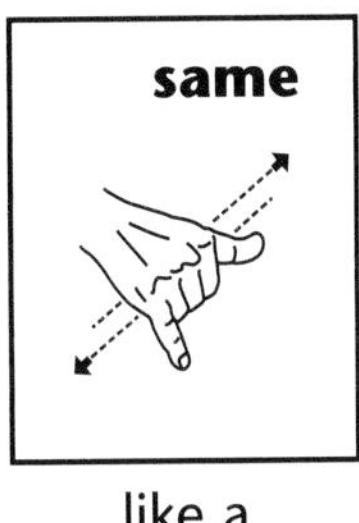

like a

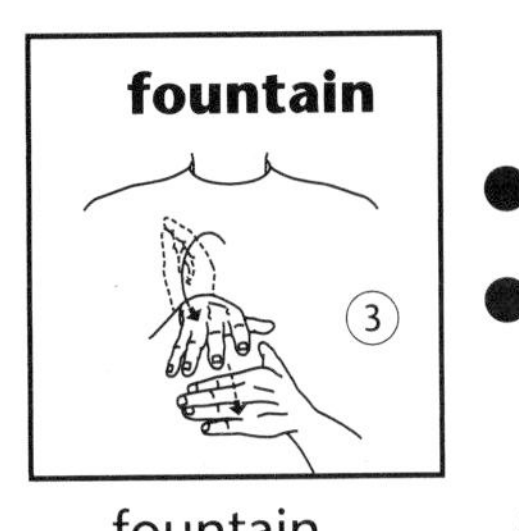

fountain,

3 times

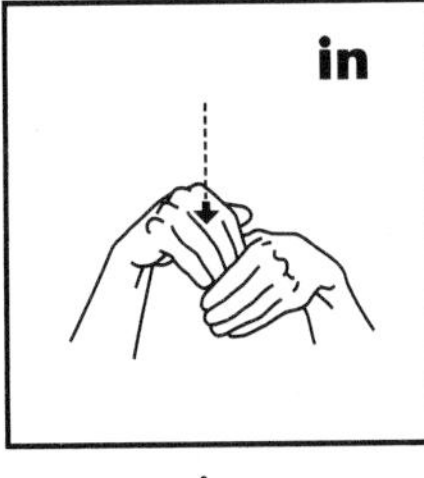

in

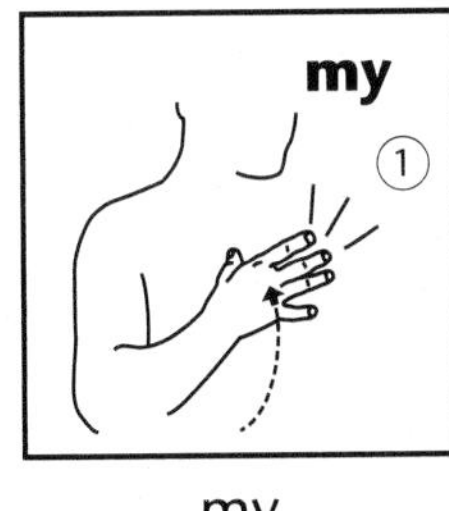

my

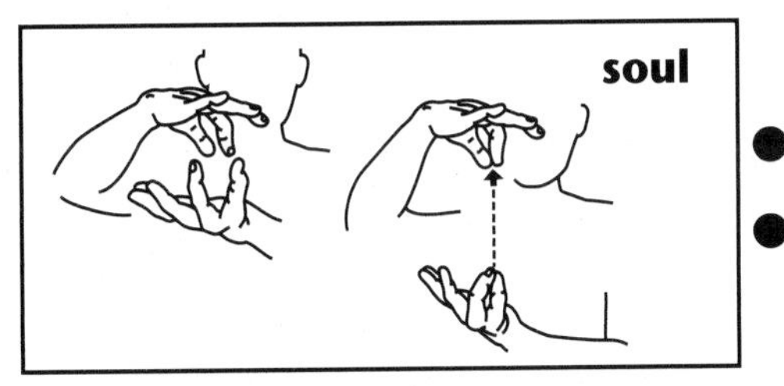

soul.

1. palm flat against chest
2. sometimes signed with both hands
3. wiggle fingers—top hand

SIGNING

Name ______________________ Class ____________

SIGNING 5 (CONTINUED)

VERSE 3

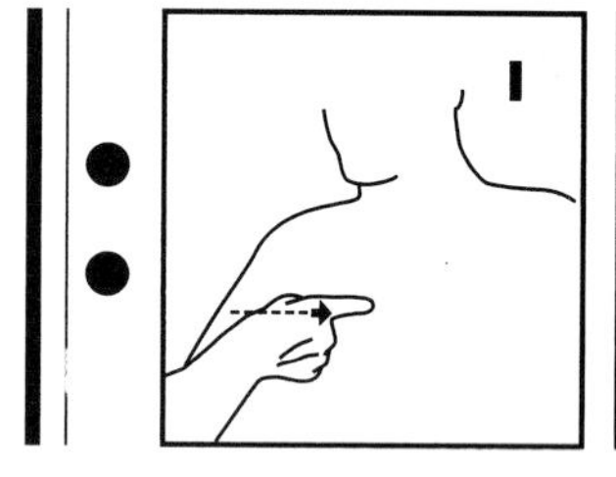

I've

got

love

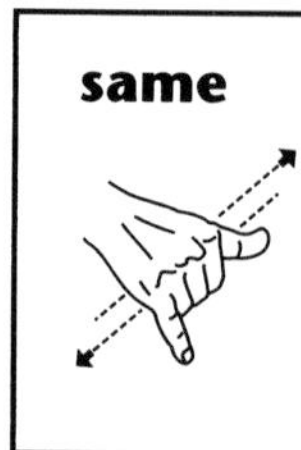

like the

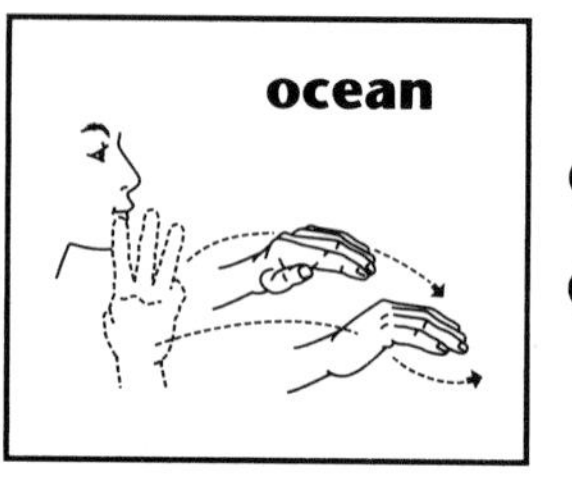

ocean,

3 times

in

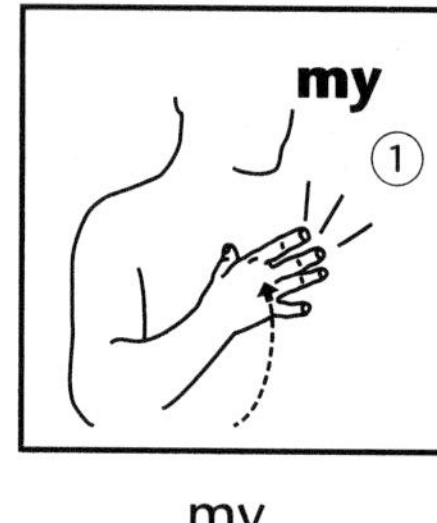

my

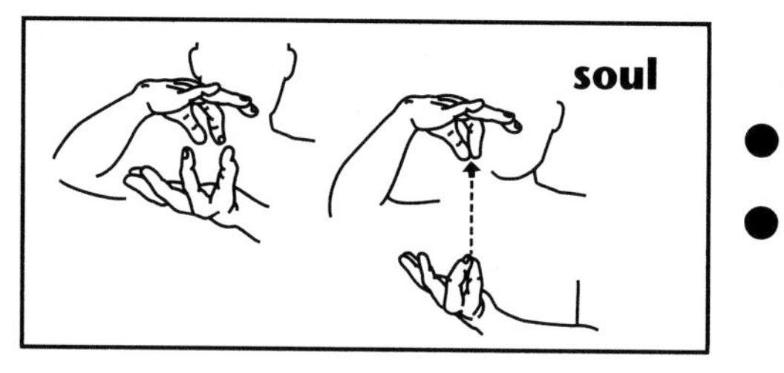

soul.

① palm flat against chest

Name ______________________ Class ______________________

Signing 6

Siyahamba

Traditional Freedom Song from South Africa
Arranged by Rick Baitz

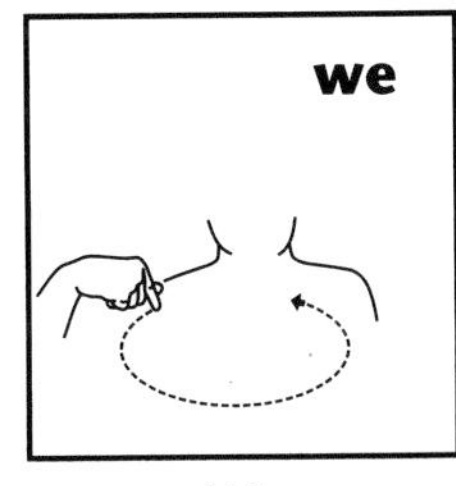

We

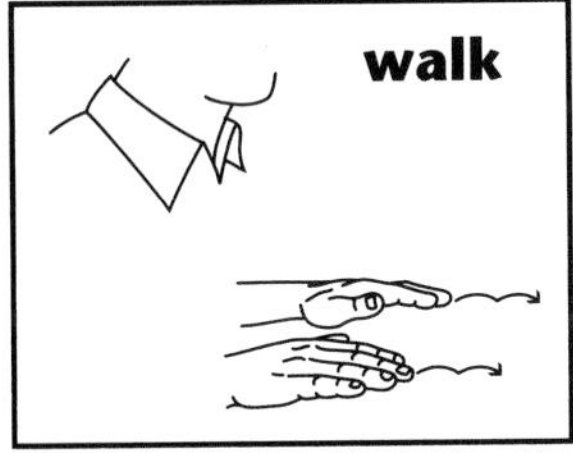

are walking

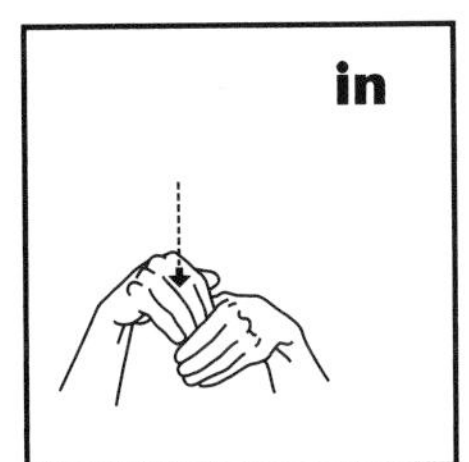

in

the light

of

God.

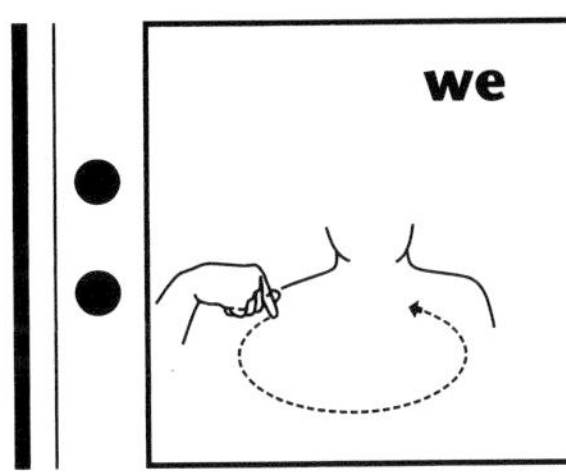

Si - ya

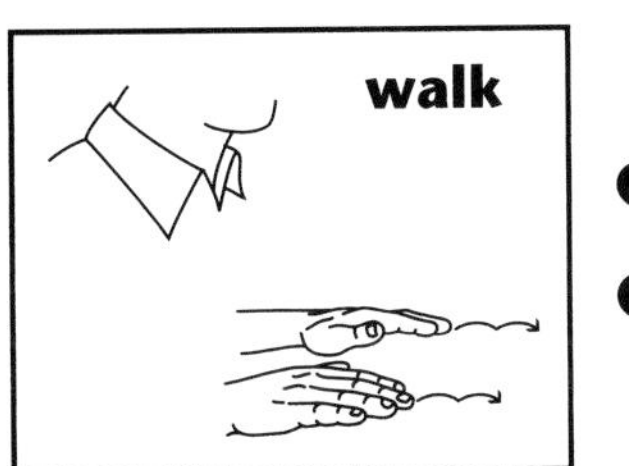

- ham - ba

Name ______________________ Class ____________

SIGNING 7

Sometimes I Feel Like a Motherless Child

African American Spiritual

VERSE 1

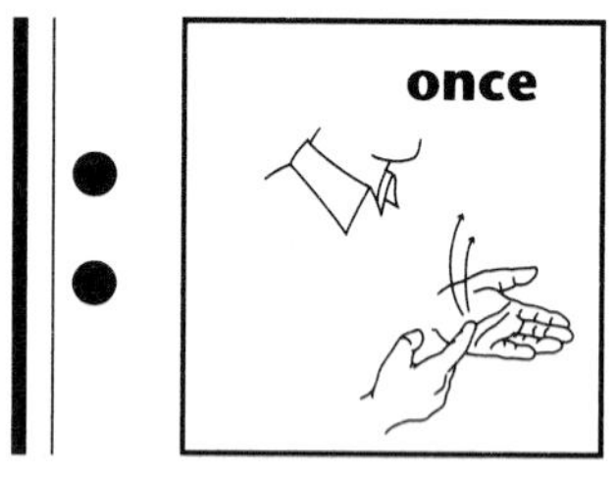

Sometimes

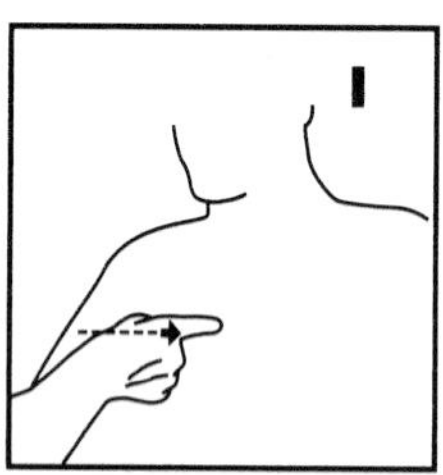

I

feel

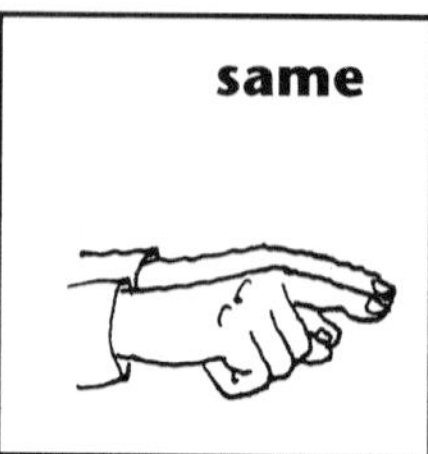

like a

mother-

less

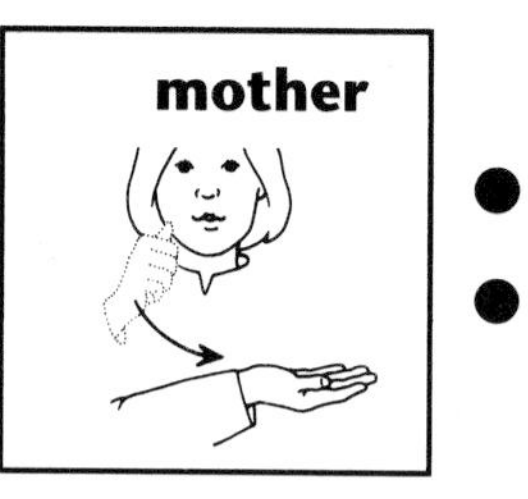

child,

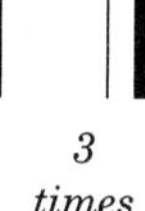

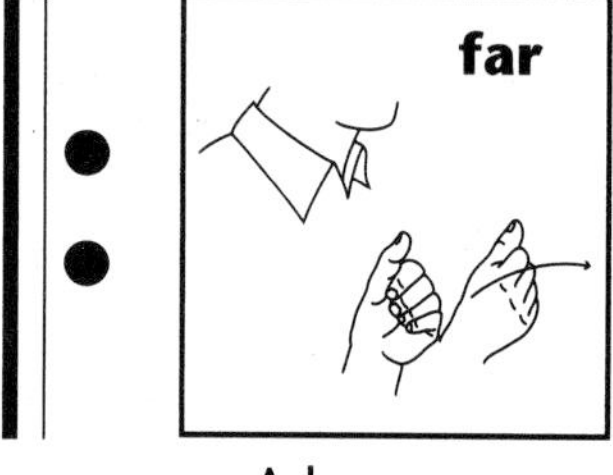

A long way

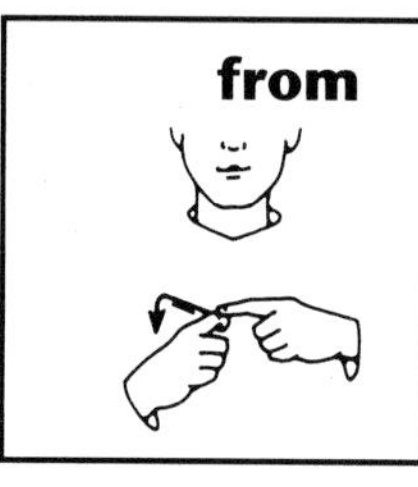

from

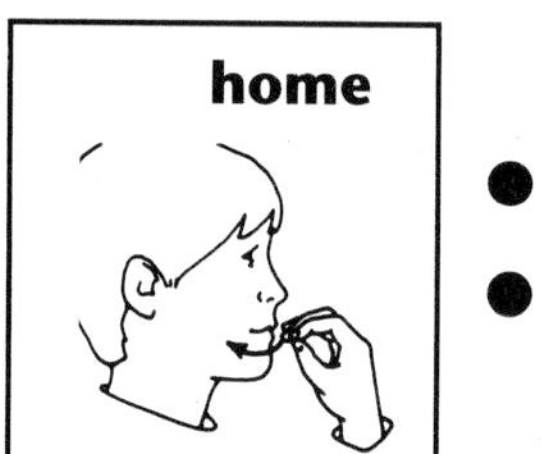

home.

Name ______________________ Class ______________________

SIGNING

SIGNING 7 (CONTINUED)

VERSE 2

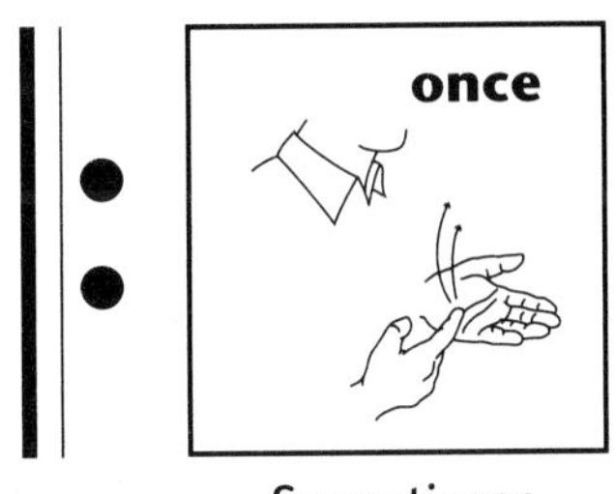

Sometimes

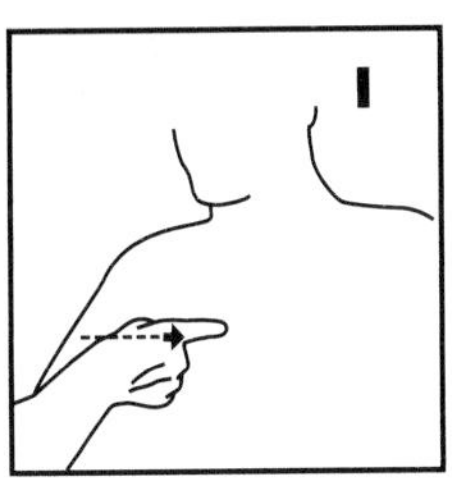

I

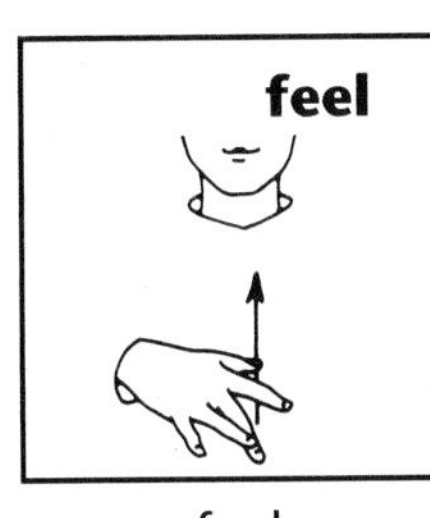

feel

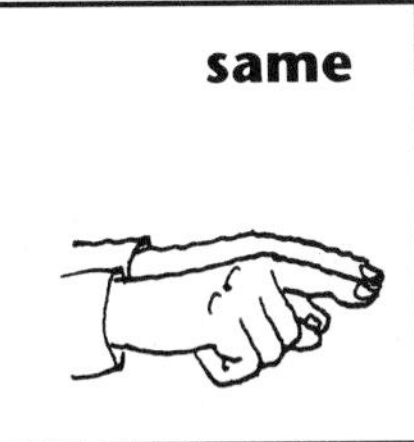

like

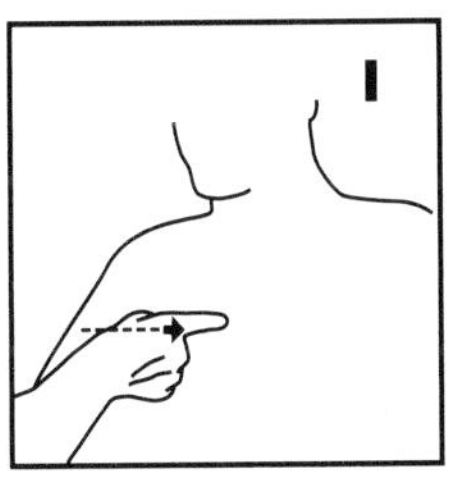

I'm

almost

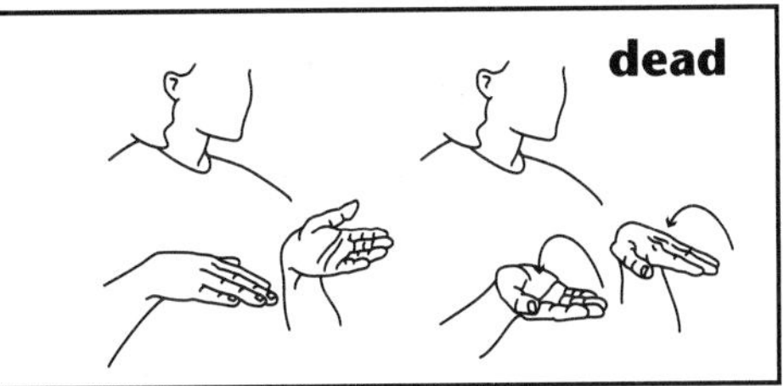

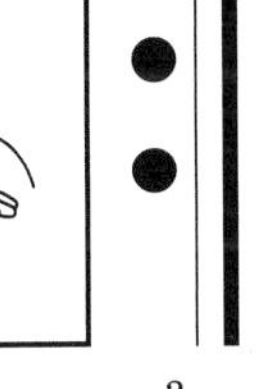
gone,

3 times

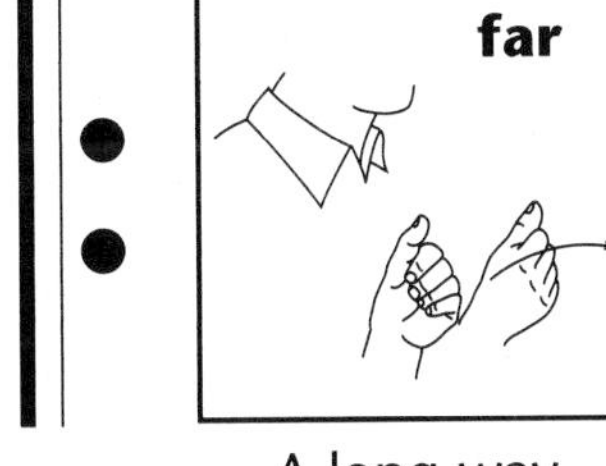

A long way

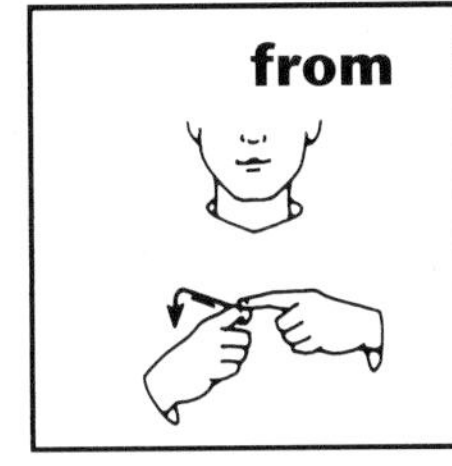

from

home.

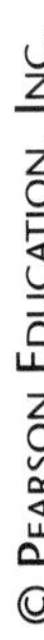

Name ______________________ Class ____________

SIGNING 8

You Are My Sunshine

Words and Music by Jimmie Davis and Charles Mitchell

REFRAIN

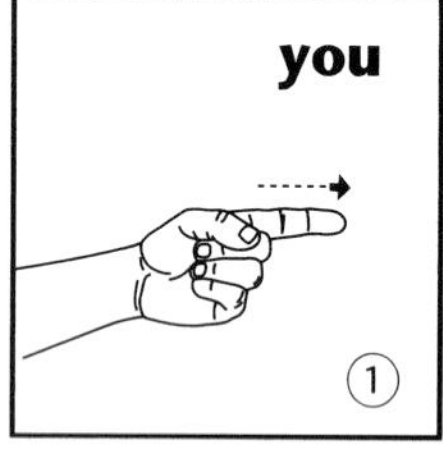

You

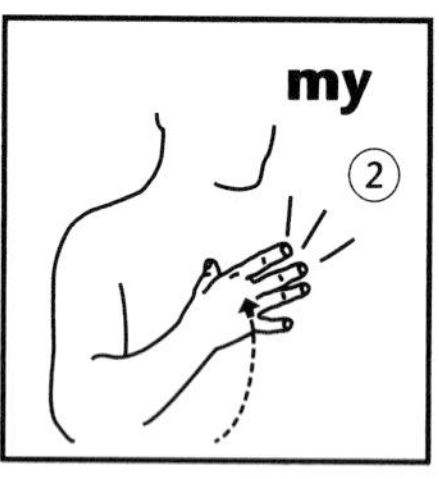

are my

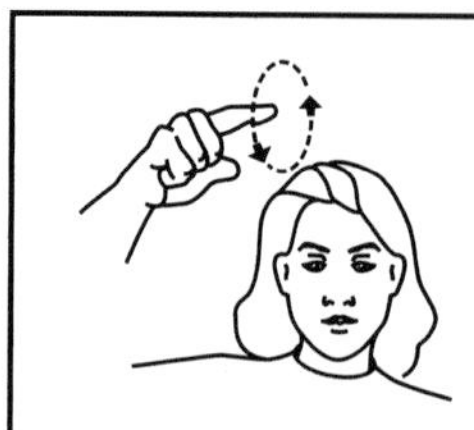

sunshine,

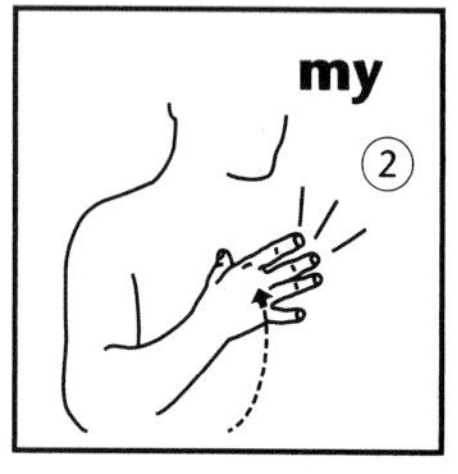

my

only

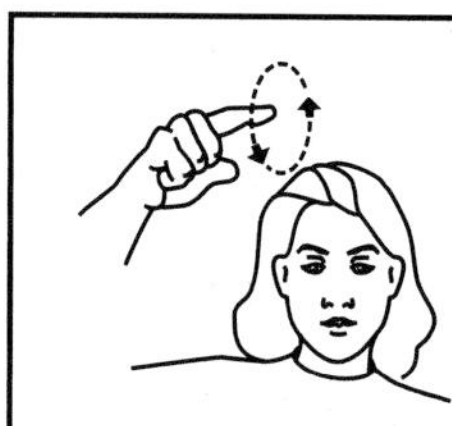

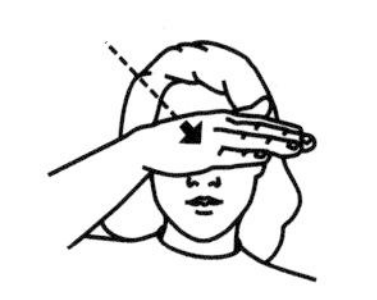

sunshine;

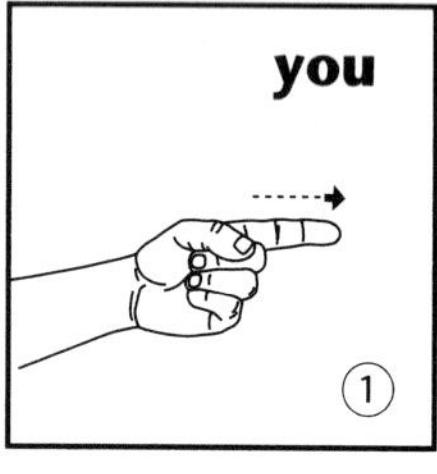

You

make

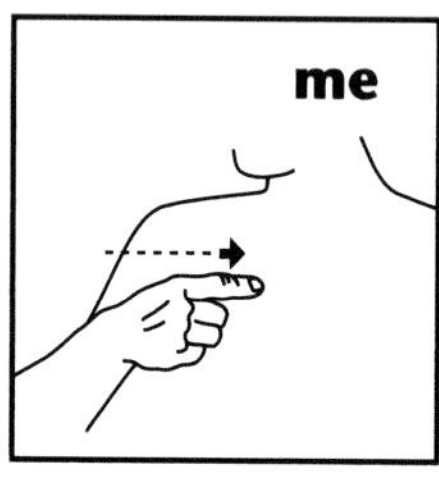

me

happy

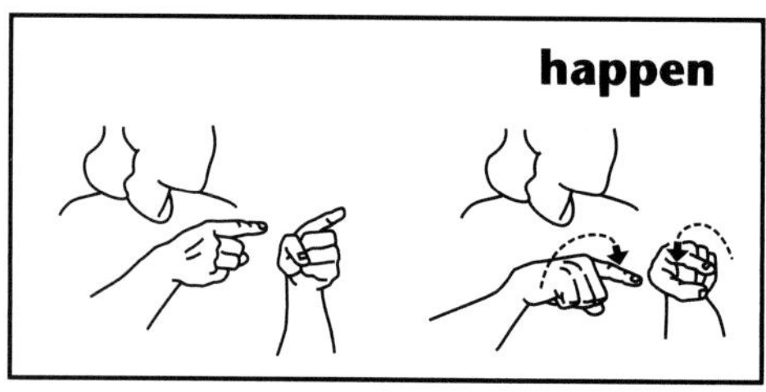

when

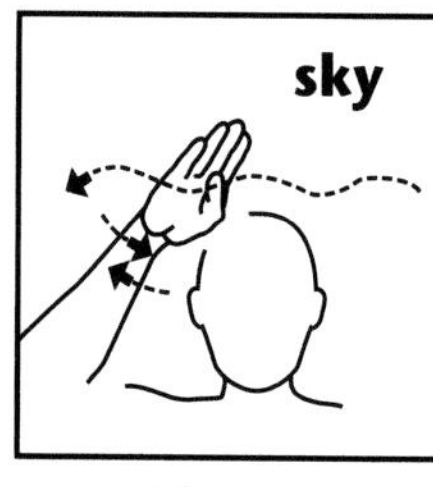

skies are

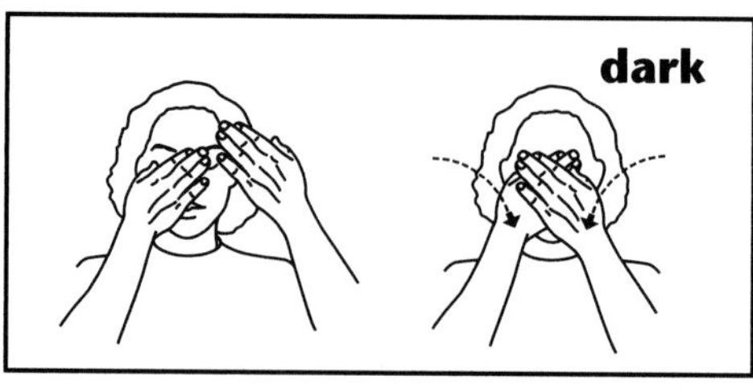

gray.

① point out or to specific person

② palm flat against chest

③ often signed with both hands

Name ______________________ Class ______________

SIGNING 8 (CONTINUED)

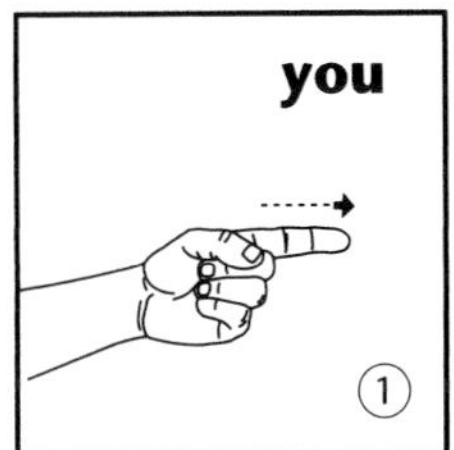

You'll

never

know

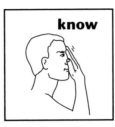

know,

dear,

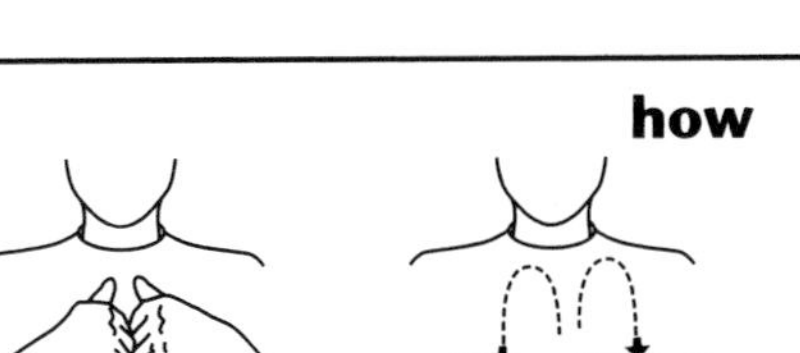

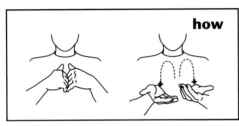

how

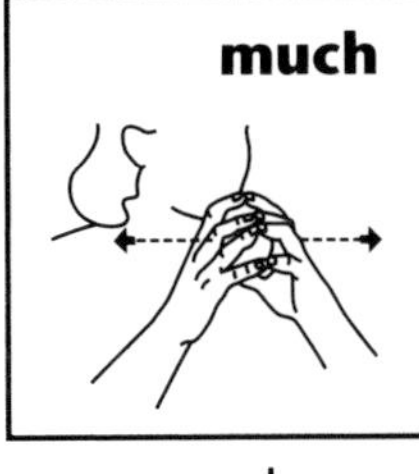

much

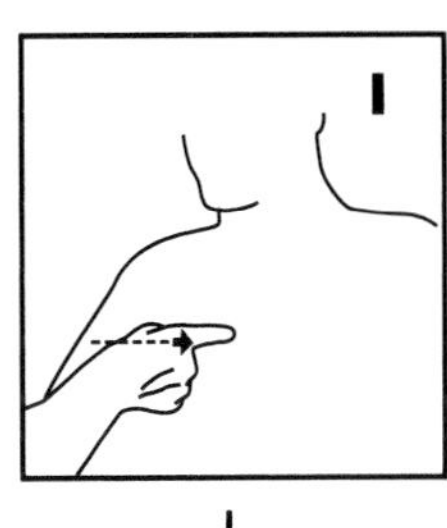

I

love

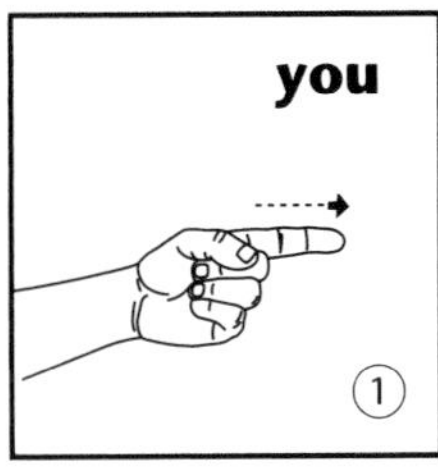

you;

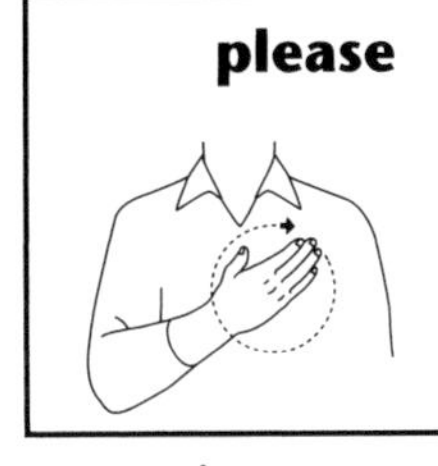

Please

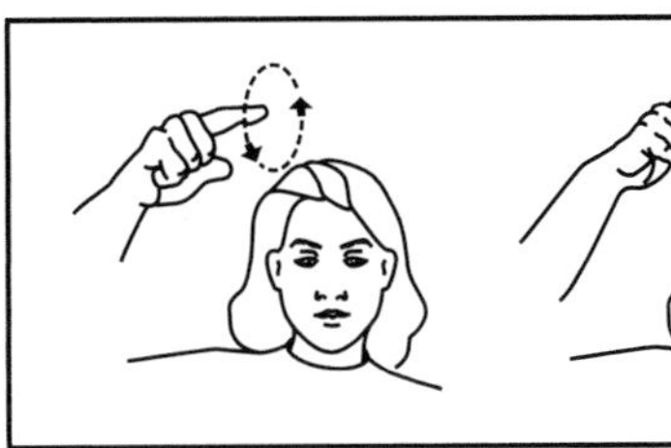
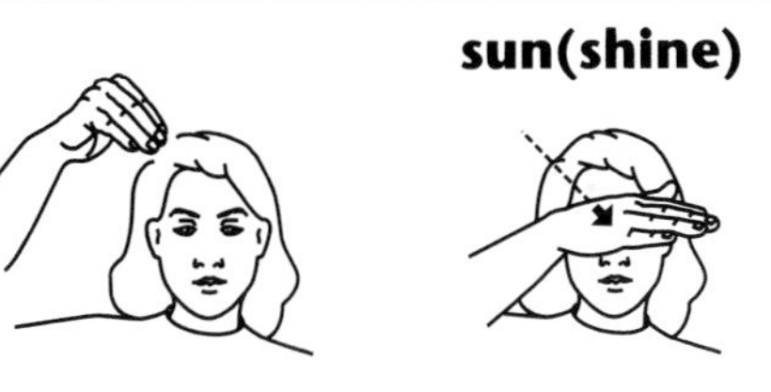

don't take my

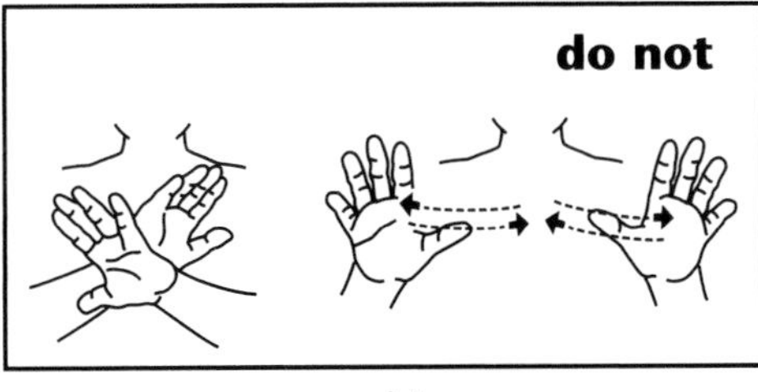

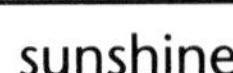
sunshine

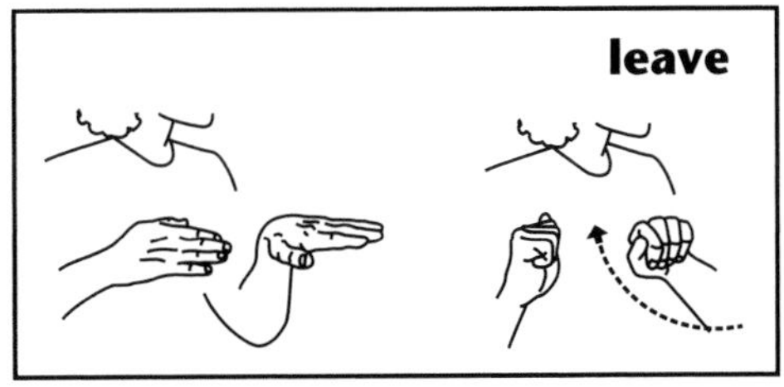

away.

Fine

① point out or to specific person

Name ______________________________ Class ______________

SIGNING 8 (CONTINUED)

VERSE 2

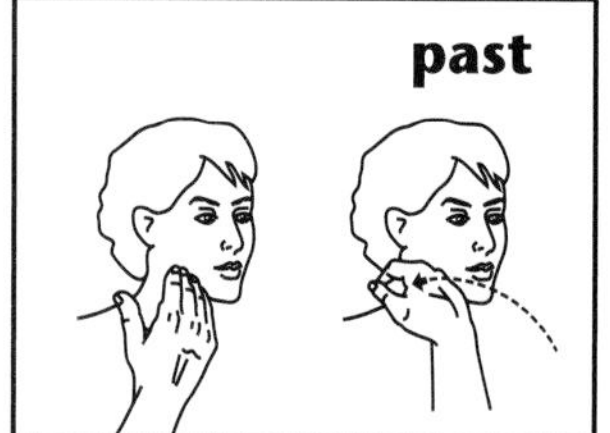

The other

night,

dear,

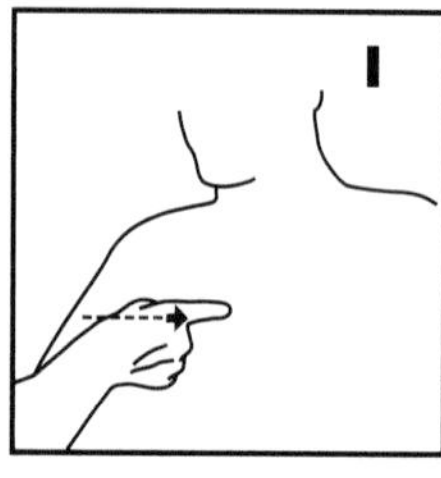

as I lay

sleeping,

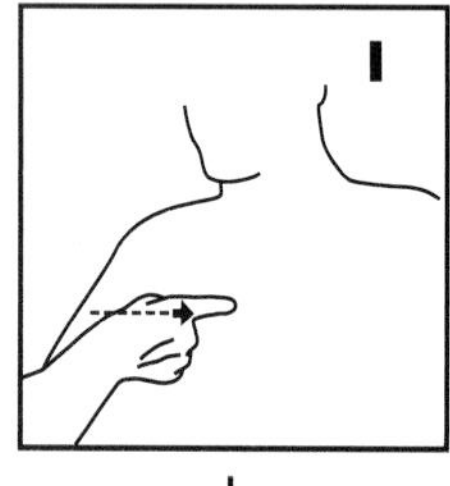

I

dreamed I

held you

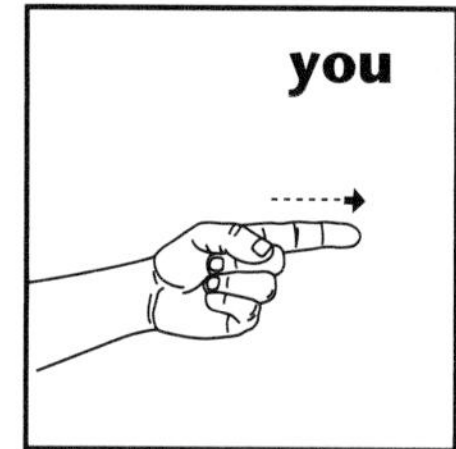

in my arms,

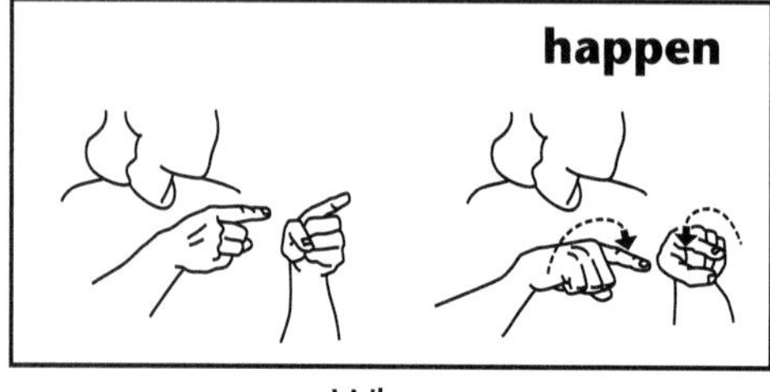

When

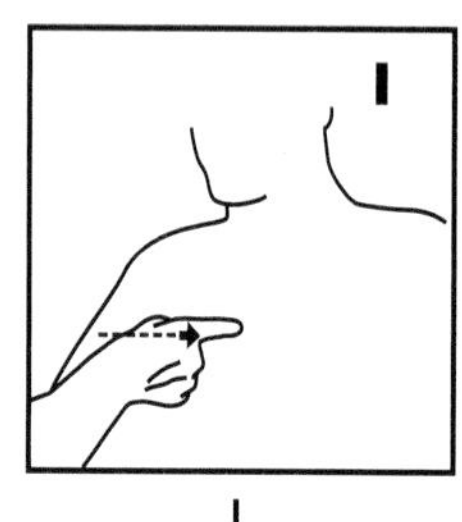

I

SIGNING 8 (CONTINUED)

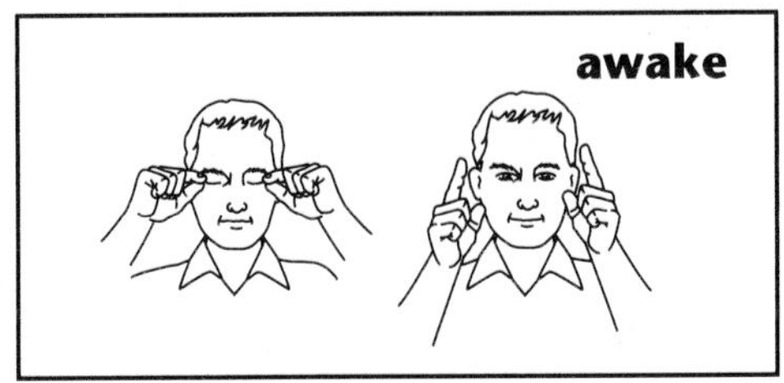

awoke,

dear,

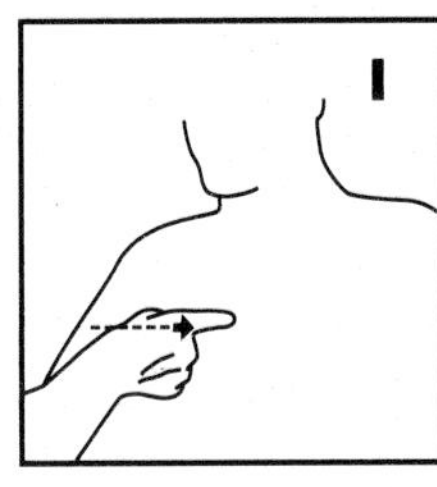

I was

mistaken

D.C. al Fine

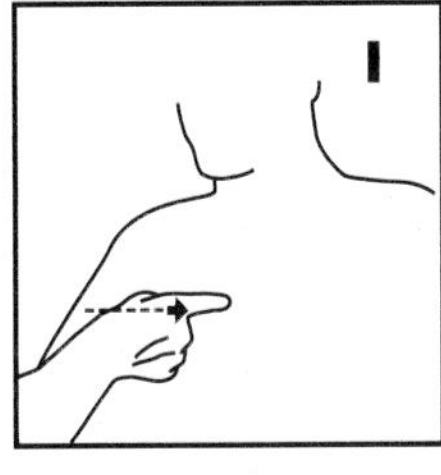

and I

(Mime sign: hang head–sad face)

hung my head and

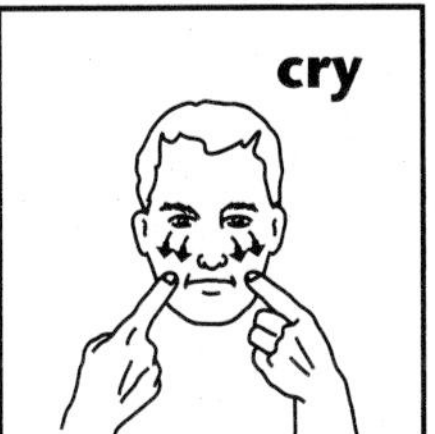

cried.

Name ______________________ Class ______________

Signing 9

Everybody Loves Saturday Night

Folk Song from West Africa

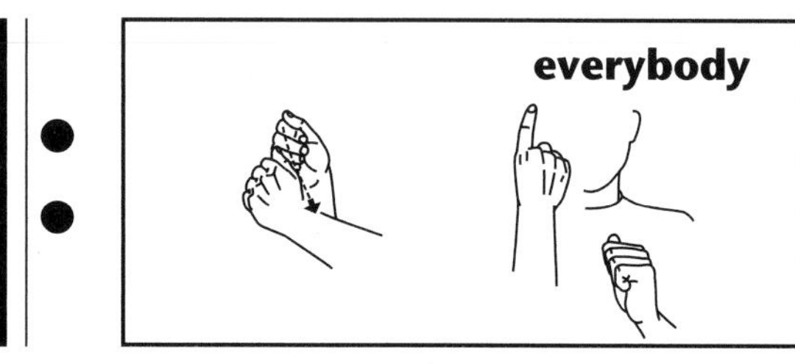

Everybody

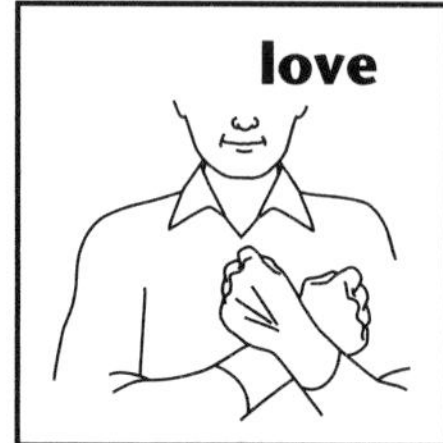

loves

Saturday

night,

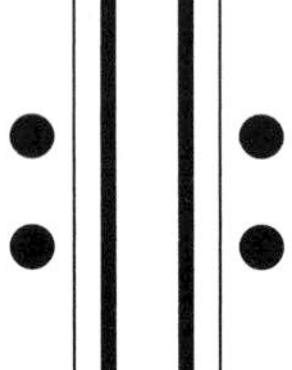

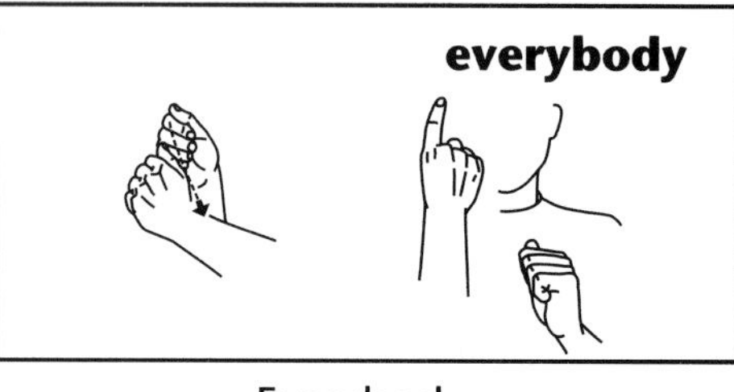

Everybody,

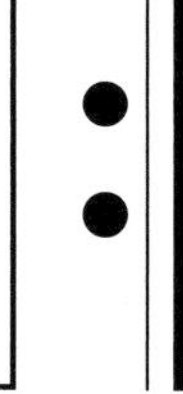

4 times

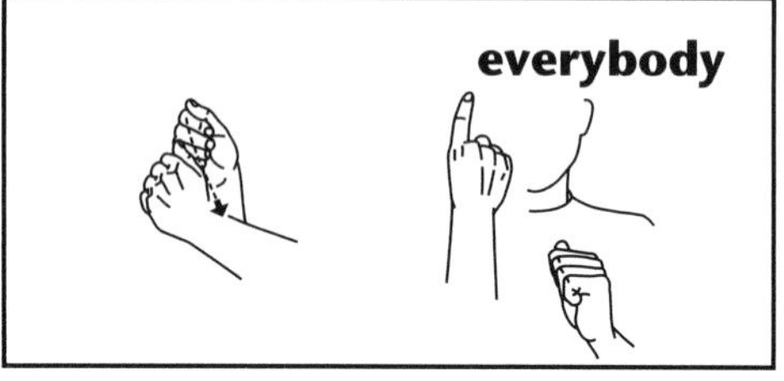

Everybody

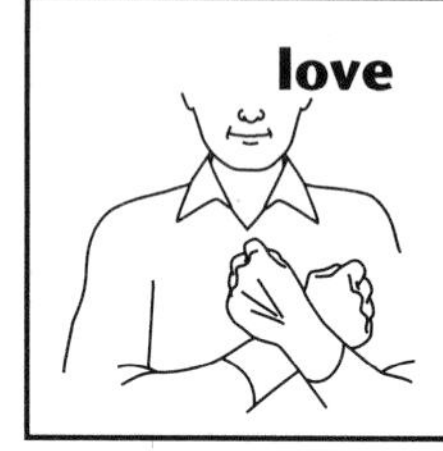

loves

Saturday

night.

① circle indicates small clockwise motion

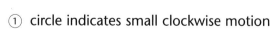

Name ____________________ Class ____________________

SIGNING 10

There Is Love Somewhere

Traditional African American Song

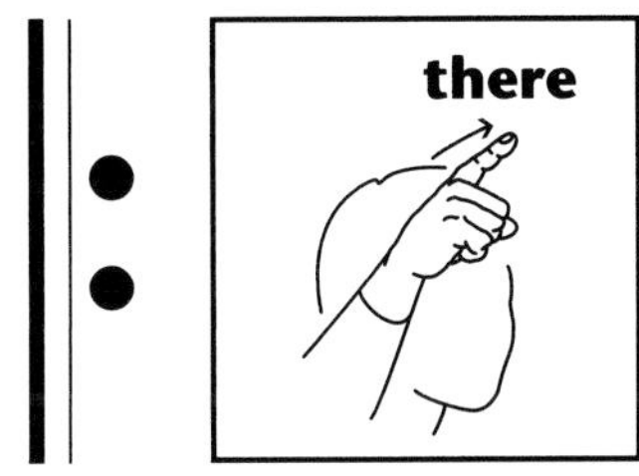

There is

love
[hope, joy, peace]

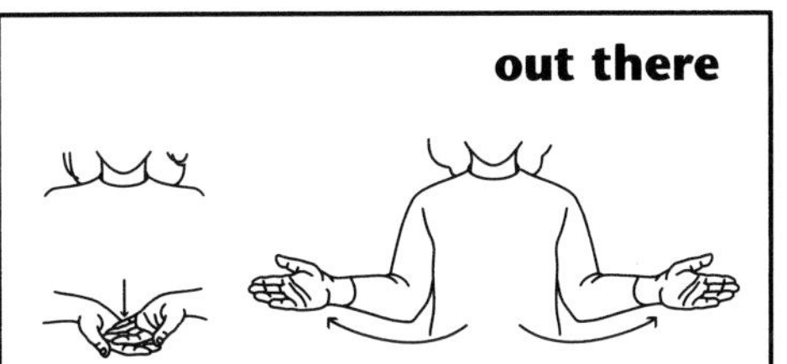

somewhere.

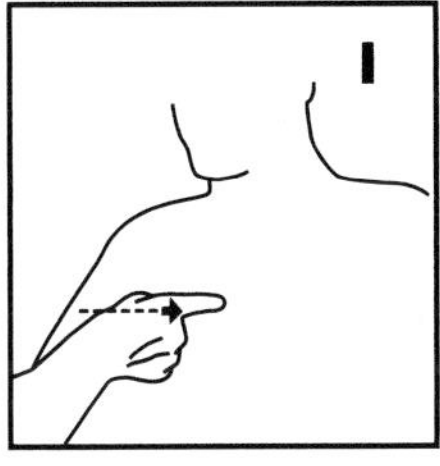

I'm

gonna

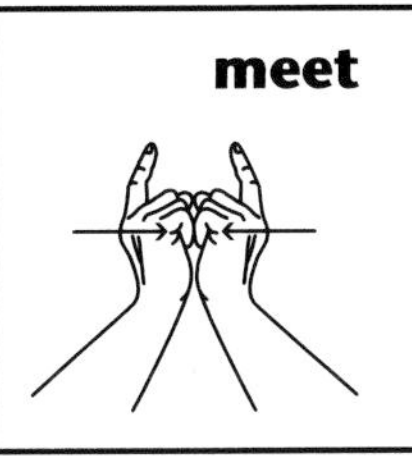

reach out

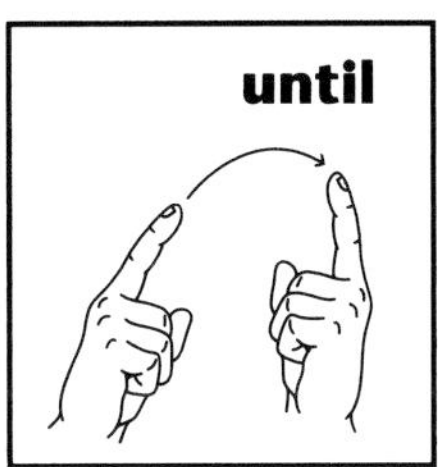

'til

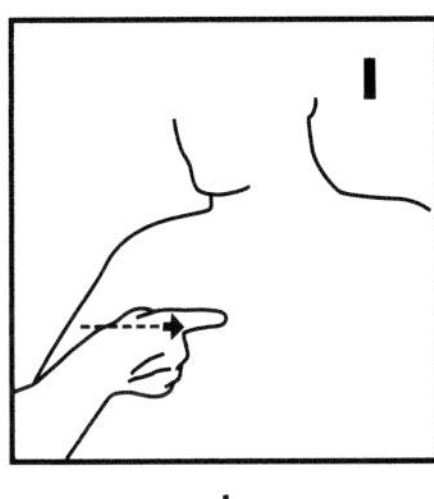

I

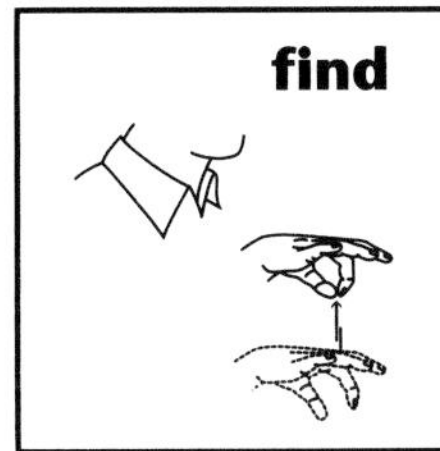

find

some.

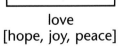

There is

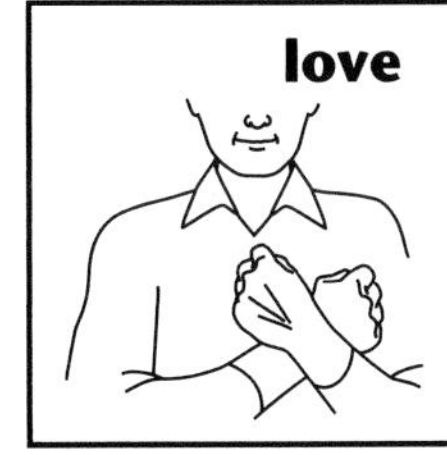

love
[hope, joy, peace]

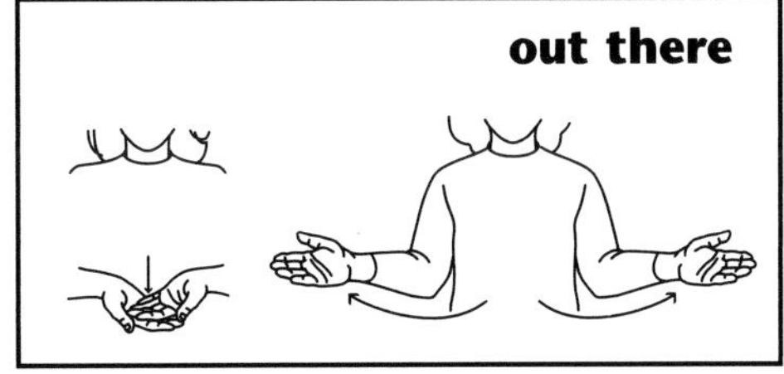

somewhere.

Name ____________________ Class ____________

SIGNING 10 (CONTINUED)

VERSE 1

love

VERSE 2

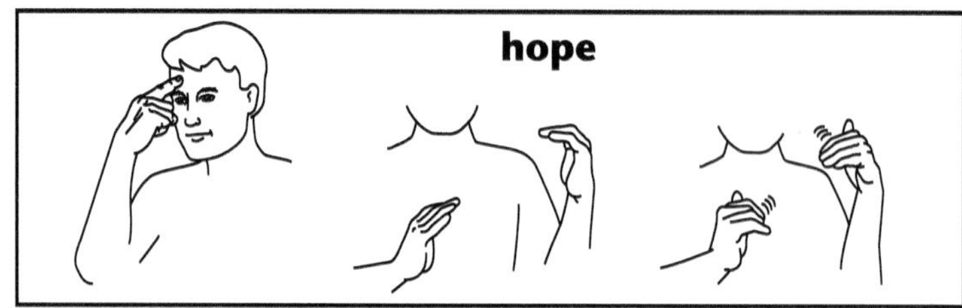

hope

VERSE 3

joy

VERSE 4

peace

Name ______________________ Class ______________________

SIGNING 11

Mama Don't 'Low

Folk Song from the United States

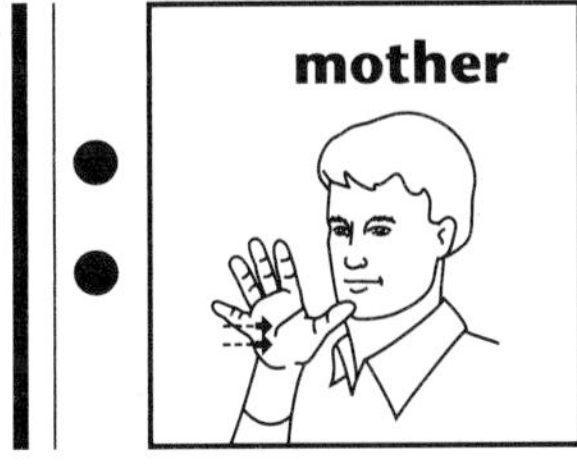

Mama don't

'low no

guitar playin' 'round here,

I don't care what

mama don't

'low, Gonna

① sign begins at the side of the nose

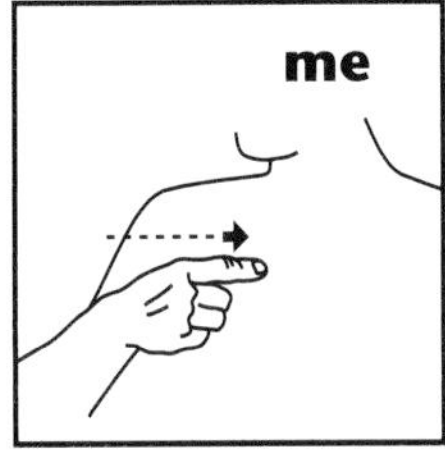

play my

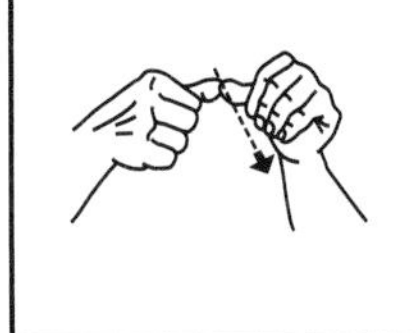
guitar

anyhow,

Mama

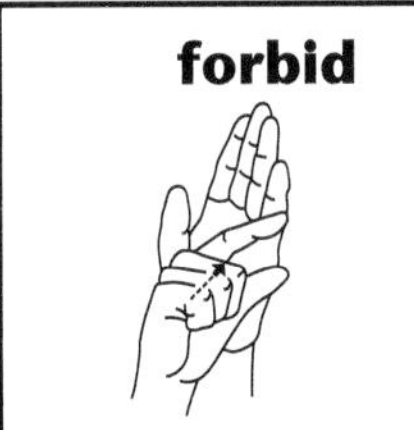

don't 'low no

(Mime: strumming guitar)

guitar playin' 'round here.

For second verse, mime picking banjo. This song incorporates mime signs. Mime signs are signs used to represent action words. This song uses the sign meaning "forbid" for the words, "don't 'low no".

Name ______________________ Class ______________

SIGNING 12

I Am But a Small Voice

Original Words by Odina E. Batnag
English Words and Music by Roger Whittaker

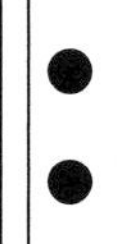

Come

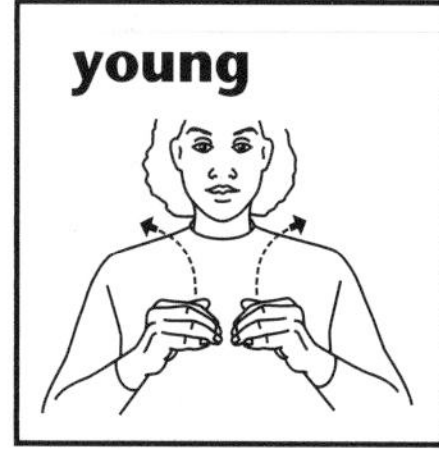

young

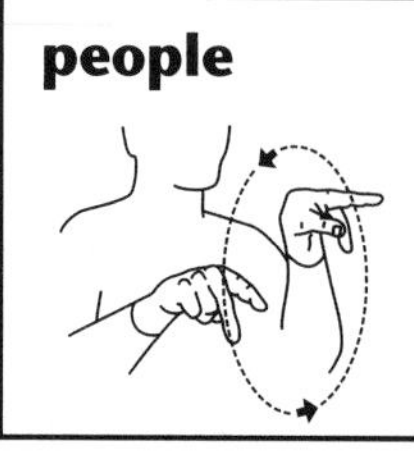

citizens

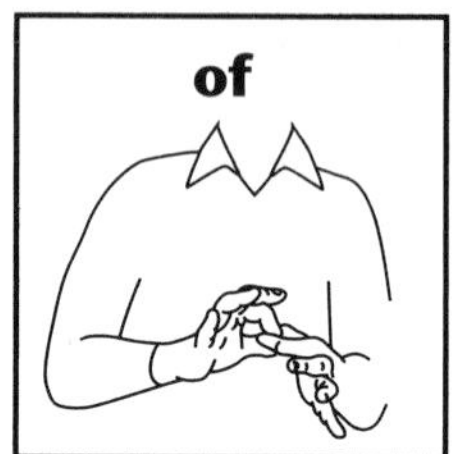

of the

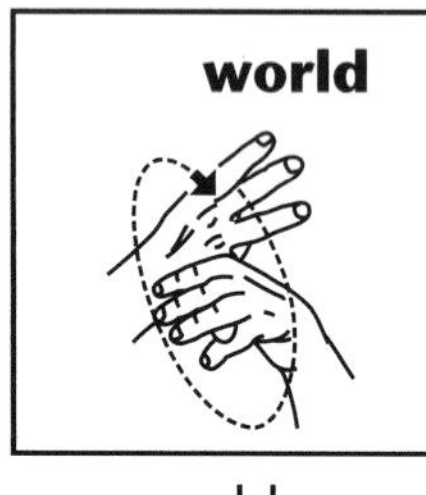

world;

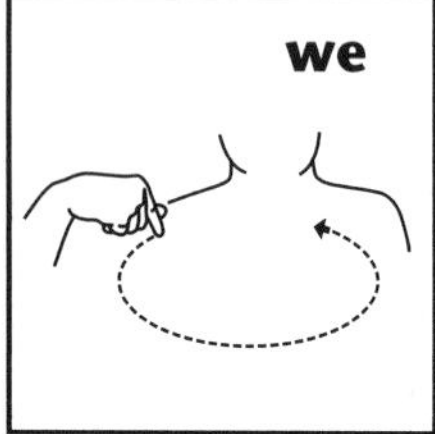

We are

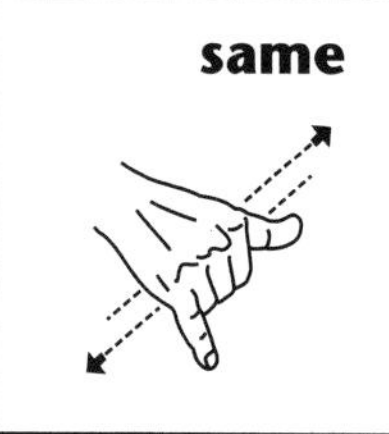

one, ______

we are

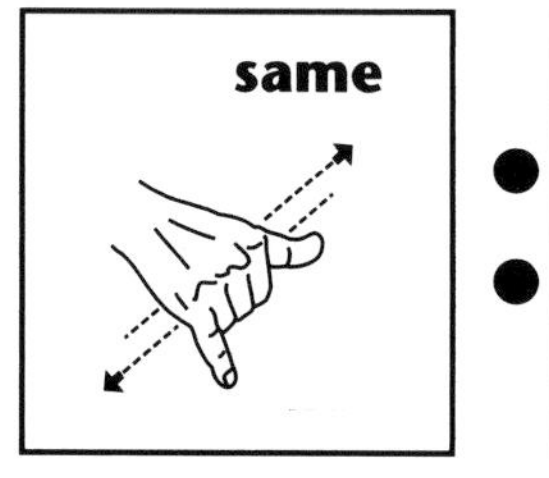

one. ______

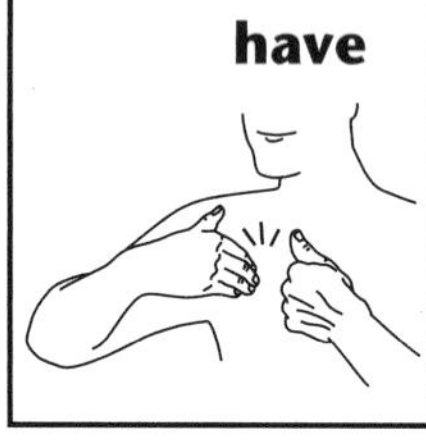

We have

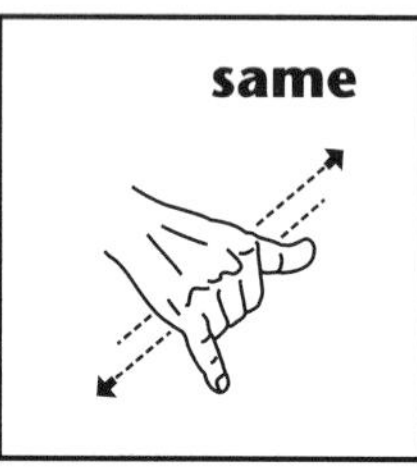

one hope,

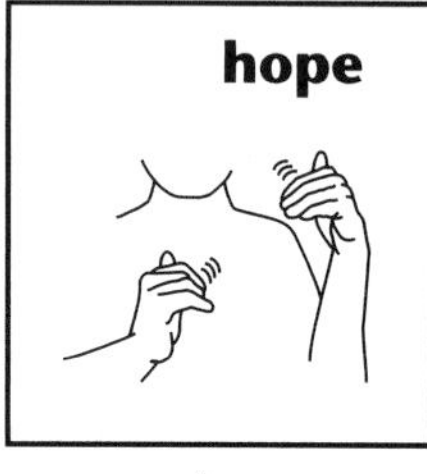

we have

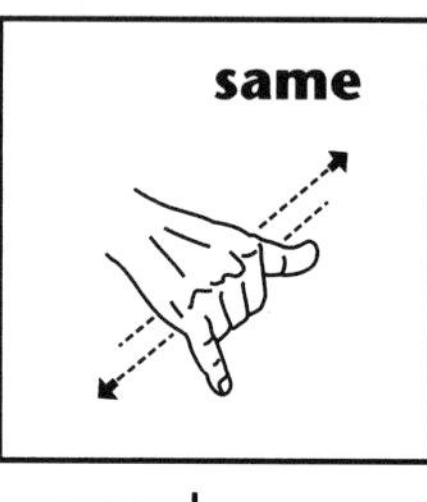

one dream,

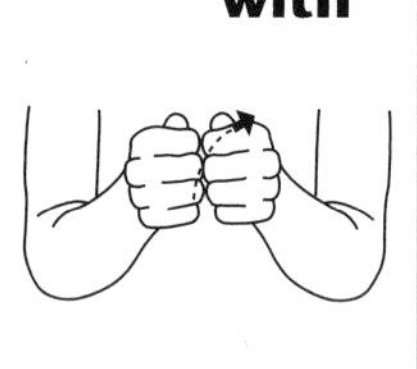

and with

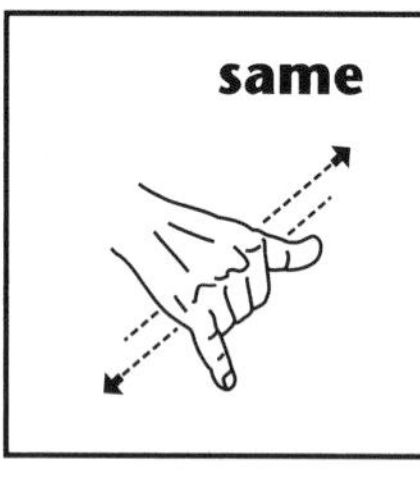

one

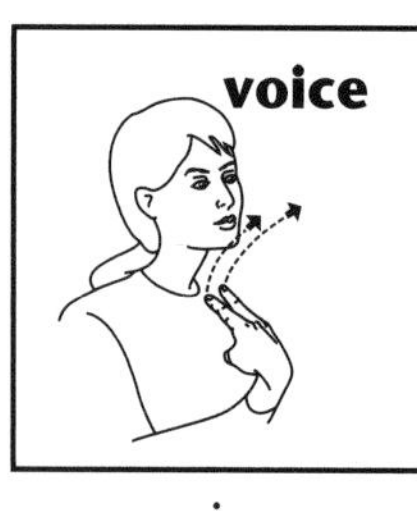

voice

we sing. ______

Name ______________________ Class ______________________

SIGNING 12 (CONTINUED)

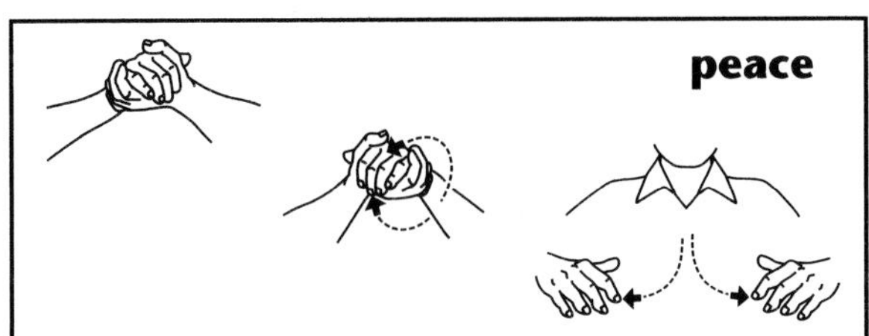

Peace, _____

prosperity, _____

And love

for

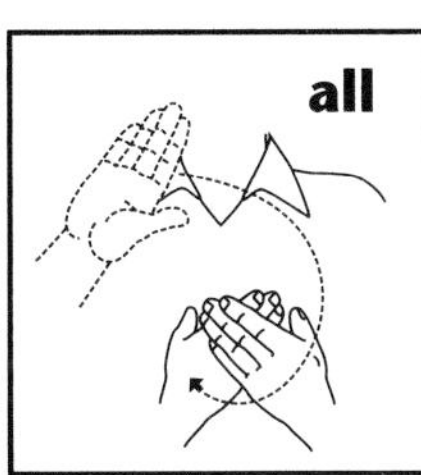

all

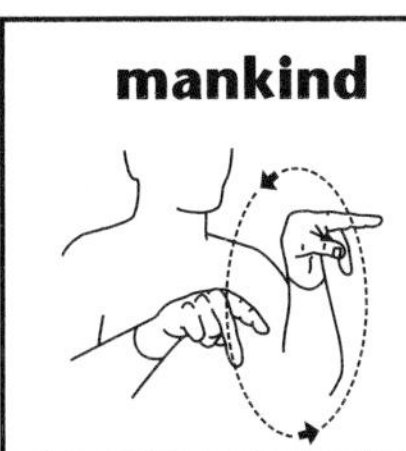

mankind.

Name ______________________________ Class ______________

Signing 13

Free at Last

African American Spiritual
Arranged by Joan R. Hillsman

REFRAIN

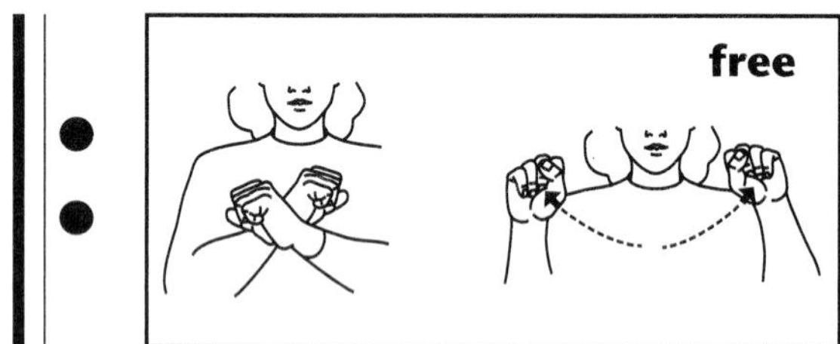

Free

at last,

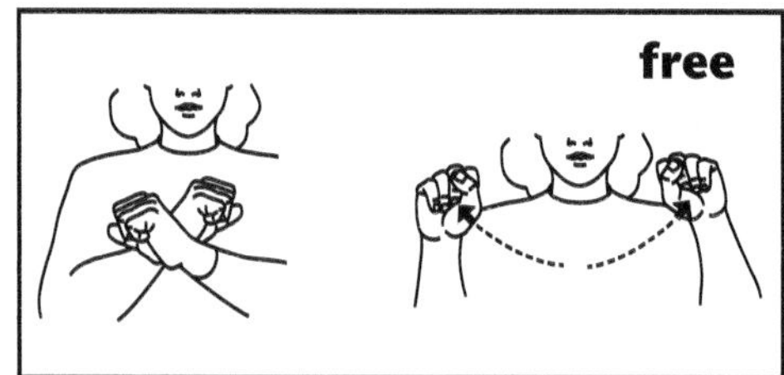

free

at last,

Thank

God Almighty

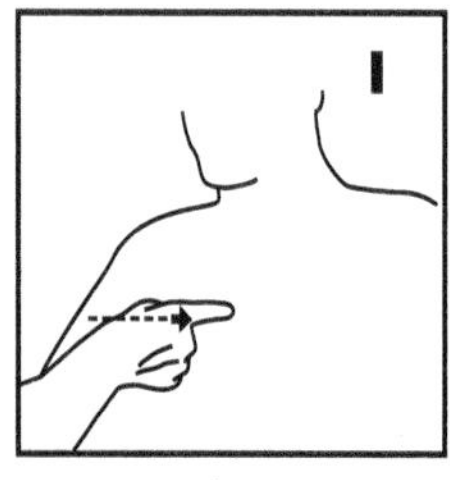

I'm

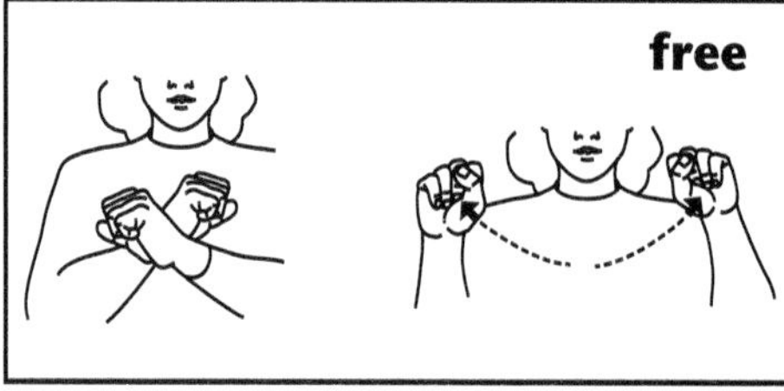

free

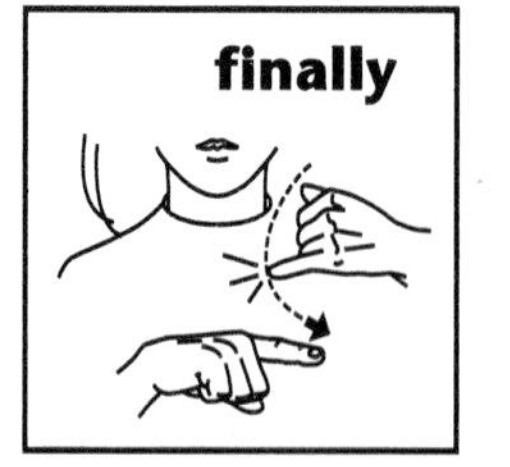

at last.

Name ______________________ Class ______________________

SIGNING 14

Love in Any Language

Words and Music by
Jon Mohr and John Mays

REFRAIN

Love in

any

language,

straight

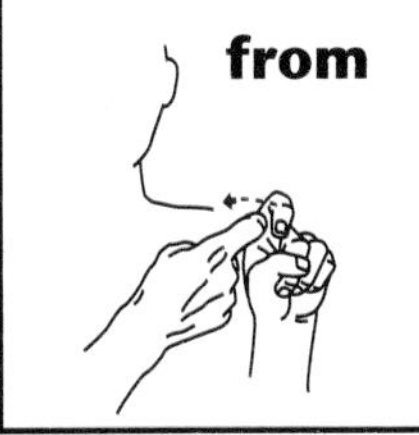

from the

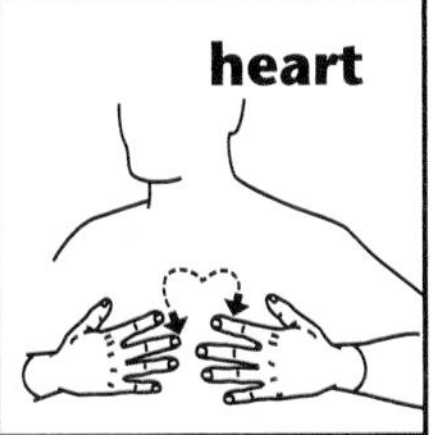

heart,

Pulls us all

together,

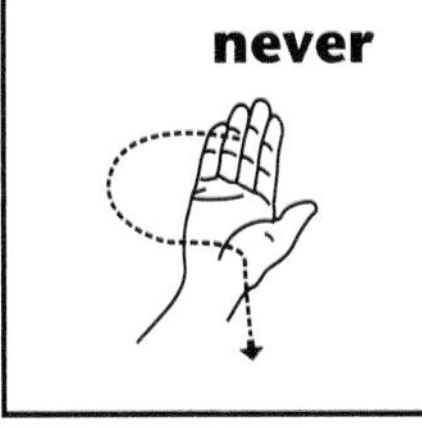

never

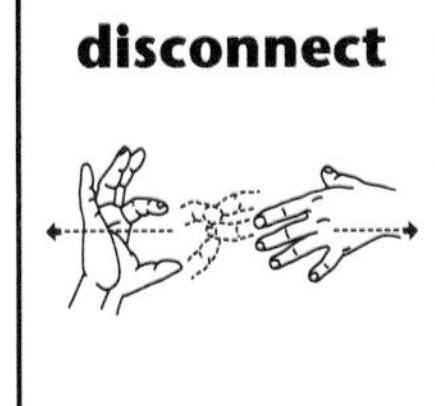

apart.

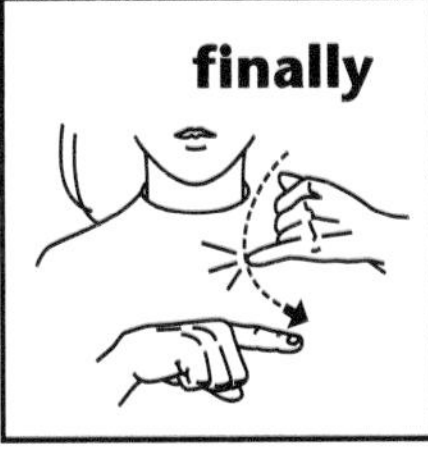

And once

we learn

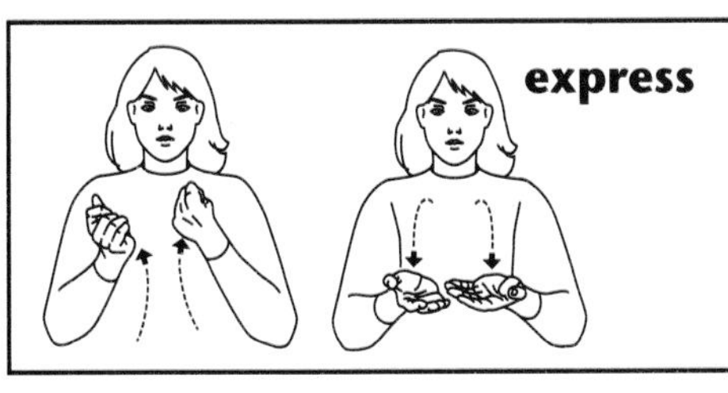

to speak

it,

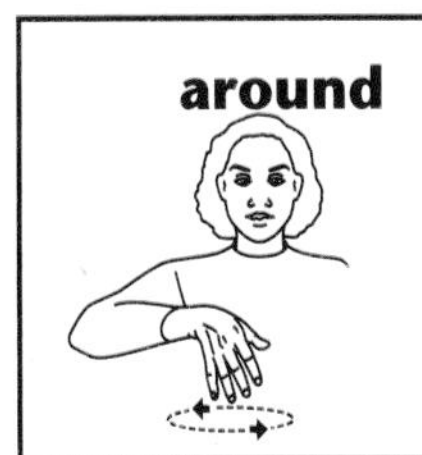

all the

Signing 14 (continued)

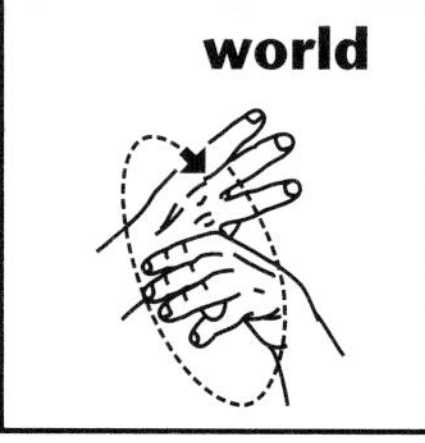

world will

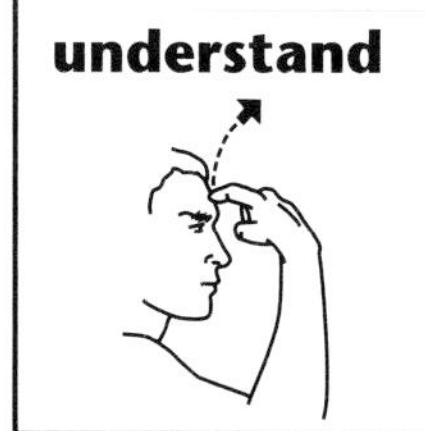

hear,

Love in

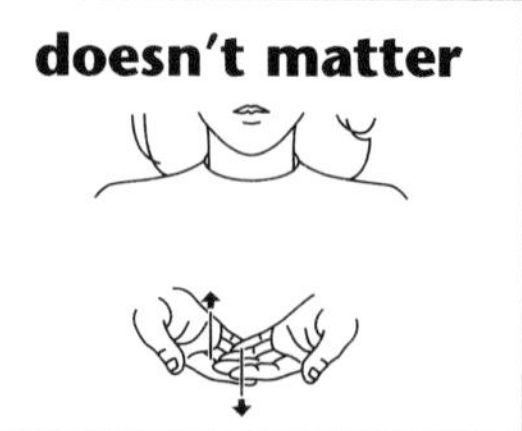

any

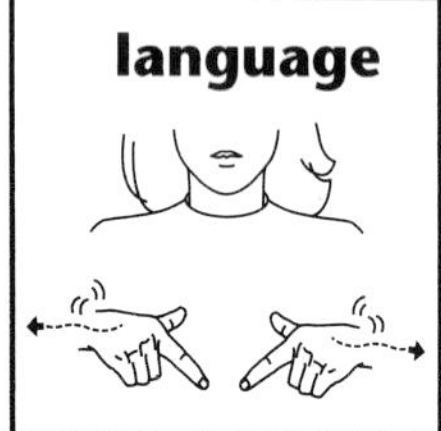

language

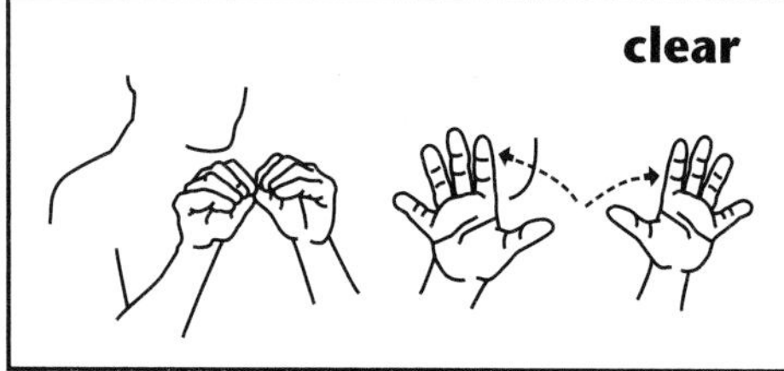

fluently

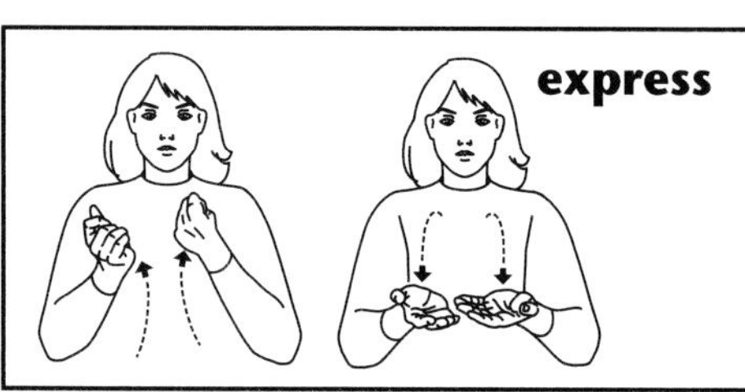

spoken

here.

The sign for "I love you" is a common sign and is used often between loved ones.

Name ______________________________ Class ____________________

SIGNING 15

Manual Alphabet

A

B

C

D

E

F

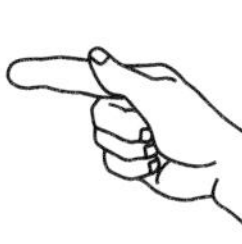
G

H

I

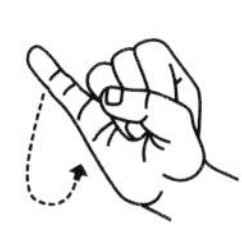
J

K

L

M

N

O

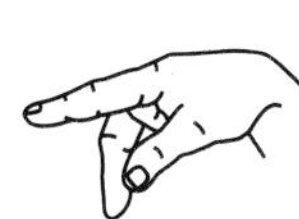
P

Q

R

S

T

U

V

W

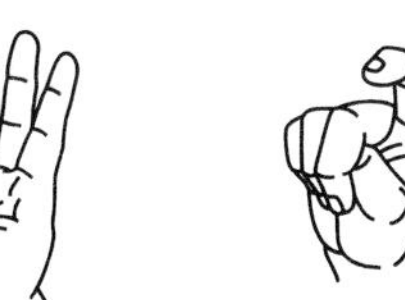

X

Y

Z

Name ______________________ Class ______________

Signing 16

Numbers

1

2

3

4

5

6

7

8

9

10

Note: Often signed with palm in for numbers 1–5 and palm out for numbers 6–9

Keyboard

Table of Contents

Name ______________________ Class ______________

Keyboard 1

One-Line, Two-Line, Three-Line Reading

Perform each pattern on a keyboard.

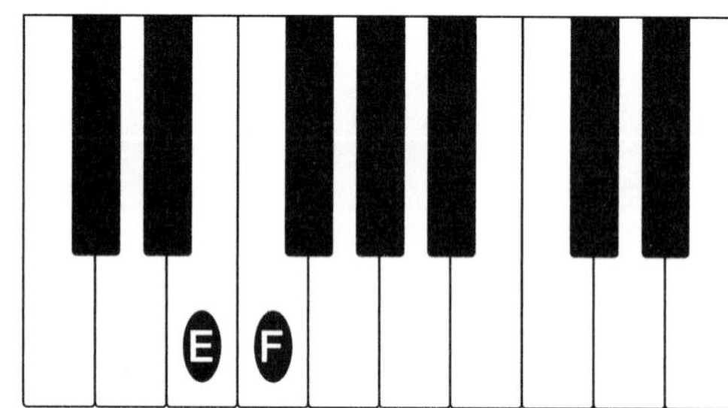

E F

Step Up

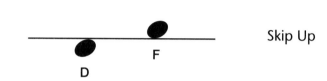

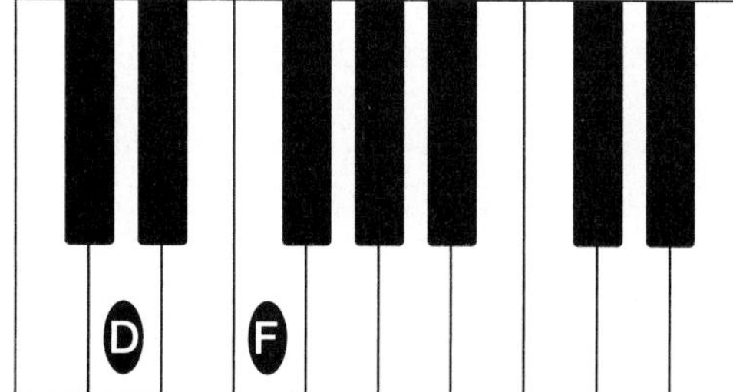

D F

Skip Up

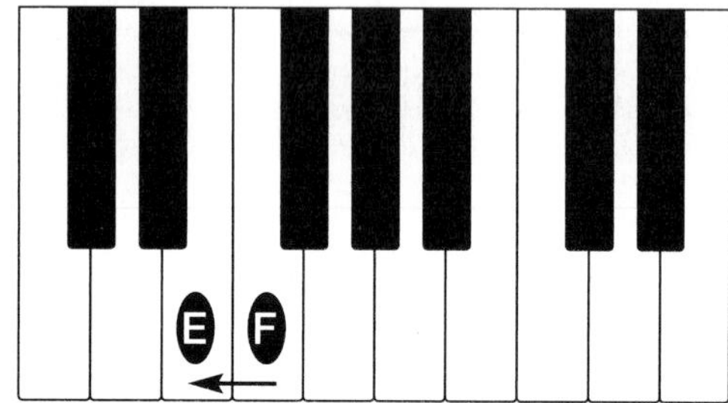

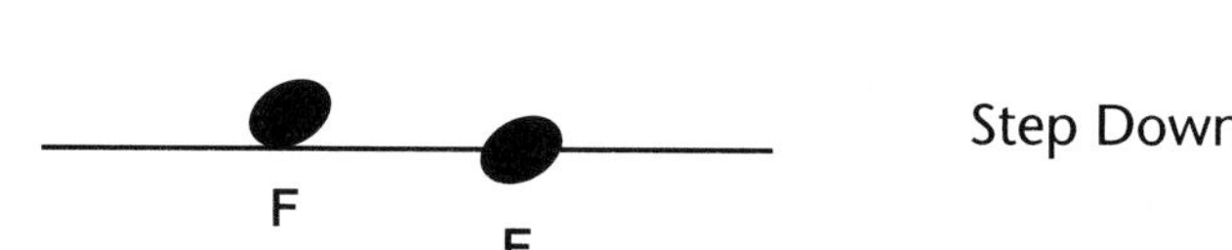

Step Down

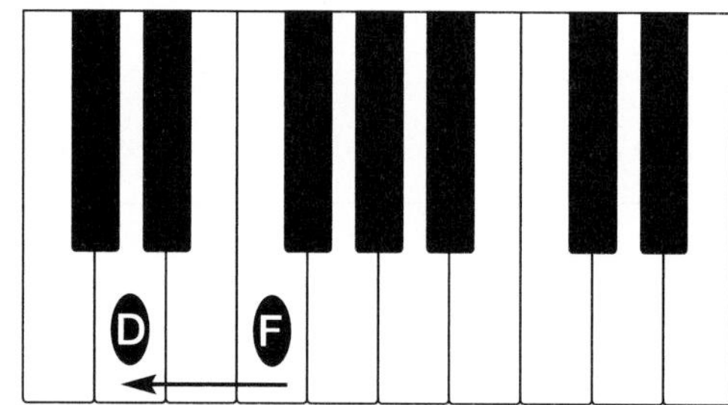

F D

Skip Down

Name ______________________ Class ______________________

KEYBOARD 2

Steps and Skips

Play each exercise on a keyboard.

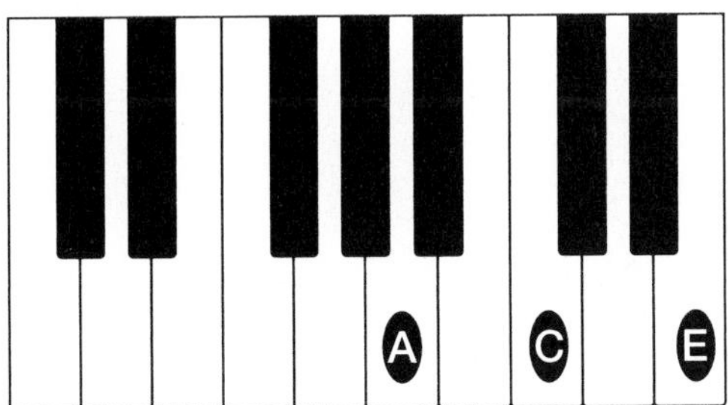

Skip Up

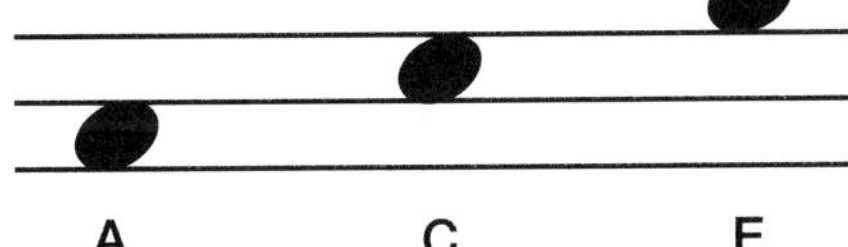

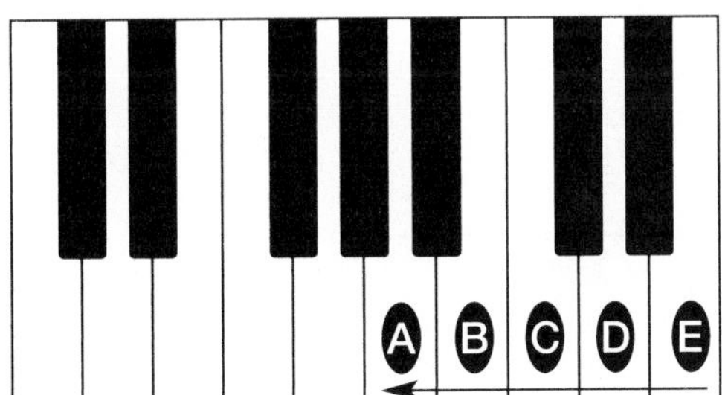

Step Down

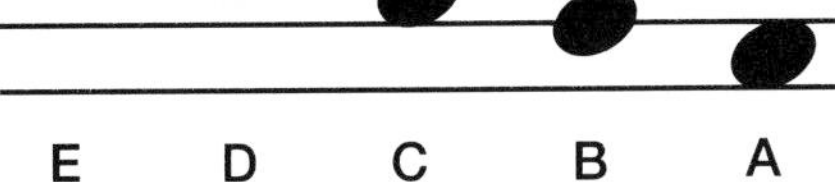

KEYBOARD

Name ______________________ Class ______________

KEYBOARD 3

Fingering Steps and Skips Using One-, Two-, and Three-Line Staff

Choose a fingering for each of the patterns below.

Write the finger numbers in the boxes above the notes.

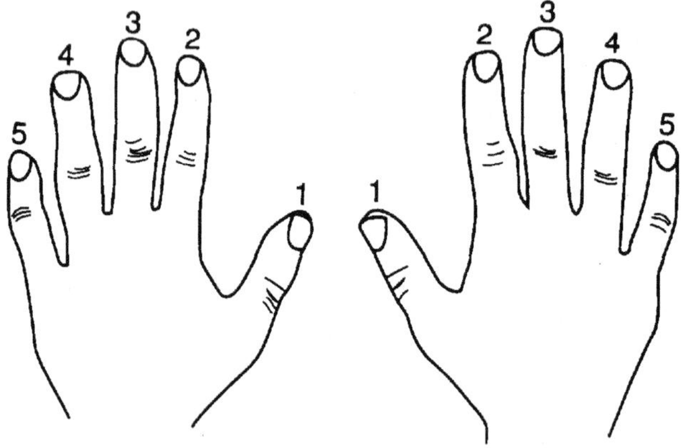

KEYBOARD 4

More Fingering

Choose a fingering for each of the patterns below.

Write the finger numbers in the boxes above the notes.

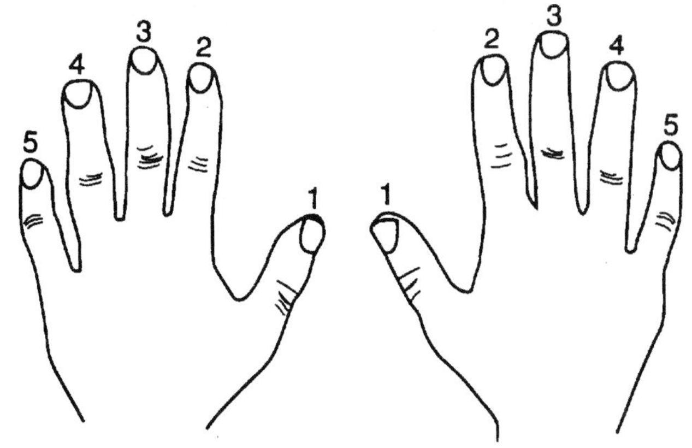

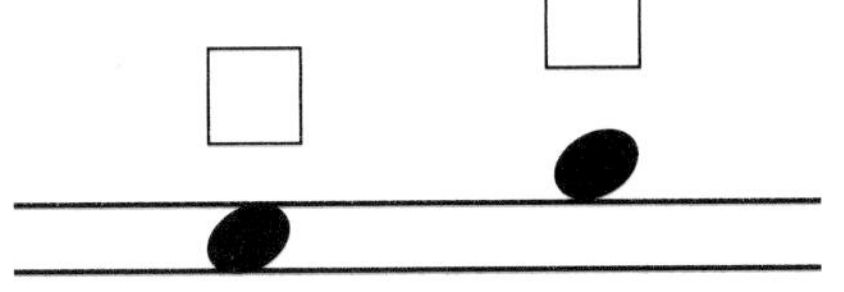

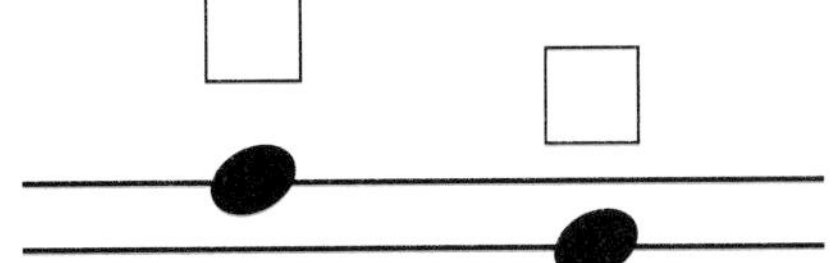

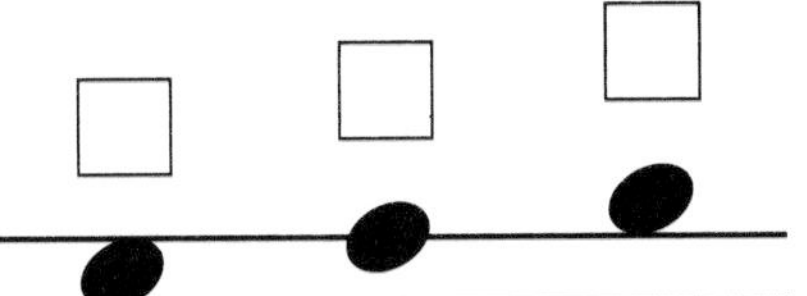

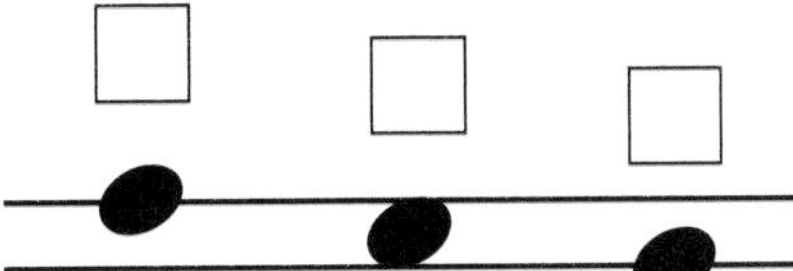

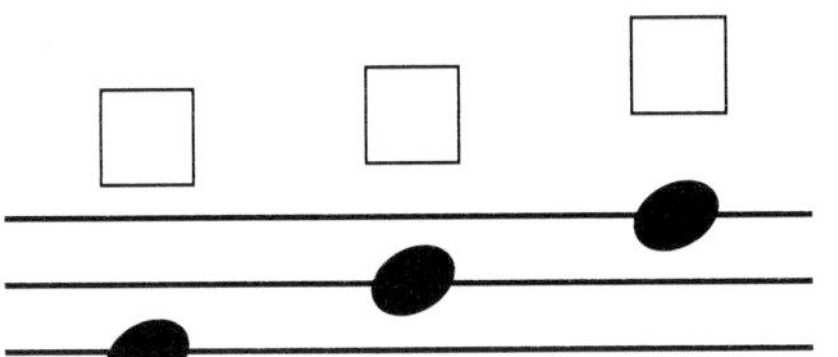

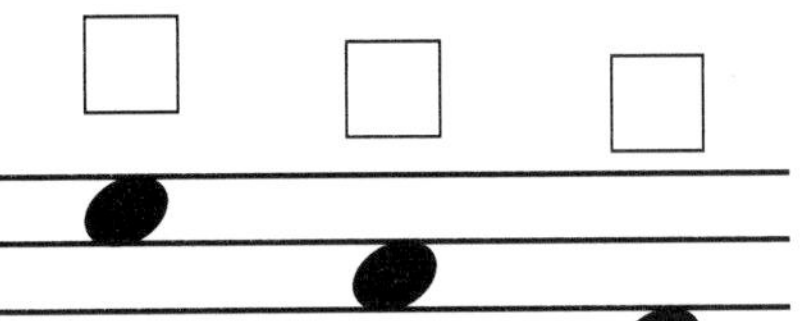

Name ______________________ Class __________

KEYBOARD 5

Five-Line Reading and Fingering

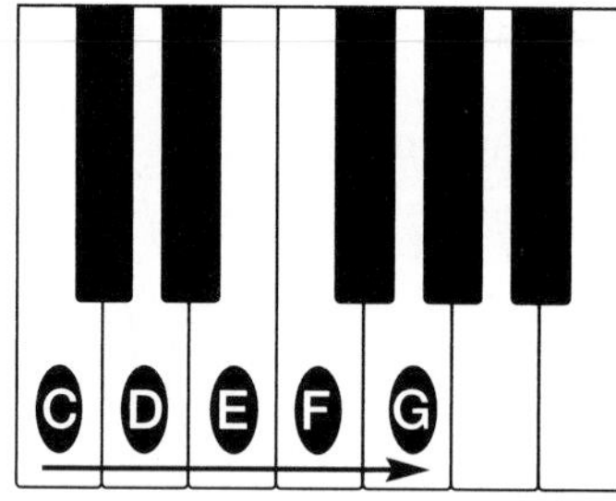

Up on the keyboard is to the right.

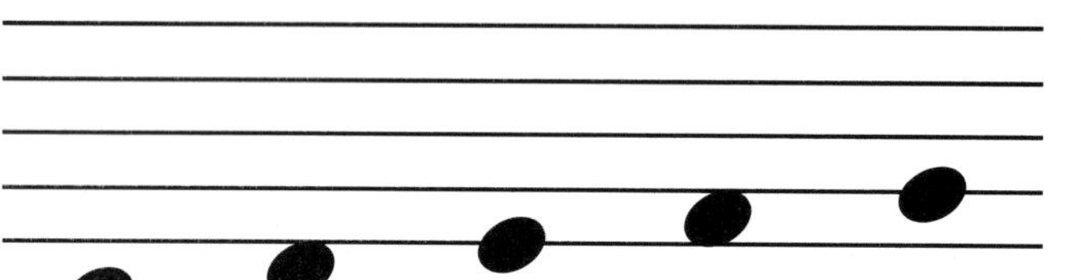

Up in music notation is UP!

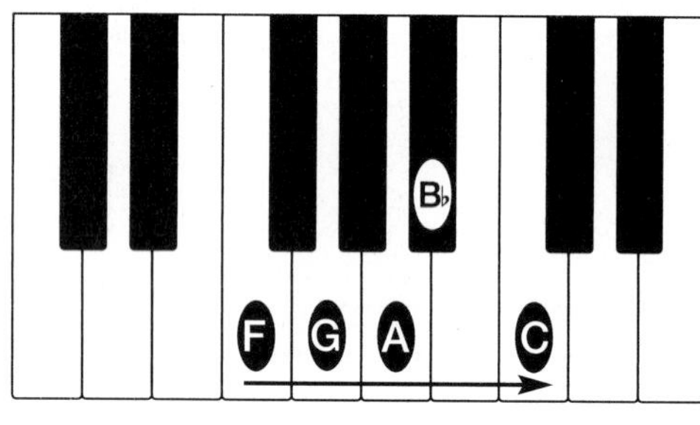

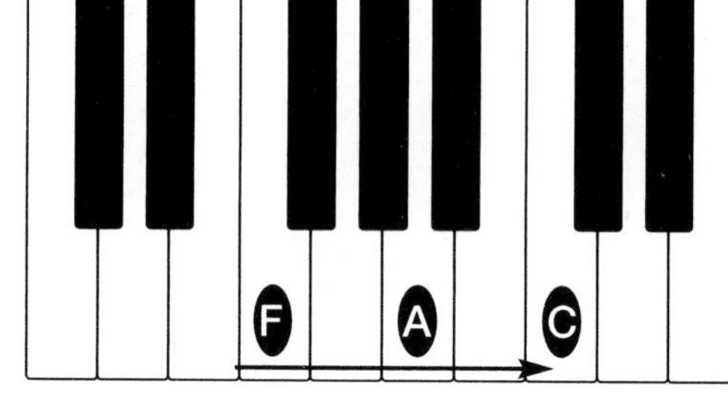

Step Up

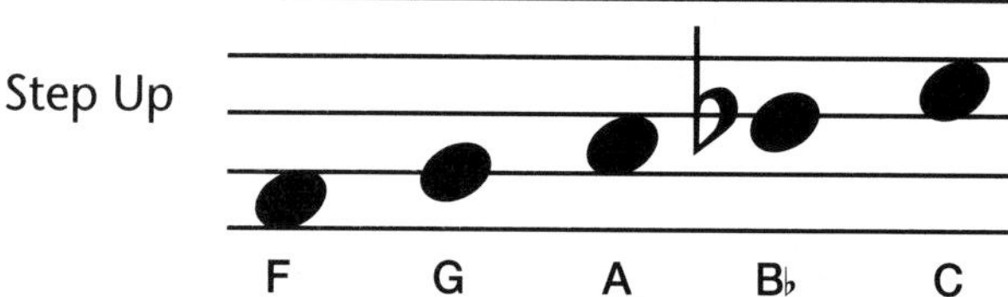

Skip Up

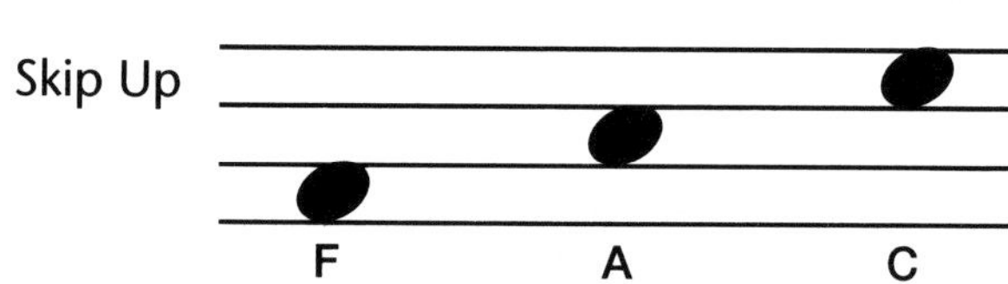

Write the finger numbers in the boxes above the notes.

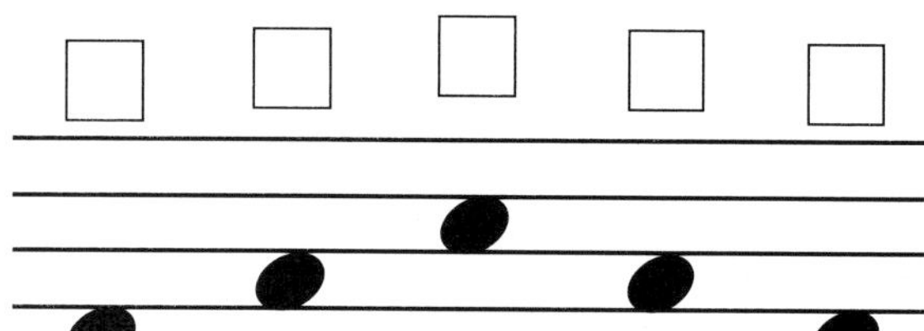

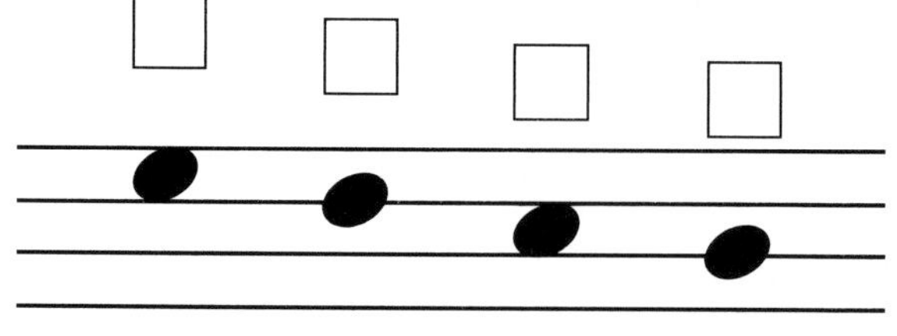

Name ______________________ Class ______________________

Keyboard 6

Rhythmic Ostinato

Play an accompaniment using a pitch pattern with an ostinato rhythm.

Bury Me Not on the Lone Prairie

Cowboy Song from the United States

Keyboard

Name ______________________ Class ____________

Keyboard 7

Harmonic Ostinato Accompaniment

Play the following ostinato accompaniment.

Hey, Ho! Nobody Home

Old English Round

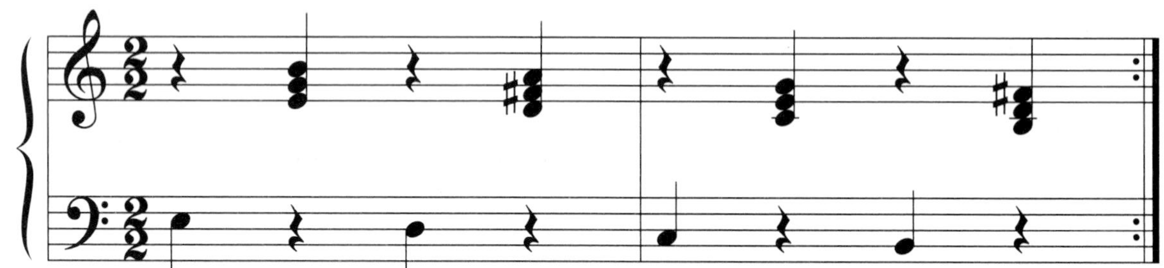

Name ______________________ Class ______________________

Keyboard 8

Dynamics

Play this accompaniment observing the dynamic markings.

Give My Regards to Broadway

Music by George M. Cohan
Arranged by Lynn Freeman Olson

Brightly

mf

From Martha F. Hilley and Lynn Freeman Olson, *Piano for Pleasure,* Third Edition, published by Wadsworth/Thomson Learning Inc. Used by permission. Original arrangement in F Major and cut time.

KEYBOARD

Name ______________________ Class ____________

KEYBOARD 8 (CONTINUED)

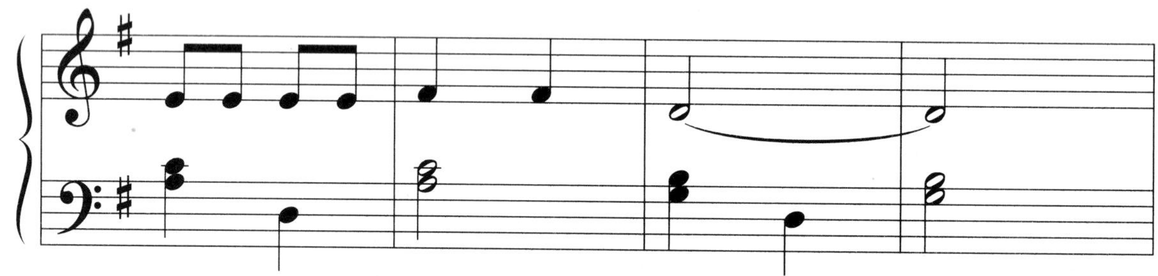

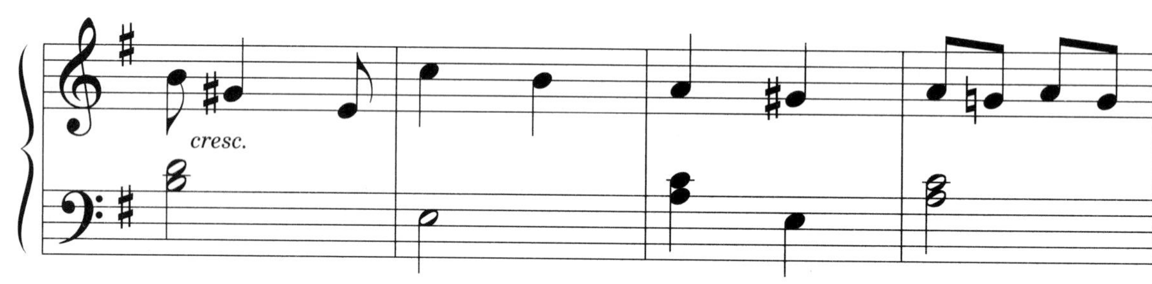

Name ______________________ Class ______________________

Keyboard 9

Playing a Countermelody

Play this countermelody on the **a** phrases only. Play one octave higher than written.

Blue Skies

Words and Music by Irving Berlin

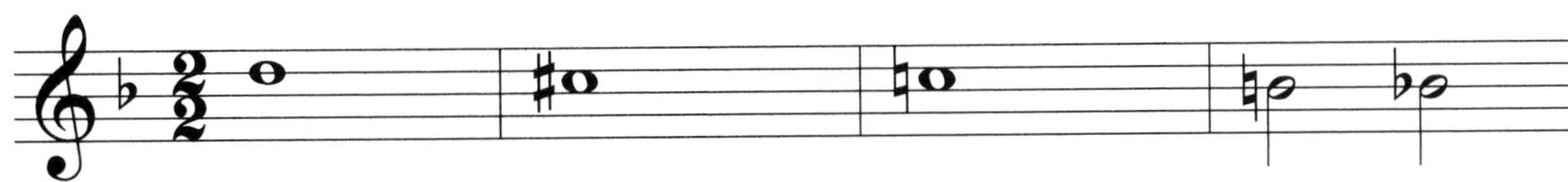

Write the appropriate finger numbers above the notes.

Keyboard

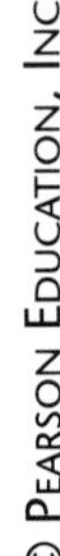

Name ______________________ Class ______________

Keyboard 10

Accompanying Using Roots and Thirds

Accompany the song with a steady half-note rhythm using the following positions. Identify each section using the form indicators.

Birthday

Music by John Lennon and Paul McCartney

Name ______________________ Class ______________________

KEYBOARD 11

Broken-Chord Accompaniment

Play this broken-chord accompaniment.

Scarborough Fair

Folk Song from England

KEYBOARD

Name ______________________ Class ______________

KEYBOARD 12

Playing a Whole-Note Accompaniment

Look closely at the four chord shapes below. They are in "closest position" which means that you move from one chord to another keeping any pitches that might be the same and moving those that change to the closest pitch possible. Practice playing these four shapes.

Swanee

Music by George Gershwin

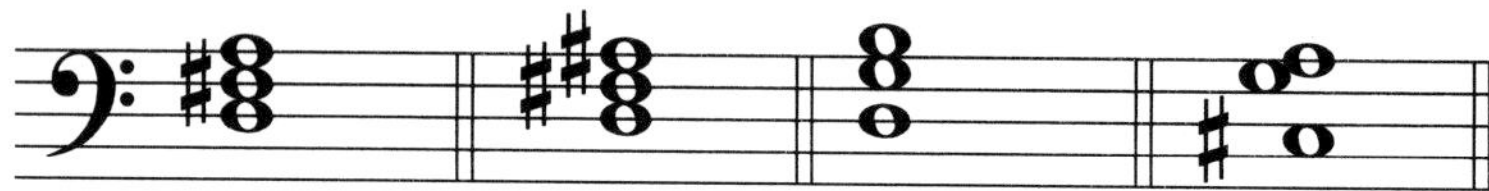

Now play the accompaniment.

Name ______________________________ Class ____________________

Keyboard 13

Playing an Ostinato Accompaniment

An ostinato accompaniment is one that repeats a pattern. Practice the four-bar pattern below until it is comfortable. The fingering is a suggestion only.

Dance for the Nations

Music by John Krumm

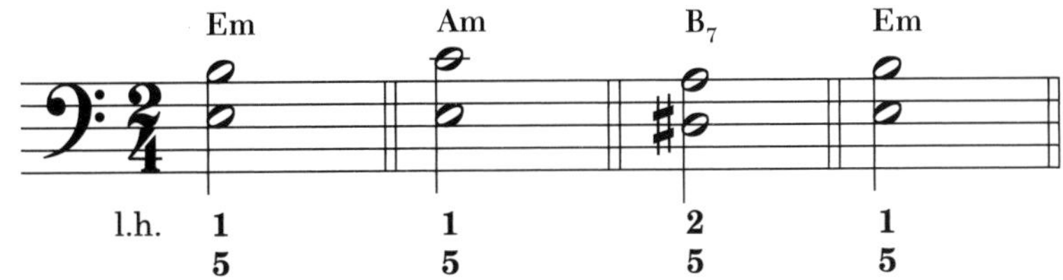

When you feel confident about moving from shape to shape, play the following left-hand ostinato accompaniment.

Keyboard

Name ______________________________ Class ______________

KEYBOARD 14

Playing an Accompaniment Using an Ostinato Rhythm

How many different chords does the following accompaniment use? Label those you find with the appropriate letter name.

Play the accompaniment.

Así es mi tierra (This Is My Land)

Music by Ignacío Fernandez Esperón

Name ______________________ Class ______________________

KEYBOARD 14 (CONTINUED)

KEYBOARD

Name ________________________ Class ____________

KEYBOARD 15

Playing a Tenor and Bass Accompaniment

"Peace Like a River" is written for two voices. Your accompaniment will furnish the other two parts (tenor and bass).

Determine the remaining fingerings before playing.

Peace Like a River

African American Spiritual

Name ______________________ Class ______________________

Keyboard 16

Playing an Accompaniment

Practice the five closest position chords shown below in keyboard style. Each chord contains three pitches in the right hand and one pitch in the bass.

Paths of Victory

Music by Bob Dylan

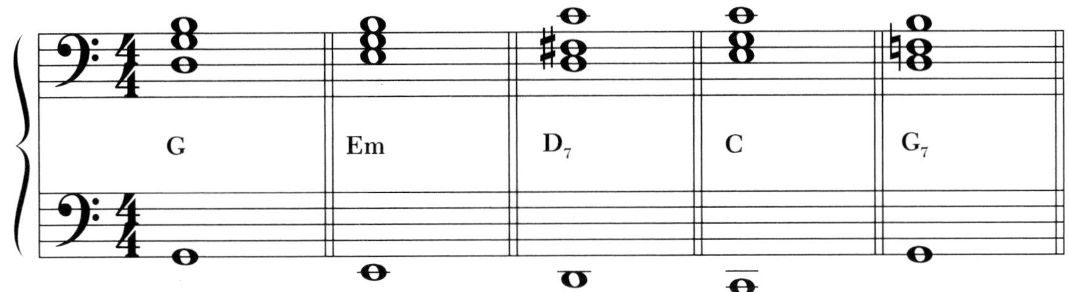

When you are comfortable with the chords, play the accompaniment.

KEYBOARD

Name ______________________ Class ____________

KEYBOARD 16 (CONTINUED)

Name ______________________ Class ______________________

KEYBOARD 17

Playing as a Trio

Invite students to individually perform one of the parts below on keyboard, using correct fingering. If a piano lab is available, invite three students to perform *"Kyrie"* as a three-part ensemble on three keyboards.

Kyrie

Round from Suriname

KEYBOARD

Name ______________________ Class ______________

KEYBOARD 18

Blues Accompaniment

Play this blues accompaniment softly.

Sometimes I Feel Like a Motherless Child

African American Spiritual

Name ______________________ Class ______________________

Keyboard 19

Tritone Blues Accompaniment

Identify and play the tritone (augmented fourth) interval. Then play the accompaniment.

Sun Gonna Shine

Traditional Blues

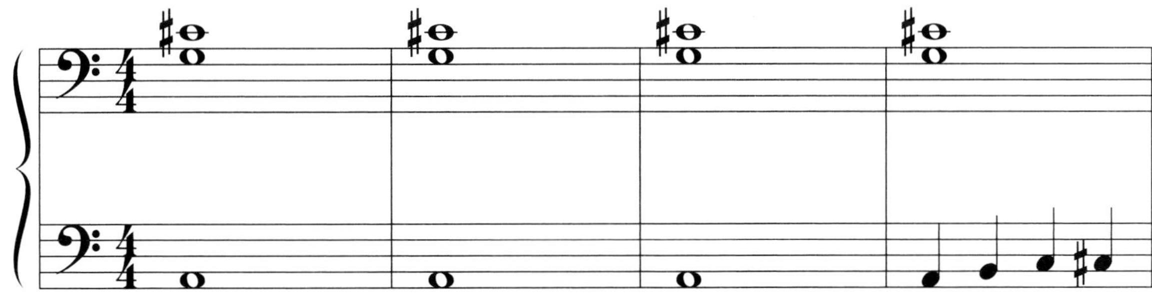

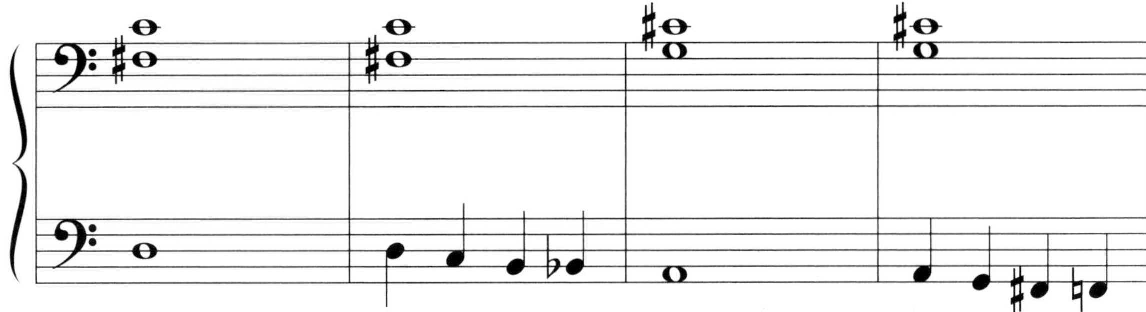

Keyboard

Name ______________________ Class ____________

KEYBOARD 20

Playing Major and Minor Chords

Play this accompaniment using major and minor chords. Notice that you always play on beats two and three in each measure.

Don't Be Cruel

Words and Music by
Otis Blackwell and Elvis Presley

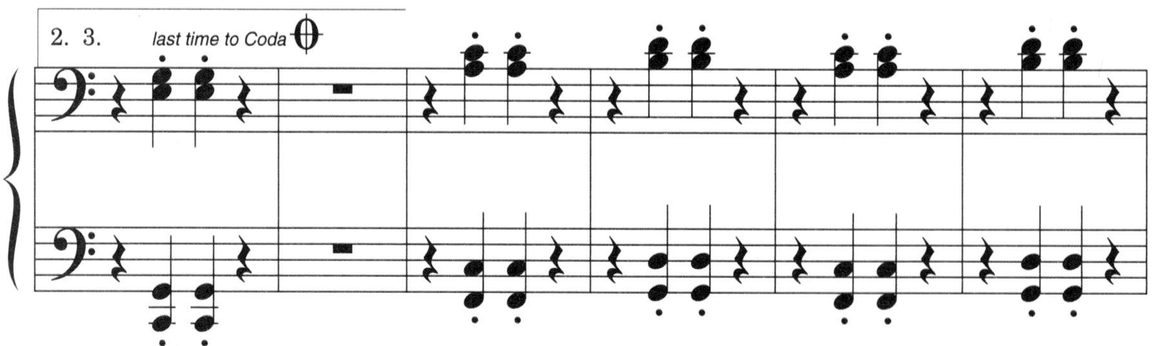

Name ______________________ Class ______________________

KEYBOARD 20 (CONTINUED)

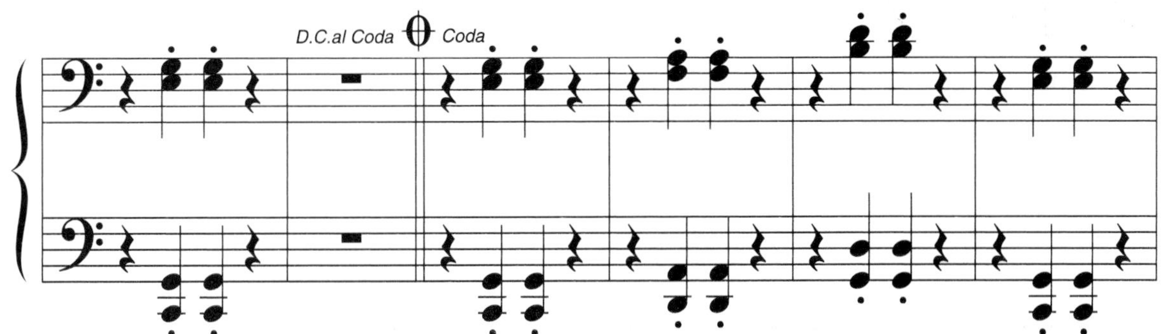

KEYBOARD

Name ______________________ Class ______________

KEYBOARD 21

Rhythm

Play this accompaniment. Notice that you always play on beats one and three.

Nana Kru

Traditional Song of the Kou Tribe of Liberia (Adapted)

Name ______________________ Class ______________

KEYBOARD 22

Fingering Positions

Perform a melody with several fingering positions. How many different fingering positions can you find? Write in your choice of fingering where indicated.

Banuwa

Folk Song from Liberia

[ ] [ ] [ ]

[ ]

[ ]

[ ] [ ] [ ] 2nd time only [ ]

[ ]

[ ] [ ] [ ]

KEYBOARD

Name ______________________ Class ______________

KEYBOARD 23

Playing a Two-Handed Accompaniment

This style of accompaniment is often called "boom-chick"—a single bass pitch alternates with a right-hand chord.

Ezekiel Saw the Wheel

African American Spiritual

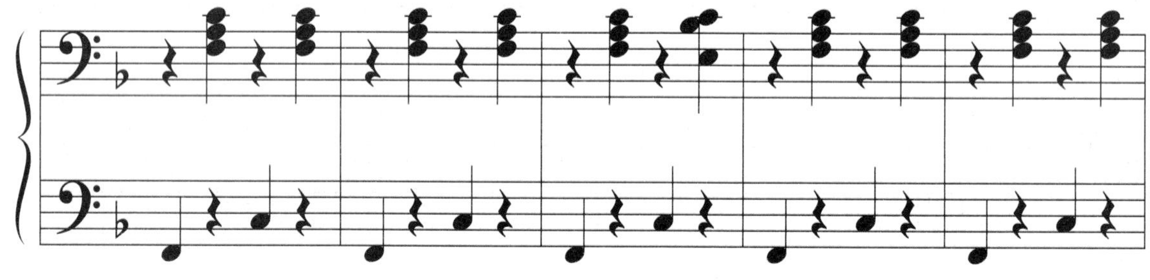

Name ______________________ Class ______________________

Keyboard 23 (continued)

Keyboard

Name ______________________ Class ______________

Keyboard 24

Playing an Accompaniment Using I, IV and V_7

The accompaniment below uses tones from the I, IV and V_7 chords in the key of F major. Pay close attention to the "cadential" measures (7 and 8, 15 and 16).

Las mañanitas

Folk Song from Mexico

Name ______________________ Class ______________________

KEYBOARD 25

Playing a Piano Piece

This arrangement of "America, the Beautiful" uses a sustain pedal. Experiment with the pedal on your keyboard. In the opening measures the sound should last from one measure to the next without "smearing" the sounds together. Notice that the indications for a pedal change occur at the beginning of the measure.

America, the Beautiful

Music by Samuel A. Ward
Arranged by Lynn Freeman Olson

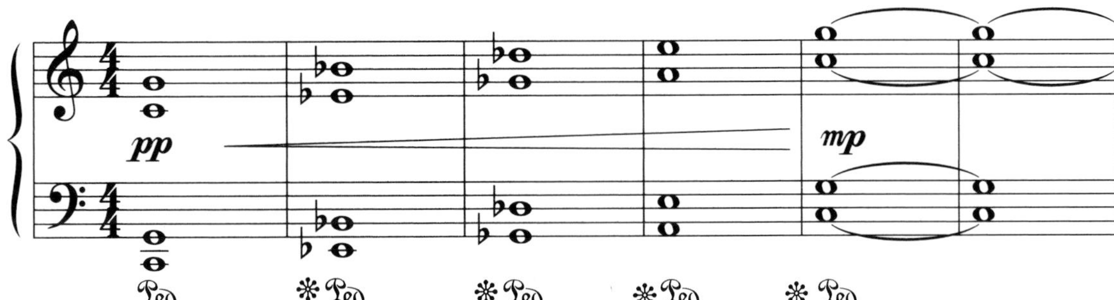

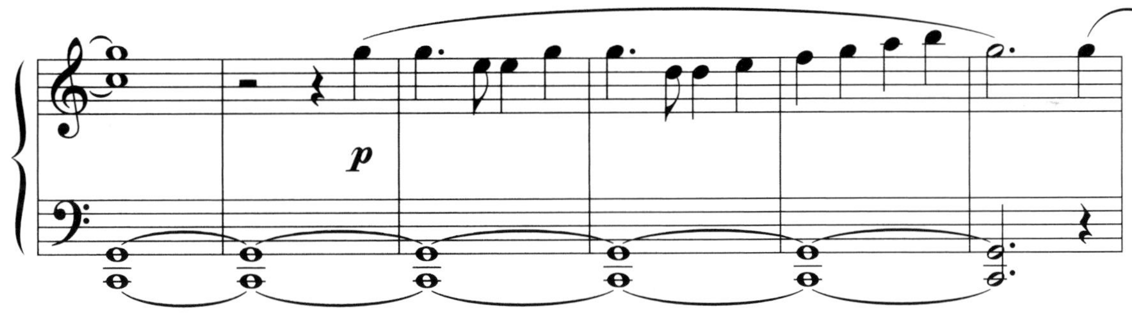

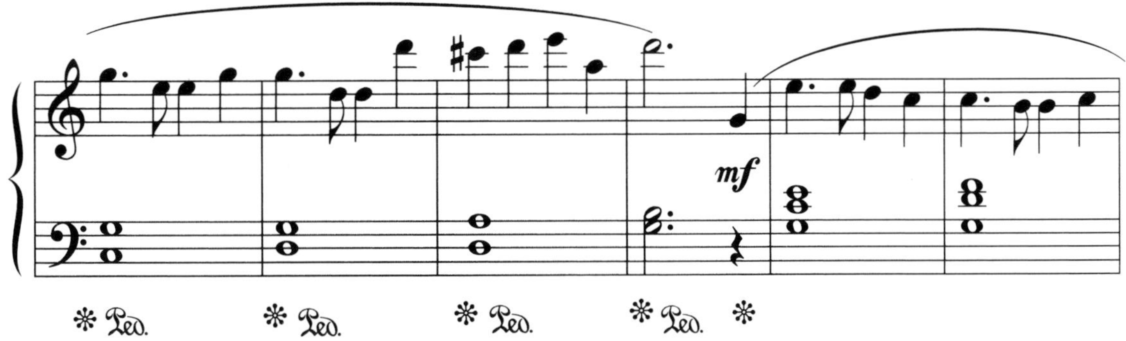

From Martha F. Hilley and Lynn Freeman Olson, *Piano for Pleasure,* Third Edition, published by Wadsworth/Thomson Learning Inc. Used by permission.

KEYBOARD

Name ______________________ Class ______________

Keyboard 25 (continued)

Recorder

Table of Contents

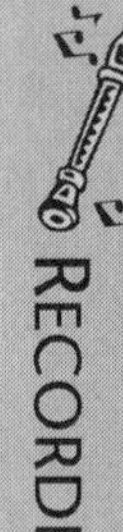

Name ______________________ Class ______________

Recorder 1

Beginning the Alto Recorder

Before playing this piece for alto recorder, review the fingering for C and D using the fingering charts below. Check to make sure that your fingers cover the holes securely and your left hand is above your right hand.

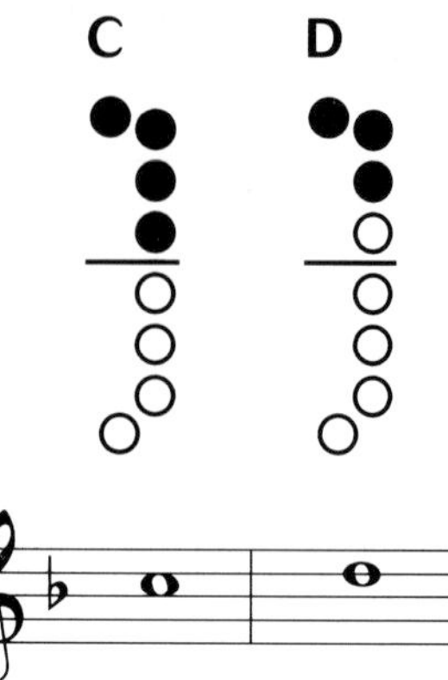

Your Life Is Now

Words and Music by John Mellencamp and George M. Green

Alto Recorder

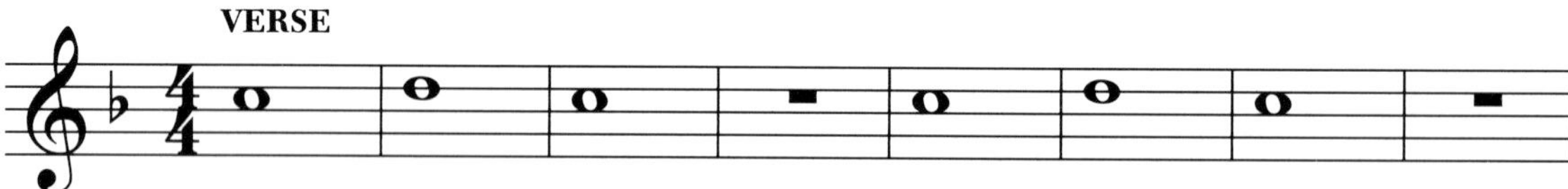

Name ______________________________ Class ____________________

Recorder 2

Playing the Alto or Soprano Recorder

You can play a countermelody to accompany "Red River Valley" on either the alto or soprano recorder. Check that your fingers are covering the holes firmly especially if you choose to play the soprano recorder.

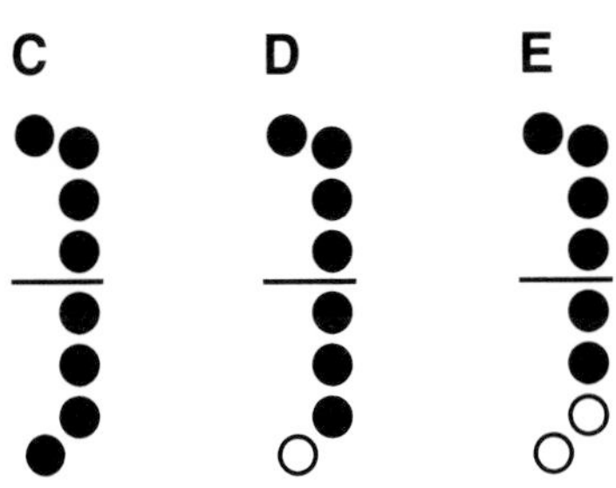

Red River Valley

Cowboy Song from the United States

Soprano Recorder

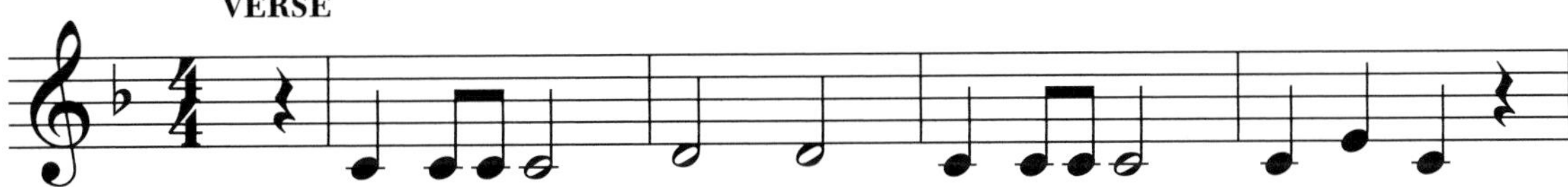

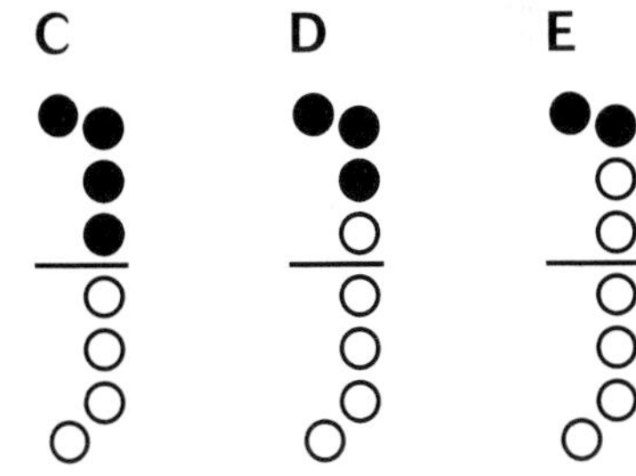

Alto Recorder

Recorder

Name ______________________ Class ____________

RECORDER 3

Playing the Soprano Recorder

Listen for the phrase endings as you play this countermelody during Section A of "Magnolia." Start each note distinctly by whispering *daah.*

A B D

Magnolia

Words and Music by Tish Hinojosa

Soprano Recorder

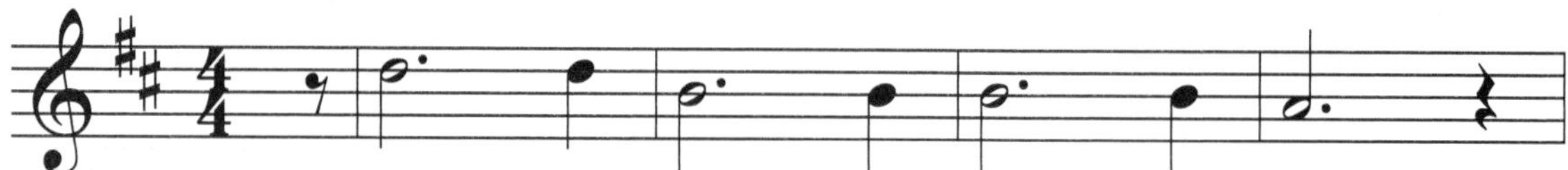

Name ______________________ Class ______________________

Recorder 4

Playing with Expression

D E F♯ G A

Play the piece below two different ways. The first time, play the melody *legato*, the second time, *staccato*. As you change your articulation, you still need to whisper *daah* on each note.

Give My Regards to Broadway

Words and Music by George M. Cohan

Soprano Recorder

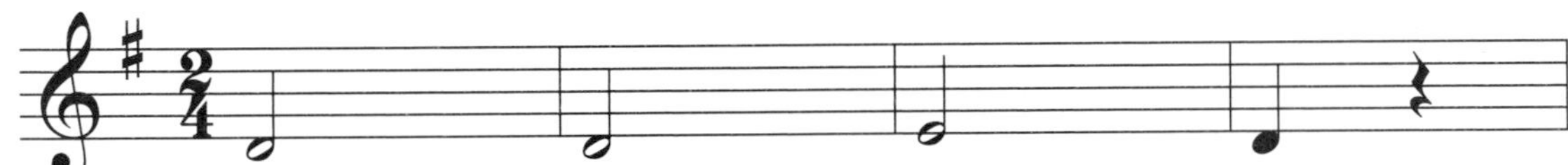

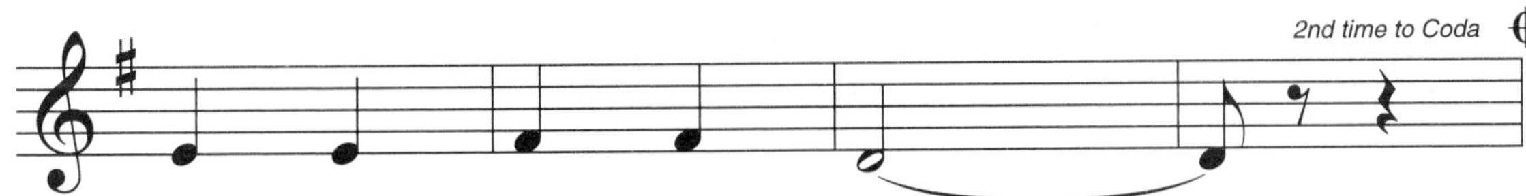

Name ______________________ Class ______________

Recorder 5

Playing the D Major Scale

Play a D Major Scale on your soprano recorder (D, E, F♯, G, A, B, C♯, D) in an upward and downward direction. Look at the melody below and notice that it begins with a D Major Scale moving in a downward direction. As you play, carefully observe the rests and repeat signs.

D E F♯ G A B C♯ D

What a Wonderful World

Words and Music by
George David Weiss and Bob Thiele

Name ______________________ Class ______________________

RECORDER 6

A Recorder Duet

Perform the countermelodies below on soprano and alto recorders. Add the recorders with the recording for an ensemble experience.

Soprano E G A B C D

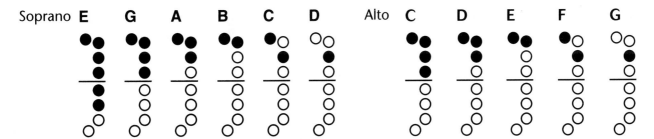

Alto C D E F G

Sing a Song of Peace

Music by Al Jacobs
Arranged by Jill Gallina

RECORDER

Name ______________________ Class ____________

Recorder 7

Another Recorder Duet

The countermelodies below can be played using soprano and alto recorders. For an ensemble experience, play the recorder part with the recording of the song.

Soprano

G A B C

Alto

C D E

I Walk the Unfrequented Road

Folk Hymn from the United States

Name ______________________ Class ______________________

Recorder 8

Playing with Style

E F♯ G A B

Look at the countermelody below. Although it only uses five notes, the rhythm is a bit tricky. If you have already sung the folk melody in class, you will notice that this countermelody and the folk melody have the same rhythm pattern.

Ain't Gonna Let Nobody Turn Me 'Round

African American Civil Rights Song

Soprano Recorder

Recorder

Name ______________________ Class ______________

Recorder 9

An Alto Recorder Countermelody

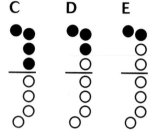

Review the fingering for C, D, and E on your alto recorder. When you are comfortable with these notes, play the countermelody below. Remember to whisper *daah* in the style of the music.

C D E

Bridges

Words and Music by Bill Staines

Alto Recorder

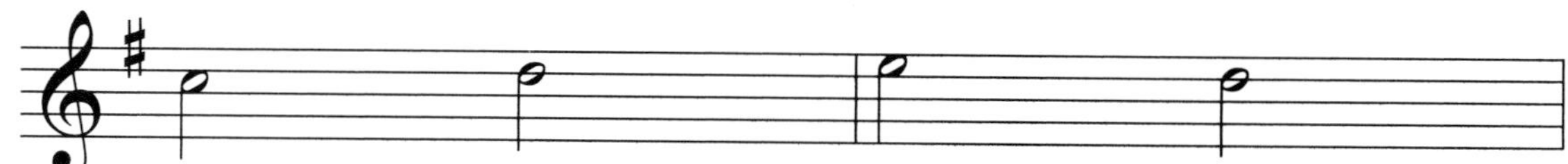

Name ______________________ Class ______________

Recorder 10

A Soprano Recorder Countermelody

This countermelody can be played on your soprano recorder. Notice that some phrases are exactly the same. Practice saying the rhythm syllables of these phrases before playing the entire piece.

G A B C D

Bridges

Words and Music by Bill Staines

Soprano Recorder

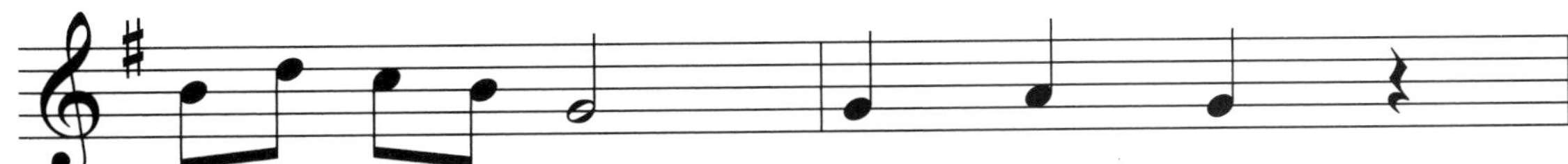

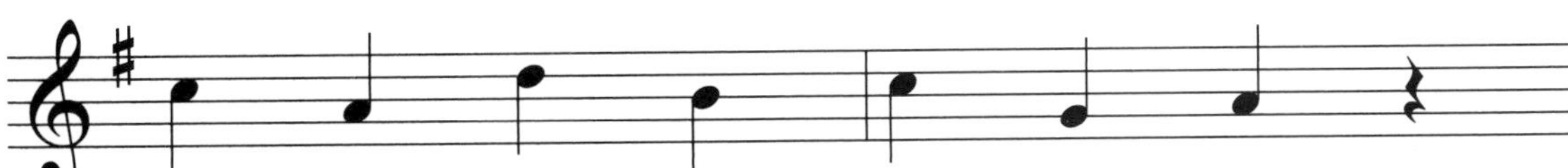

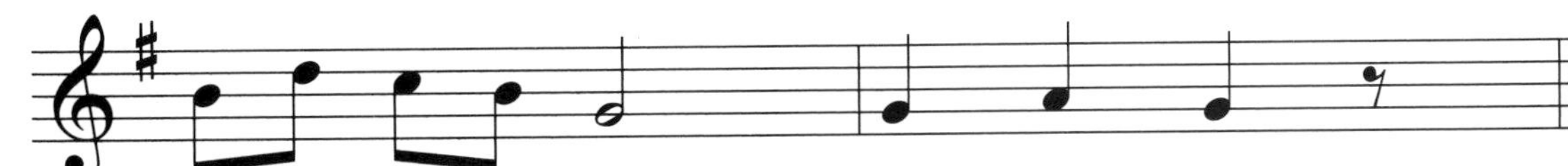

Name ______________________________ Class ______________

Recorder 11

Playing the Alto Recorder

C D E

Review the fingering for C, D, and E on the alto recorder. Follow the music below and finger the notes without playing. Play the countermelody by yourself or with the recording of the song.

Harrison Town

Folk Song from the Ozarks
Adapted by Jill Trinka

Alto Recorder

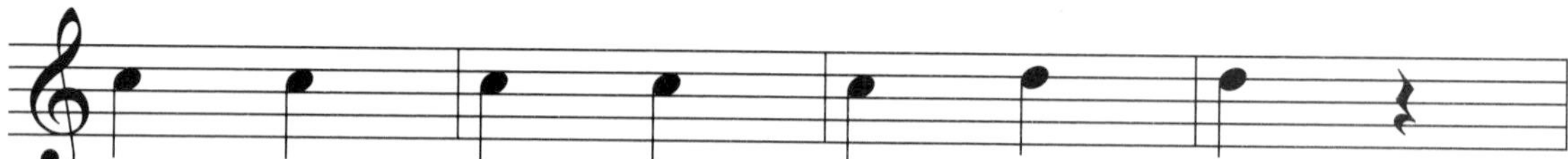

Name ______________________ Class ______________________

Recorder 12

Soprano

G A♭ A B♭ C D

Feeling Beats in Two

Before playing the countermelody below, review the fingering for B♭ and A♭. Use the fingering for G♯ when playing A♭. They are enharmonic tones.

Strike Up the Band

Music by George Gershwin

Soprano Recorder

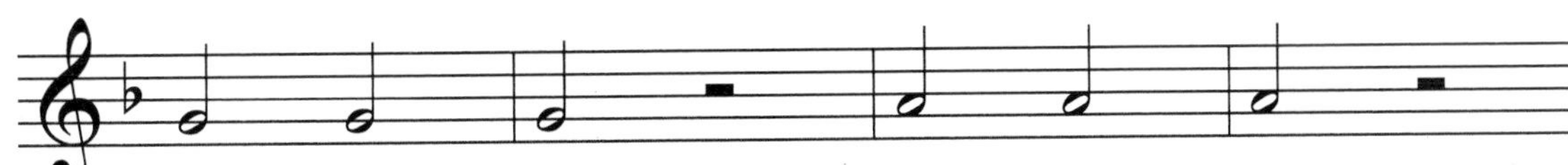

Recorder

Name ______________________ Class ____________

Recorder 13

Playing B♭

Soprano

G A B♭ C D

Practice the last two phrases of this recorder piece before playing the entire countermelody. Because the song is in the key of F, you will need to play B♭. The half-step rule will help you to remember the fingering for this note.

El payo (The Cowpoke)

Folk Song from Mexico

Soprano Recorder

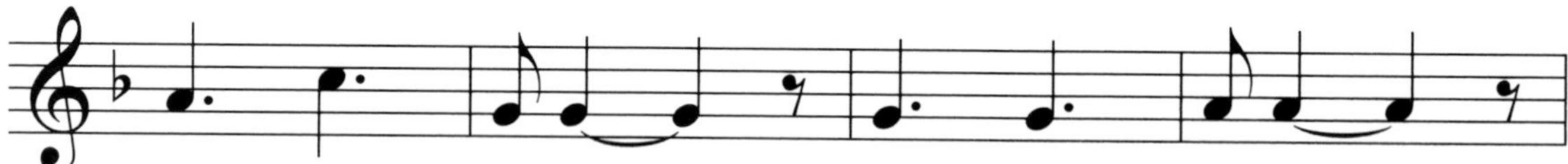

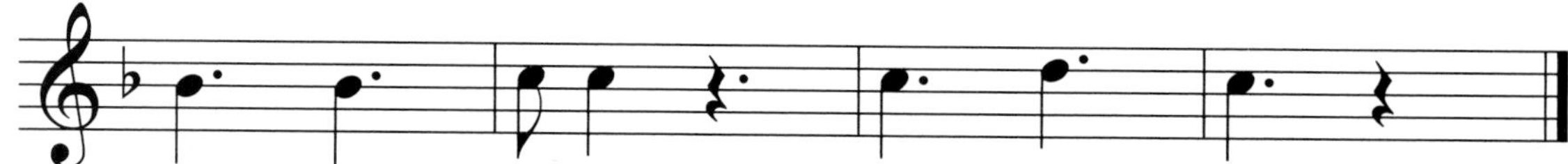

Name ______________________ Class ______________________

RECORDER 14

Dueling Recorders

Play the beginning of this countermelody on your alto recorder. When indicated, switch to your soprano recorder and play the ending of the piece. For another challenge, play the entire piece on soprano recorder. You will need to transpose the first two phrases down one octave as you play.

Alto C D G

Hava nagila

Jewish Folk Song

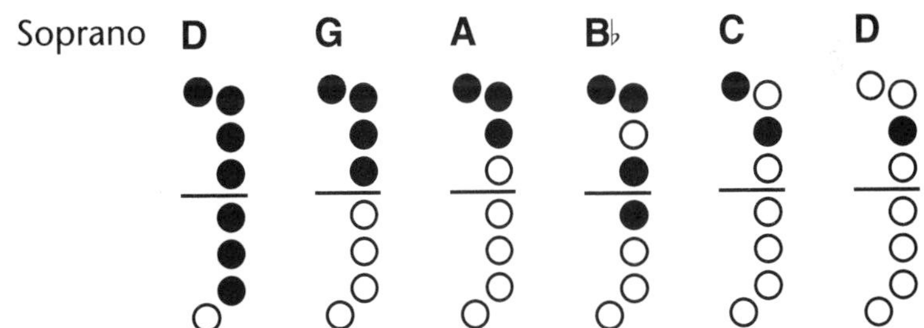

Soprano Recorder

RECORDER

Name ______________________ Class ____________

RECORDER 15

More Harmony

The countermelody below can be played on your alto recorder or on your soprano recorder if you transpose the melody down one octave. With the recording, try playing the countermelody first on the soprano recorder and then on the alto recorder. Which recorder sound do you like best with the recording? Why?

Soprano: D E G

Alto: D E G

Four Strong Winds

Words and Music by Ian Tyson

REFRAIN

Name ______________________ Class ______________________

Recorder 16

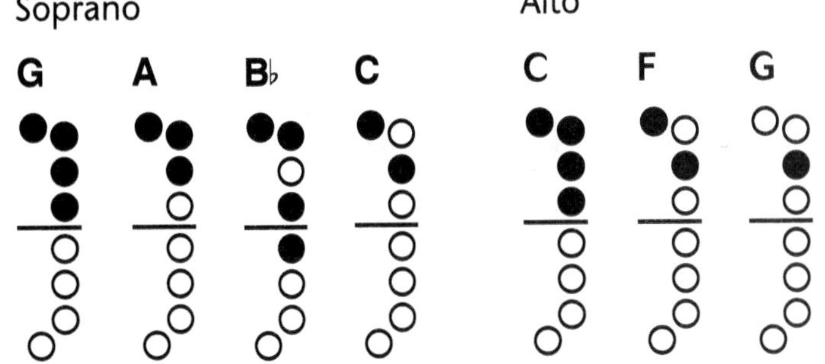

A Recorder Duet

Play this recorder duet with a friend. Blend the recorder sound by listening to the other part as you play.

Mary Ann

Calypso Song from the West Indies

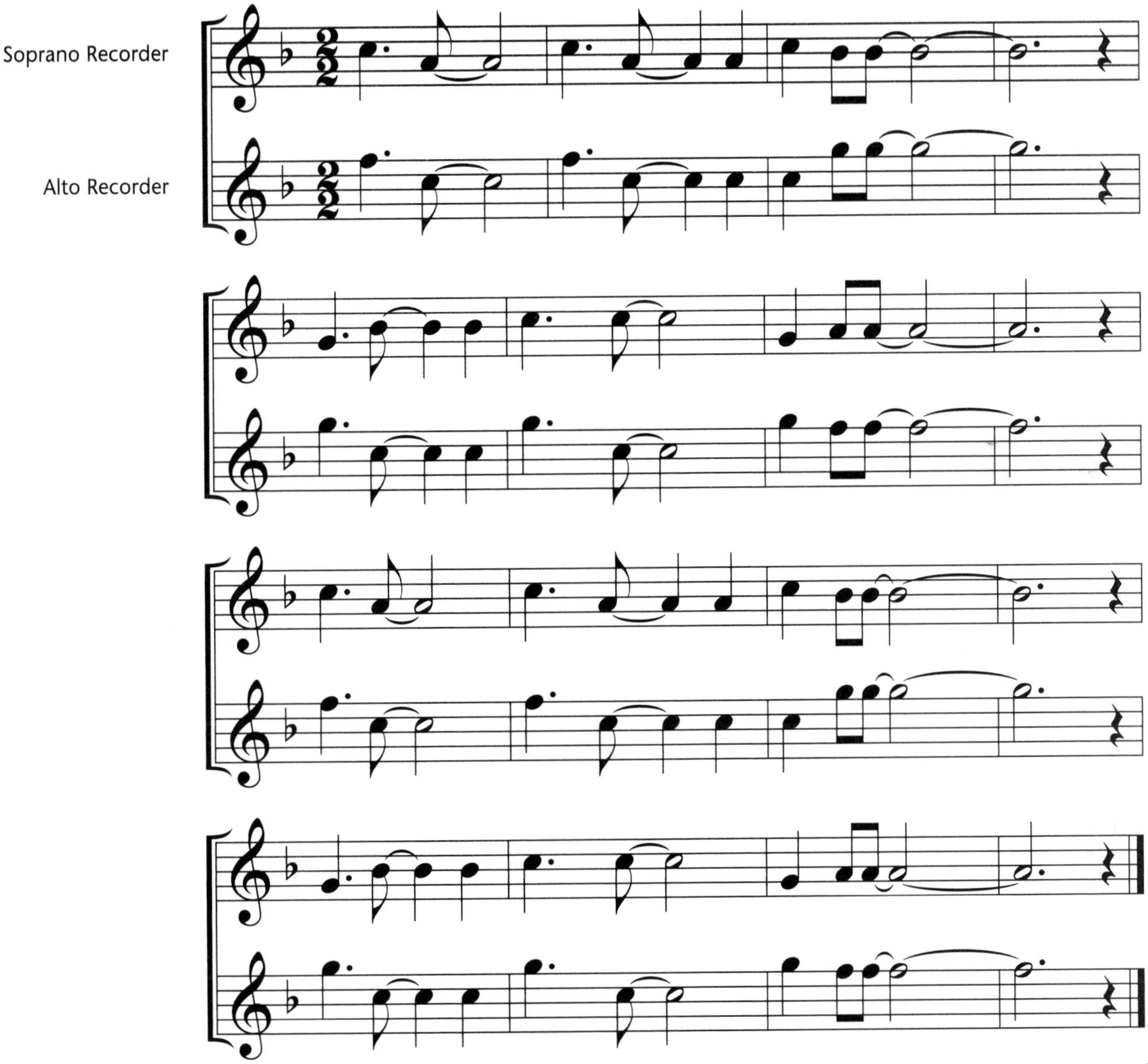

Soprano Recorder

Alto Recorder

Recorder

Name ______________________ Class ______________

Recorder 17

A Recorder Duet

Play this recorder duet with a friend. One of you will play the soprano recorder while the other plays the alto recorder. Listen to each other and try to blend your sound.

Soprano: G A C D

Alto: C D E

Blue Mountain Lake

Lumberjack Song from New York
Adapted by Susan Brumfield

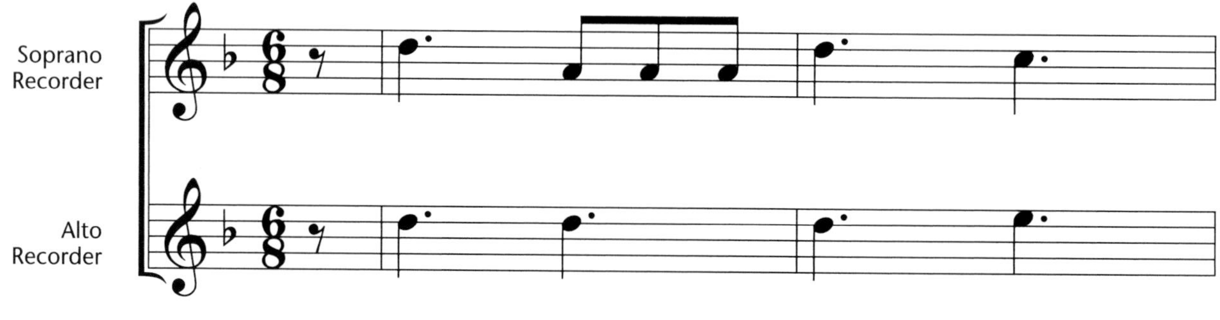

Name ______________________________ Class ____________________

Recorder 18

Recorder Descant

Play a recorder descant during the introduction on the recording. Use the fingering chart in your book to help you learn any new notes. Listen to this descant played by a wood flute on the recording of this song.

D E F♯ G A B C♯ D

This Little Light of Mine

African American Spiritual
Arranged by Linda Twine and Joseph Joubert

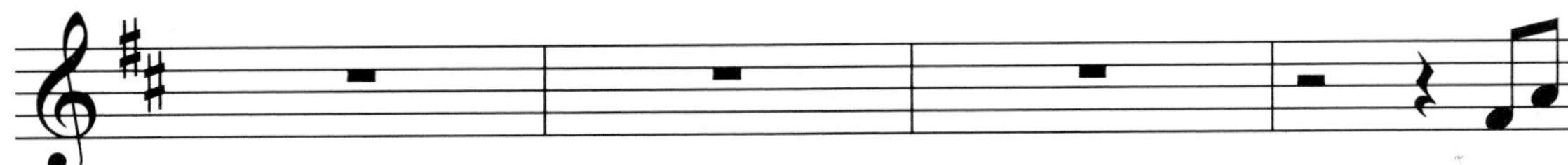

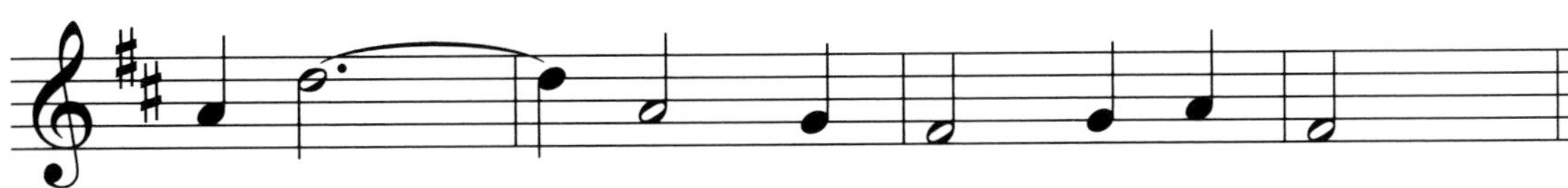

Recorder

Name ______________________________ Class ______________

RECORDER 19

Stylized Recorder Playing

Try this warm-up before playing the part below. Play E for four beats followed by F♯ for four beats and repeat. Then play each note for two beats and then each note for one beat. When playing with the recording, sing the odd numbered verses and play on the even numbered verses. Try to blend the recorder with the sound of the guitar.

E F♯ A B

Sun Gonna Shine

Traditional Blues

Soprano Recorder

Name ______________________________ Class ____________________

Recorder 20

Ensemble Playing

This recorder piece can be used to accompany the refrain of "Green, Green Grass of Home." When playing in ensembles, listen to the other parts as you play.

Soprano

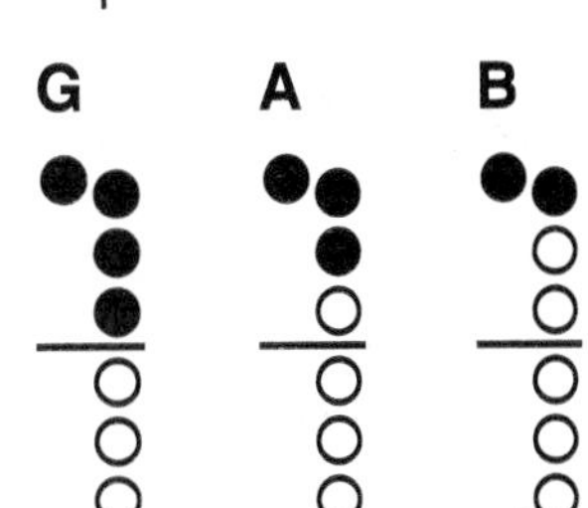

Alto

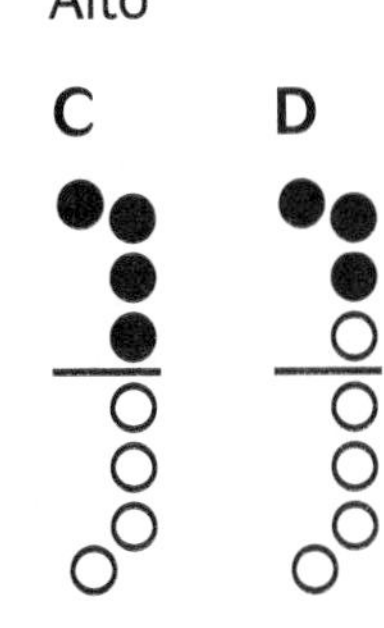

Green, Green Grass of Home

Words and Music by Curly Putman

Recorder

Name ______________________ Class ______________

Recorder 21

Playing Recorders in Harmony

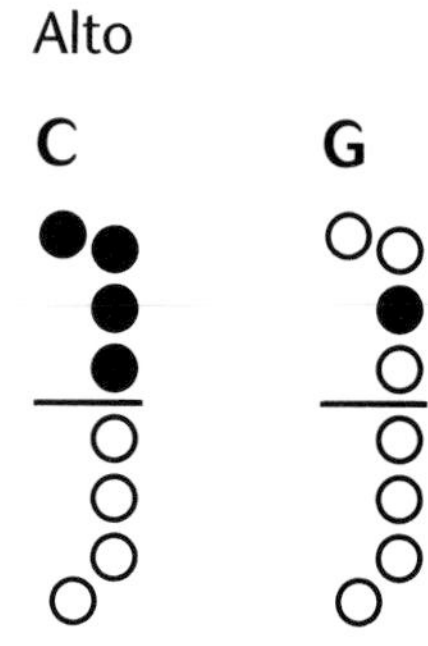

Play the parts below using soprano and alto recorders. Notice the soprano recorder part is the same as the traditional melody from Trinidad; the alto recorder part can be played to add harmony.

Water Come a Me Eye

Folk Song from Trinidad

Soprano Recorder

Alto Recorder

Name ______________________ Class ______________________

Recorder 22

Reviewing B♭

Practice the fingering for B♭ before playing the countermelody below. Accompany the first eight phrases of the song melody on your recorder and then sing the remainder of the song.

B♭ C D

On My Way

Music by Jeanine Tesori
Arranged by Michael Rafter

Soprano Recorder

Recorder

Name ____________________ Class ____________

Recorder 23

Accompanying a Show Tune

The recorder part below can be played on the alto recorder to accompany the recording *The Circle of Life.* Review the fingering for C, D, F, and G before performing this arrangement.

C D F G

The Circle of Life

Music by Elton John

Alto Recorder

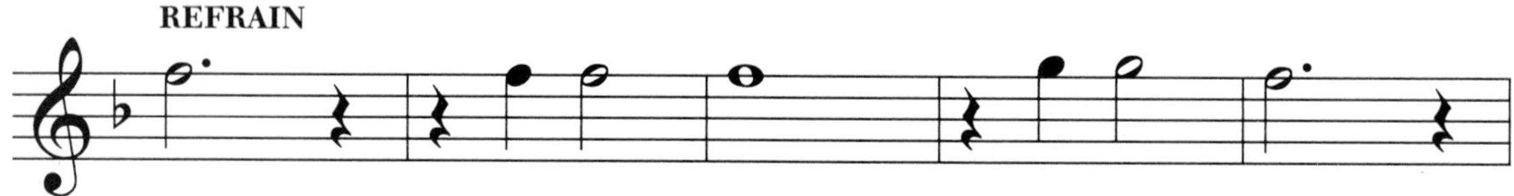

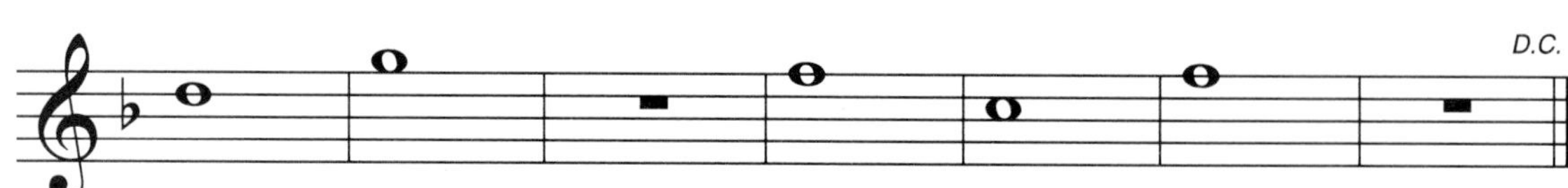

* *Last time to Refrain*

Name ______________________ Class ______________________

RECORDER 24

Feeling Beats in Sets of Two

As you play this countermelody, whisper *daah* on each note in the style of the music. Make sure you clearly articulate the sound of each eighth note. Take a breath at the end of each four-measure phrase.

G A B C D

Mama Don't 'Low

Folk Song from the United States

Soprano Recorder

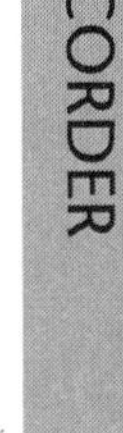

RECORDER

Name ______________________ Class ______________

Recorder 25

Playing Alto Recorder

Review the fingering for C, D, F, and G on your alto recorder. When you can finger those notes, play the countermelody below. You may need to practice slowly in order to play the leaps accurately. Remember to move your fingers together.

C D F G

Corta la caña (Head for the Canefields)

Folk Song from Puerto Rico

Alto Recorder

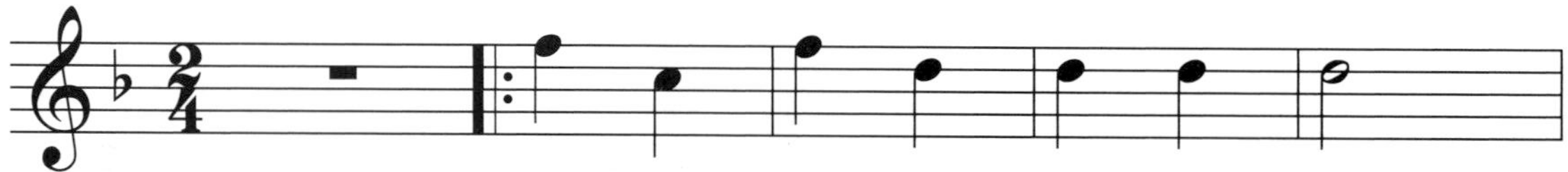

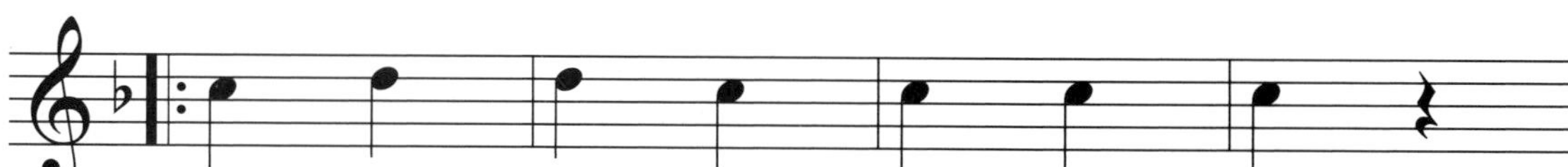

Name ________________________ Class ________________

Recorder 26

Playing Soprano Recorder

Review the fingering for D, G, and A on your soprano recorder. Move your fingers together when playing leaps. Whisper *daah* in the style of the music as you play.

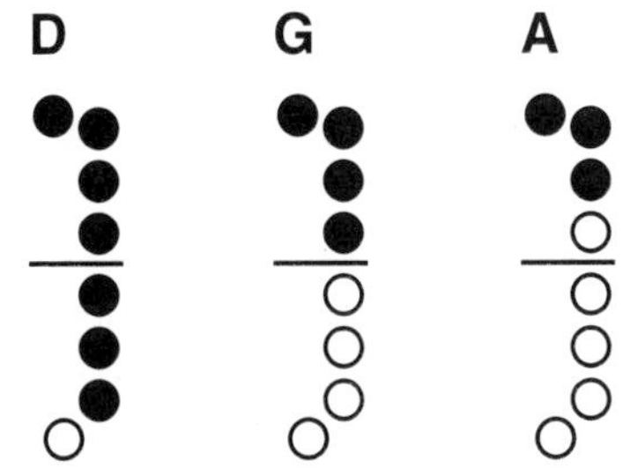

Corta la caña (Head for the Canefields)

Folk Song from Puerto Rico

Soprano Recorder

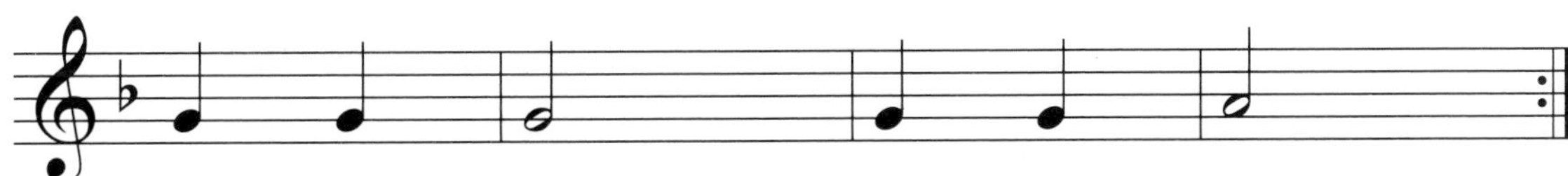

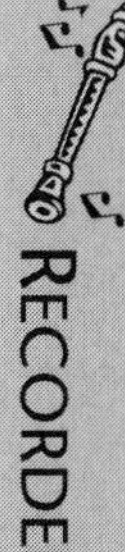

Name ______________________ Class ______________

Recorder 27

Accompanying the Soprano Recorder

Learn the countermelody below on your alto recorder. If a friend can play the traditional melody on soprano recorder, play this alto part as an accompaniment. Listen to each other and blend your sound as you play.

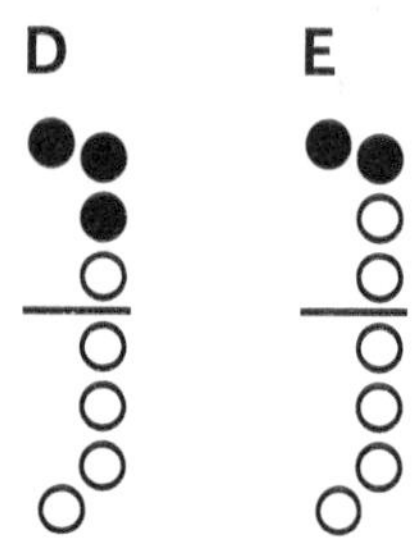

Worried Man Blues

Traditional Blues

Alto Recorder

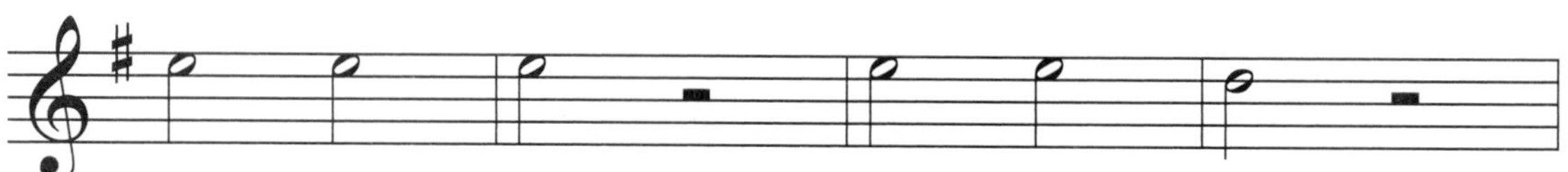

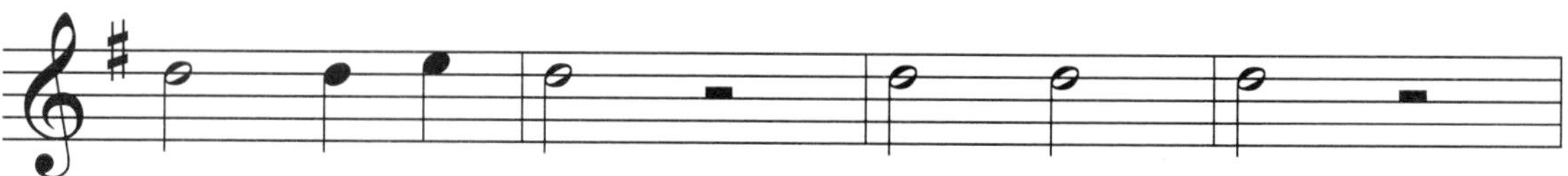

Name ______________________ Class ______________________

RECORDER 28

Accompanying an Entire Song

Review the fingerings for D, E, F♯, G, A, B and C on the soprano recorder. Practice the part below by playing each phrase. Then, perform the accompaniment for the entire song as the class sings.

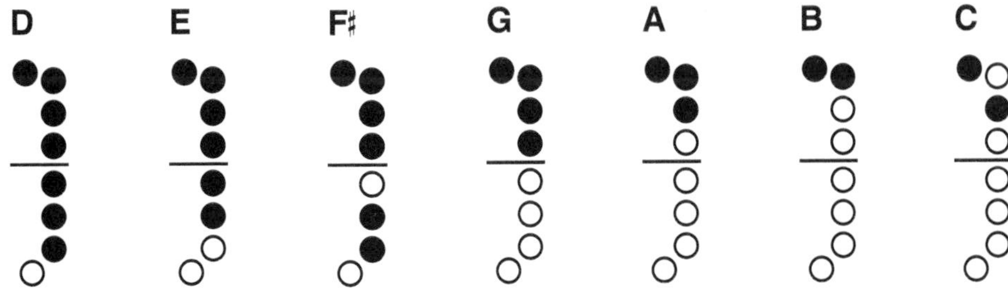

I Am But a Small Voice

English Words and Music by Roger Whittaker

RECORDER

Name ______________________ Class ______________

Recorder 28 (continued)

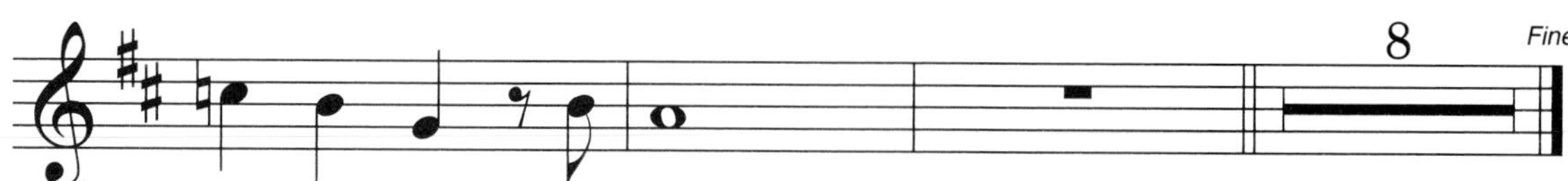

Name ______________________ Class ______________________

Recorder 29

Notes in the Lower Register

Practice fingering the notes D, E, F♯, G, and A before playing the countermelody below. As you play, be sure to feel the beats grouped in sets of two. Play the verse on your soprano recorder and sing the refrain.

D E F♯ G A

Abraham, Martin, and John

Words and Music by Dick Holler

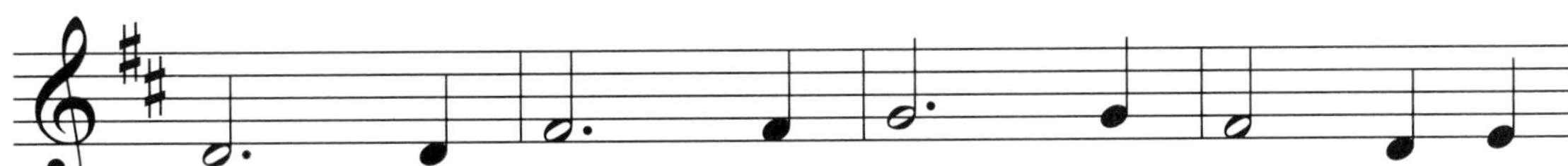

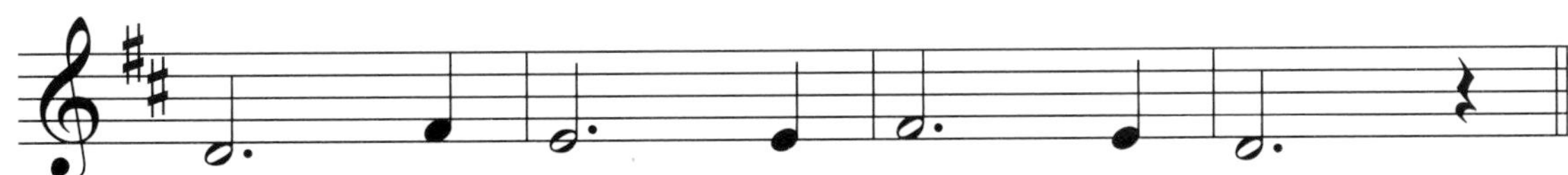

Recorder

Name ______________________ Class ______________

RECORDER 30

Soprano Recorder Fingerings

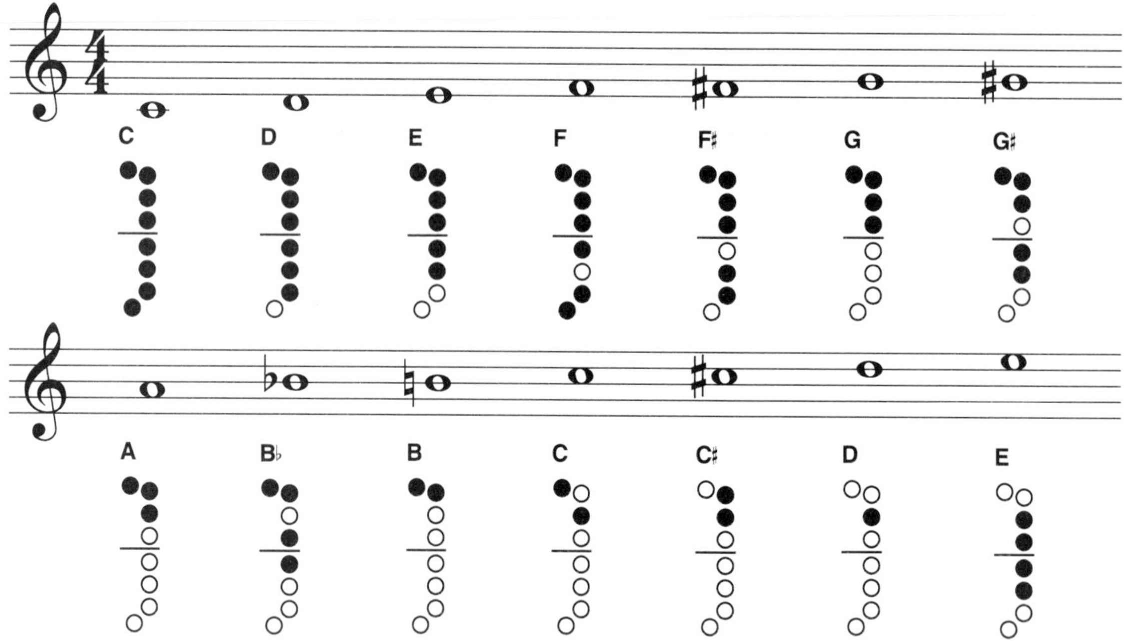

Alto Recorder Fingerings

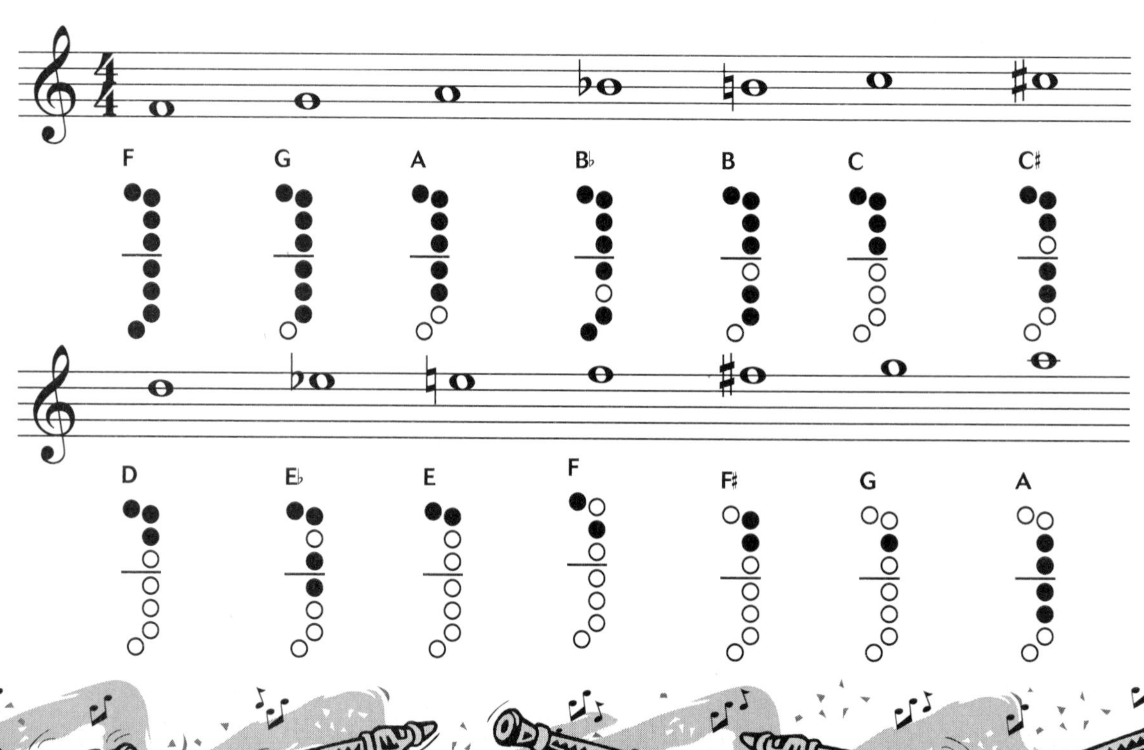

ACTIVITY MASTERS

Table of Contents

Name ______________________________ Class ______________

Activity Master 1

A Letter to Home

This year, your child will be participating in a music class designed to foster lifelong appreciation of music through active music making. The sequenced music instruction will help your child develop musical skills and understanding, using music of various styles from the United States and around the world. In addition to developing specific musical skills, your child's studies in other areas will be enhanced by instruction that links concepts across the curriculum.

Your child will also have opportunities to participate in theme-based music making. Some possible themes include American music, world music, friends, families, self-esteem, animals, ecology, storytelling, choral singing, seasons, and celebrations. Your child may also be involved in classroom and/or school-wide performances, and you will be invited to attend or volunteer to assist with these performances.

You can also reinforce your child's music learning at home. Consider listening to music together and talking about it. Ask your child to share songs learned in music class. Attend local concerts to help foster appropriate audience behavior. These experiences will help make music meaningful at school, at home, and in the community.

Sincerely,

Name ______________________ Class ______________

Activity Master 2

Una Carta al Hogar

Este año, su niño(a) tomará parte en una clase de música que le ayudará a adquirir una apreciación de música durante toda la vida mediante su participación en actividades musicales. La instrucción de música, que está estructurada en una secuencia lógica, le ayudará a su niño(a) a desarrollar destrezas y conocimientos musicales, al experimentar distintos estilos de música de los Estados Unidos y de todas partes del mundo. Además del desarrollo de destrezas musicales, su niño(a) mejorará en los otros campos de estudio porque la instrucción relaciona conceptos provenientes de todo el plan de estudios.

Su niño(a) también tendrá oportunidades de tomar parte en actividades musicales basadas en un tema. Entre estos temas hay música americana, música mundial, amigos, familias, auto-estima, animales, ecología, cuentos, canto coral, estaciones y celebraciones. Tal vez su niño(a) pueda estar envuelto en actuaciones en la clase y/o para toda la escuela, y se le invitará a usted(es) a asistir o a ayudar con estas actuaciones como voluntario(a). Usted(es) también puede(n) reforzar en casa el aprendizaje de música de su niño(a). Consideren escuchar a música juntos y después hablar sobre lo que oyeron. Pídale a su niño(a) que comparta con usted(es) las canciones que ha aprendido en la clase de música. Llévelo(la) a conciertos de la zona para ayudarle a experimentar en la audiencia conducta apropriada. Todo esto ayudará a hacer que la música sea una experiencia significativa para su niño(a) en la escuela, en casa y en la comunidad.

Sinceramente,

Name ______________________ Class ______________

ACTIVITY MASTER 3

Real World Dynamics

Look at page 38 in your textbook for definitions of words and symbols having to do with dynamics. Although dynamics are used to add to the expressive quality of music, our environment is filled with variations in dynamic levels. On the chart below, fill in the meaning of each symbol. Then, write in a sound from the environment that corresponds to this dynamic level.

	Dynamic Marking	Definition	Environmental Sound
1.	*pp*		
2.	*p*	soft	whispering
3.	*mp*		
4.	*f*		
5.	*ff*		
6.	*mf*		

Bonus Questions

7.	***crescendo***		
8.	***decrescendo***		

Name ______________________ Class ______________

Activity Master 4

Twelve-Bar Blues

Using I, IV, and V, fill in the chord numeral that goes in each measure to create a twelve-bar blues progression in a rock style.

1	2	3	4
5	6	7	8
9	10	11	12

Create lyrics for your rock song. The lyrics for lines 1 and 2 are the same. The lyrics for line 3 are different. The last word of line 3 should rhyme with the last word of lines 1 and 2.

Line 1

____

____

Line 2

____

____

Line 3

____

____

Name ______________________ Class ____________

Activity Master 5

Simple Rhythms and Not-So-Simple (Compound) Meters

Each rhythm is either simple meter or compound meter. Mark with an S the rhythms that show simple meter. Mark with a C the rhythms that show compound meter.

1. ___ 2/4
2. ___ 3/8
3. ___ 4/4
4. ___ 6/8
5. ___ 3/8
6. ___ 6/8
7. ___ 3/4
8. ___ 2/4
9. ___ 3/4
10. ___ 6/8

Create a four-measure rhythm pattern that is in simple meter.

Create a four-measure rhythm pattern that is in compound meter.

Name ______________________ Class ______________

ACTIVITIES

ACTIVITY MASTER 6

Crossword Puzzle 1

aeolian	diminution	major	ornamentation	*staccato*
Armstrong	*erhu*	*mbira*	ostinatos	tie
augmentation	*fortissimo*	minimalism	poetry	timbre
Beatles	harmony	minor	Schuman	time
contour	improvisation	mixolydian	*sforzando*	tonic
crescendo	*legato*	mode	sight	Vandross

Across

3. This composer started his career singing jingles (p. 9)
5. When rhythm is notated to be twice as fast (p. 80)
7. The home note of a scale (p. 56)
9. Extra notes singers add to the melody (p. 55)
12. These can be motives, melodic ideas, rhythms, or chords (p. 29)
13. _____ reading is a skill singers and instrumentalists use to learn new music from written notation (p. 126)
15. A style of music using ostinatos to create harmonies and layered textures (p. 30)
18. Melodic _____ is the shape of a musical phrase (p. 20)
20. Another name for the "*do*-diatonic" scale (p. 56)
21. An important musician in jazz history (p. 65)
22. The tone color of an instrument or voice (p. 24)
23. An important form of written expression (p. 40)
25. English rock group (p. 91)
27. An African thumb piano (p. 27)
28. He composed a "baseball opera" (p. 83)
29. A symbol that joins two notes of the same pitch together to make the note longer (p. 10)

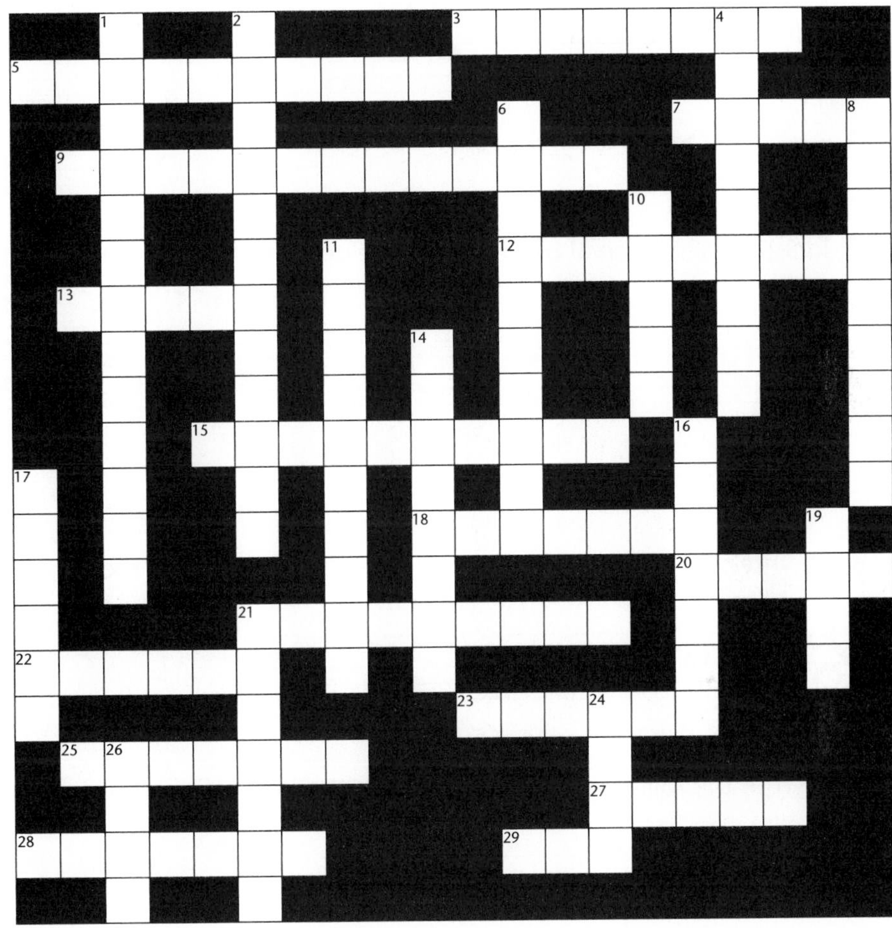

Down

1. The art of making up the music as you perform (p. 55)
2. When rhythm is notated to be twice as slow (p. 80)
4. A sudden accent on a note or chord (p. 78)
6. The mode in which the seventh degree is lowered one half step (p. 96)
8. Gradually louder (p. 76)
10. When a scale ends on "*la*" it is called _____ (p. 58)
11. Very loud (p. 38)
14. When notes are short and separated from each other (p. 38)
16. Two or more different tones sounding at the same time (p. 26)
17. When notes are connected to each other and played or sung smoothly (p. 38)
19. A musical scale whose sound is determined by a specific pattern of whole steps and half steps (p. 94)
21. Name of a mode (p. 94)
24. A ___ signature is the musical symbol that shows how many beats are in a measure and which note gets the beat (p. 42)
26. Chinese stringed instrument (p. 103)

Name ______________________________ Class ______________

ACTIVITY MASTER 7

Notating Intervals

1. Identify each of the following intervals. Write your answers in the spaces provided.

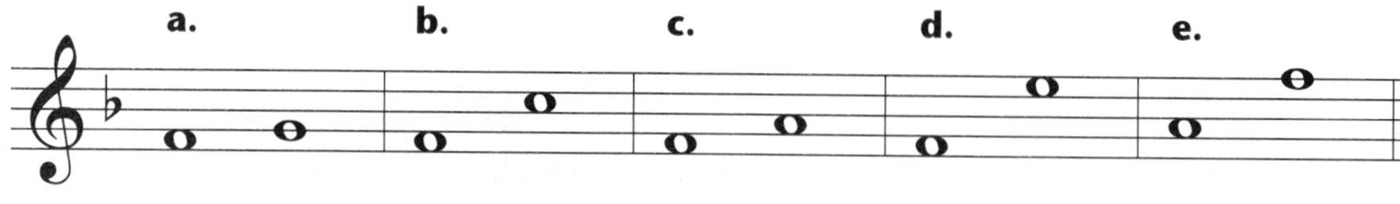

______ ______ ______ ______ ______

2. Identify each interval between the melody and harmony parts.

____ ____ ____ ____ ____ ____ ____ ____ ____

3. Rewrite the following pitches to create the interval of a sixth.

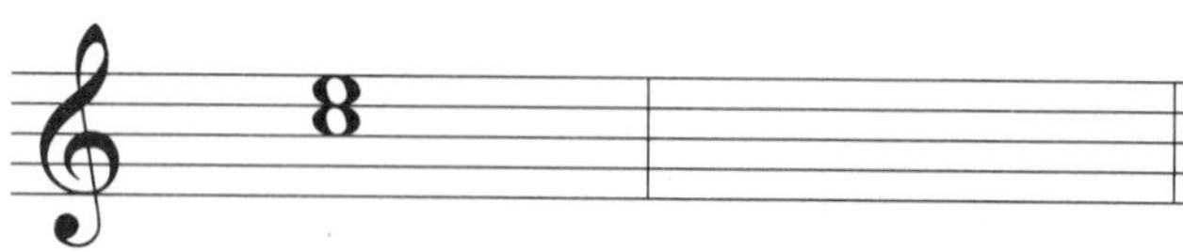

4. Rewrite the following pitches to create the interval of a third.

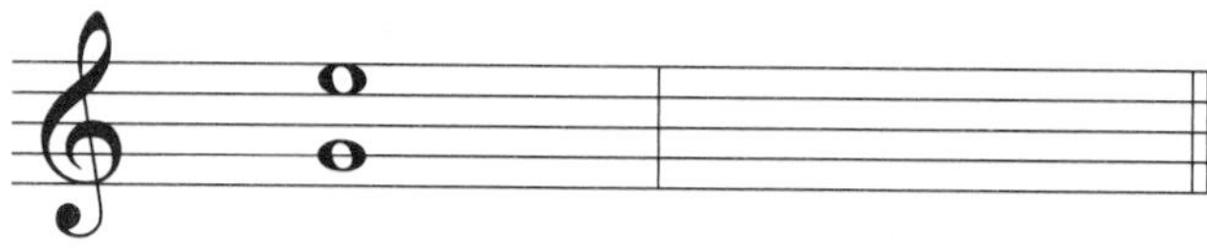

5. Add a note above each of the following pitches to create the interval indicated.

a.	**b.**	**c.**	**d.**	**e.**
4th	5th	2nd	octave	3rd

Name ______________________ Class ______________

ACTIVITIES

ACTIVITY MASTER 8

Music By Chance

1. Cut out the six boxes and put them on your desk face down. Scramble them. Then, pick up each box one at a time, turn it over, and put it down in the order that you have selected by chance. Invite several friends to help you perform the piece you have created.
2. On the back of each piece of paper, or on any number of pieces of paper, create some musical ideas that can be performed as a chance piece. Scramble and perform as above.
3. Select a poem that is in your book. Ask some classmates to perform it with you in this fashion: Each can read any line or fragment of a line whenever they like. Have one person decide when the poem should start and when it is finished.

Vocal Sounds

s s s s s s s
Br Br Br Br Br
sing random high note

Desk Sounds

(write your own)

Foot Sounds

scrape floor for 6 seconds

tap toe:

stomp foot:

Speech

"watch" (high voice)
"watch" (low voice)
"watch" (high voice)
"watch" (low voice)

Hand Sounds

rub palms together

clap and pat:

Vocal Sounds

(write your own)

Name ______________________ Class ______________

Activity Master 9

Crossword Puzzle 2

accelerando	canon	ground	*prestissimo*	theme
accompaniment	compound	homophonic	*ritardando*	triple
adagio	crab	interval	round	variation
Bach	cut	Mehta	simple	*vivace*
Berg	Danube	metronome	syncopation	Vivaldi
Berlin	fugue	position	tempo	Ziggy

Across

1. Gradual decrease in tempo (p. 152)
3. A canon in which the melody is performed backwards (p. 125)
6. ___ time is a meter of two beats per measure; the half note gets the beat (p. 119)
8. An important melody that occurs several times in a piece of music (p. 160)
9. As fast as possible (p. 114)
12. A device which is set to play the desired number of beats per minute (p. 114)
15. A texture in a melody supported by harmony (p. 173)
17. Music that changes a theme in some important ways (p. 160)
19. Quite slow (p. 114)
20. ___ meter is subdivided into three equal parts. The dotted quarter note gets the beat (p. 120)
24. A _____ bass is a bass line that continuously repeats throughout a composition (p. 202)
25. This meter is subdivided into two equal parts. The quarter note gets the beat (p. 119)
26. He wrote "Alexander's Ragtime Band" (p. 136)
27. First name of the son of reggae legend Bob Marley (p. 143)
28. A musical form in which the main melody is imitated by two or more additional, overlapping melodies (p. 128)

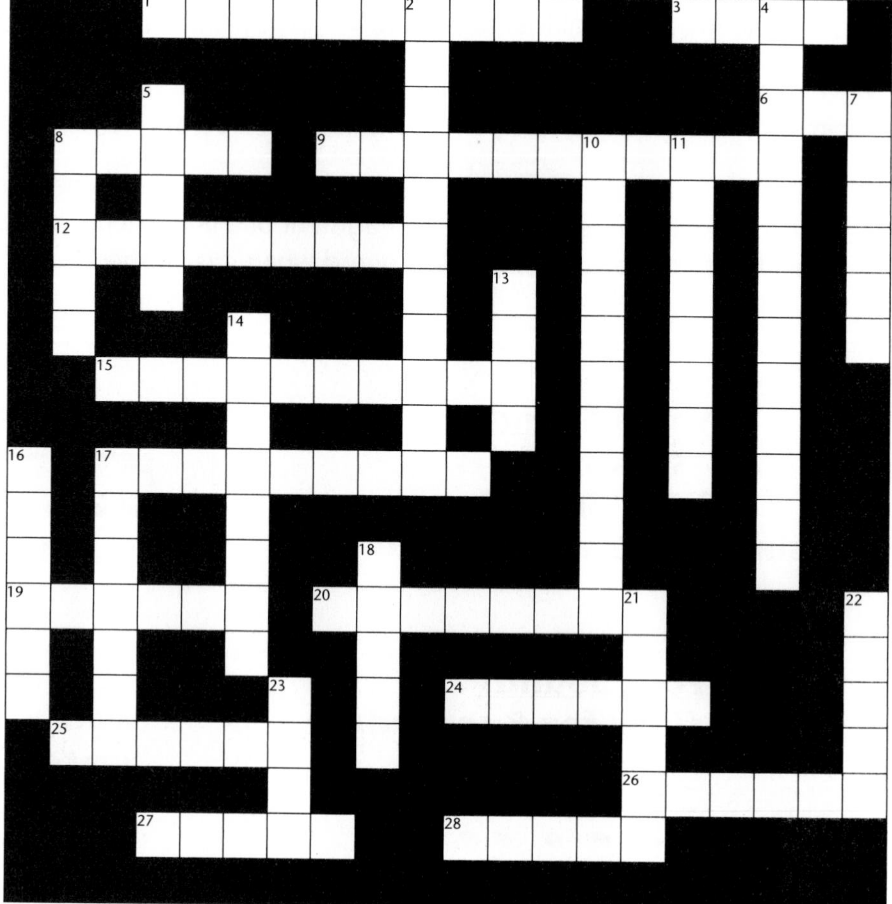

Down

2. A gradual increase in tempo (p. 152)
4. Music that supports the sound of the featured performer (p. 142)
5. Music conductor known for his grandiose and intense conducting style (p. 154)
7. This meter has three beats in each measure (p. 120)
8. The speed of the music (p. 114)
10. A term used to describe accented rhythms that occur off the beat (p. 156)
11. The distance between two notes (p. 130)
13. One of the most famous composers of fugues (p. 128)
14. Root _____ means that the root of the chord is the lowest note (p. 144)
16. Lively (p. 114)
17. Known as the "Red Priest" (p. 211)
18. A "follow-the-leader" form in which all sing the melody but start at different times (p. 122)
21. A river that flows from Germany's Black Forest to the Black Sea (p. 192)
22. A round in which the melody can enter on the same or different pitches (p. 124)
23. He composed in the "atonal" style of music (p. 169)

Name ______________________ Class ____________

ACTIVITIES

Activity Master 10

Musical Questions and Answers

Pretend that the following rhythm patterns, each having two beats, have been played by a drum leader. Create and notate an answer pattern for each existing pattern. When you are finished, ask several classmates to join you. One of you play the leader's pattern and the others can play what they have written. Play one at a time and then together. Establish a basic beat before starting.

Question **Answer**

1. 

2.

3.

4.

5. 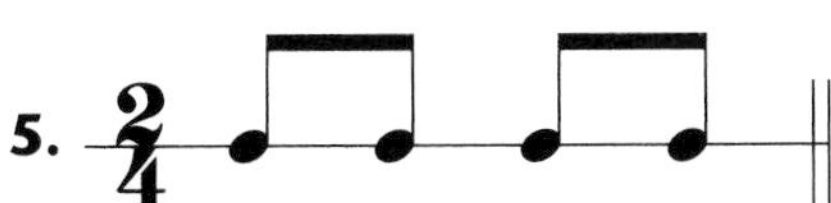

Name ____________________ Class ____________

Activity Master 11

The Three "L's" of Pitch

Circle the instrument in each set that plays lower pitches.

1. Bassoon — Flute

2. Violin — Cello

3. Tuba — Trumpet

4. Small timpani — Large timpani

5. Trumpet — Trombone

6. What happens to the pitch when a player tightens a string on a violin?

____

7. What happens to the pitch when a player tightens a string on a cello?

____

8. What happens to the pitch when the trombone player moves the slide out, making the instrument longer?

____

9. What happens to the pitch when a timpani player loosens the head of the drum?

____

10. What happens to the pitch when a trumpet player pushes a valve that allows the air to travel further through the tubing of the instrument?

____

Name ______________________ Class ______________

Activity Master 12

"Techno" Road Map

Use the road map below to create your own "techno" song. You may use any of the motives and rhythm patterns on the following page, you may create your own, or you may use any combination you choose.

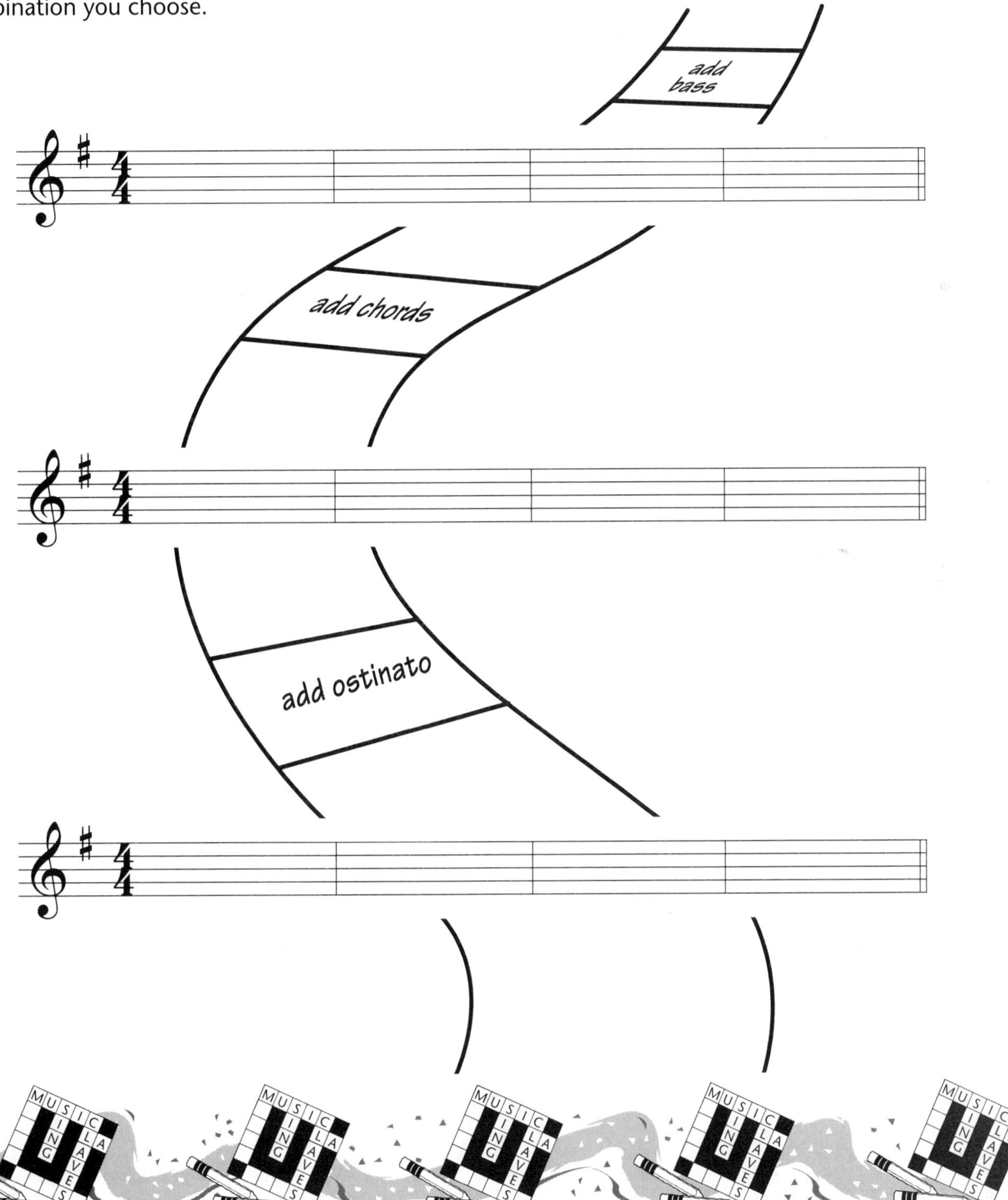

Name ______________________________ Class ______________

ACTIVITY MASTER 12 (CONTINUED)

Bass 1

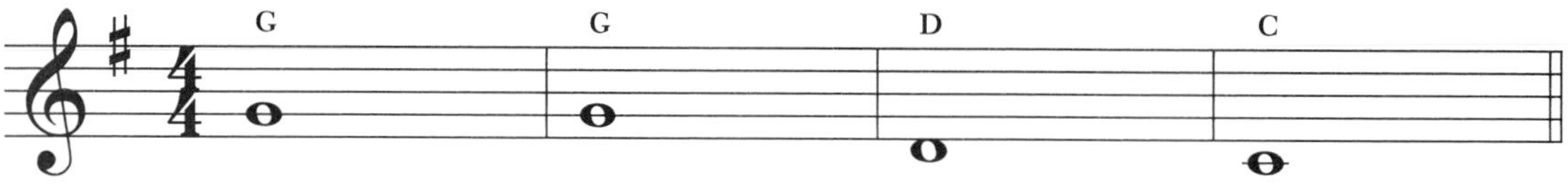

G G D C

Bass 2

G G D C

Chords 1

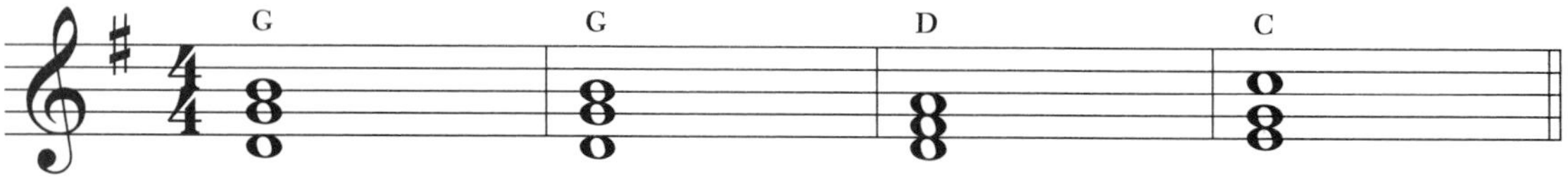

G G D C

Chords 2

Chords 3

Ostinato 1

Ostinato 2

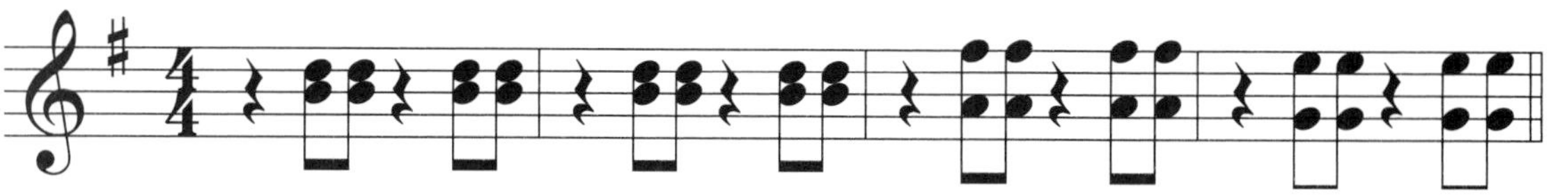

Try this rhythm for a challenge.

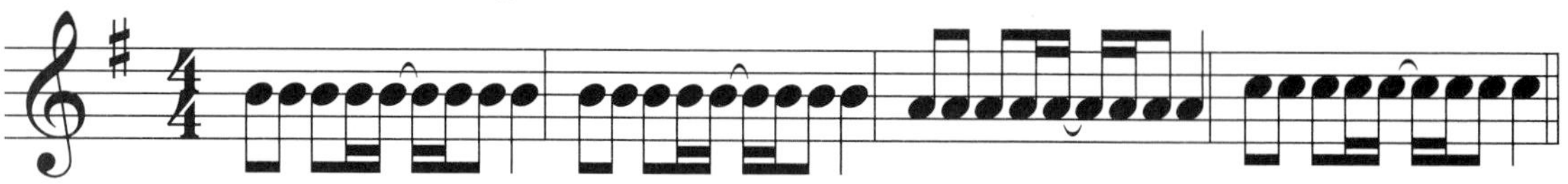

Name ______________________________ Class ______________

ACTIVITIES

ACTIVITY MASTER 13

Find the Motive

The rhythmic motives below appear in the song *"Vem kan segla"* on page 417 in the book. For each example, write the measure number in which each motive begins.

1. ______________

2. ______________

3. ______________

4. ______________

5. ______________

6. ______________

Name ____________________ Class ____________

ACTIVITY MASTER 14

Manuscript Paper

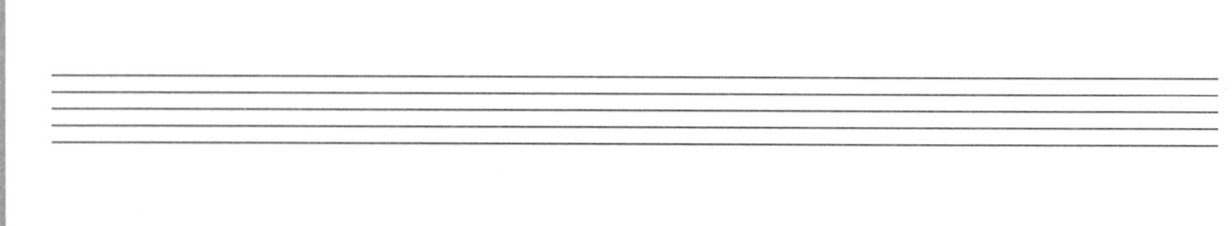

Name ______________________ Class ______________

ACTIVITY MASTER 15

Percussion Manuscript Paper

1. Percussion Manuscript

2. Percussion Ensemble Manuscript

Name ____________________ Class ____________

ACTIVITY MASTER 16

Keyboard Diagram

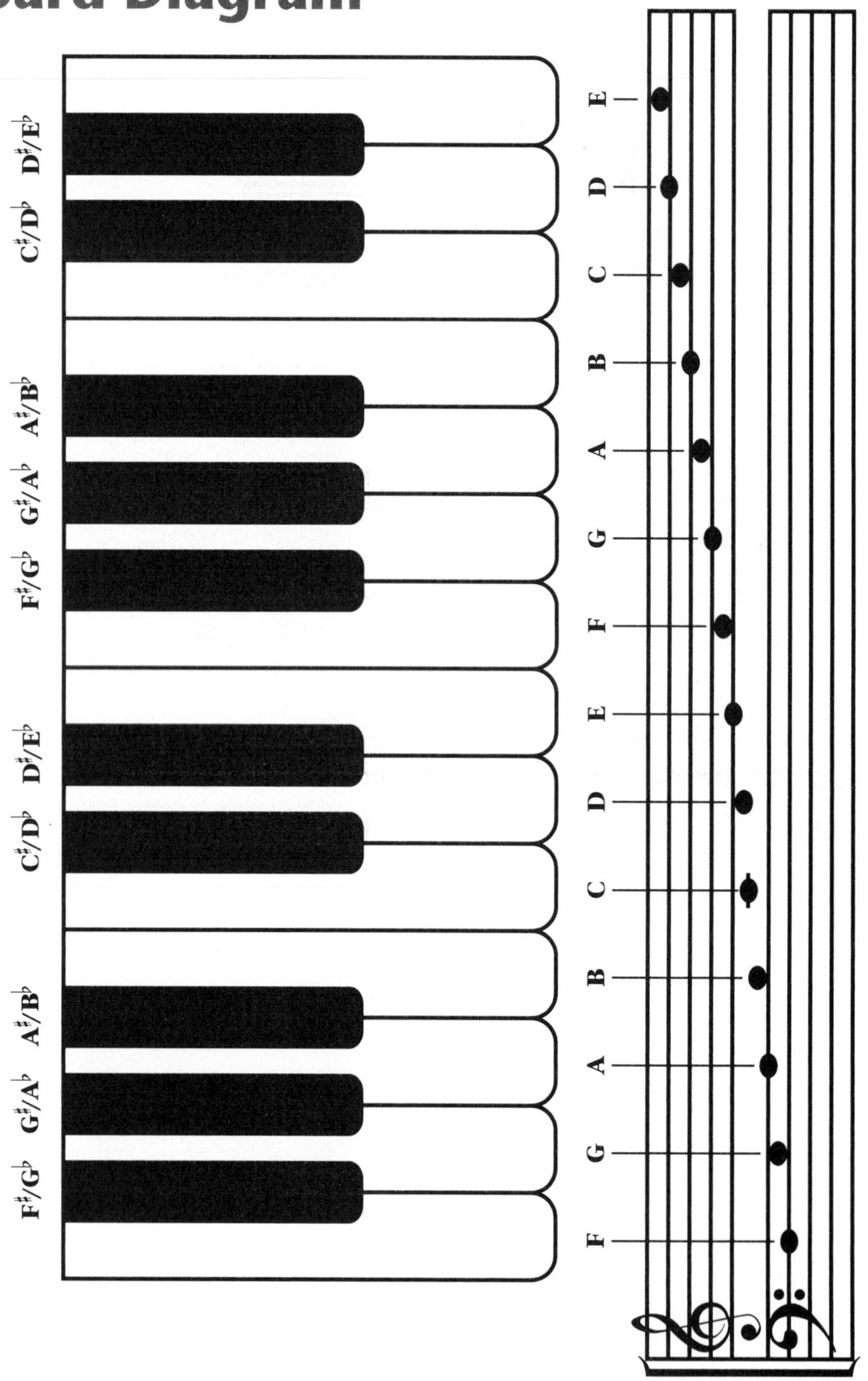

C♯/D♭ D♯/E♭ F♯/G♭ G♯/A♭ A♯/B♭ C♯/D♭ D♯/E♭ F♯/G♭ G♯/A♭ A♯/B♭

E D C B A G F E D C B A G F

Name ______________________ Class ______________

ACTIVITY MASTER 17

Bell Diagram

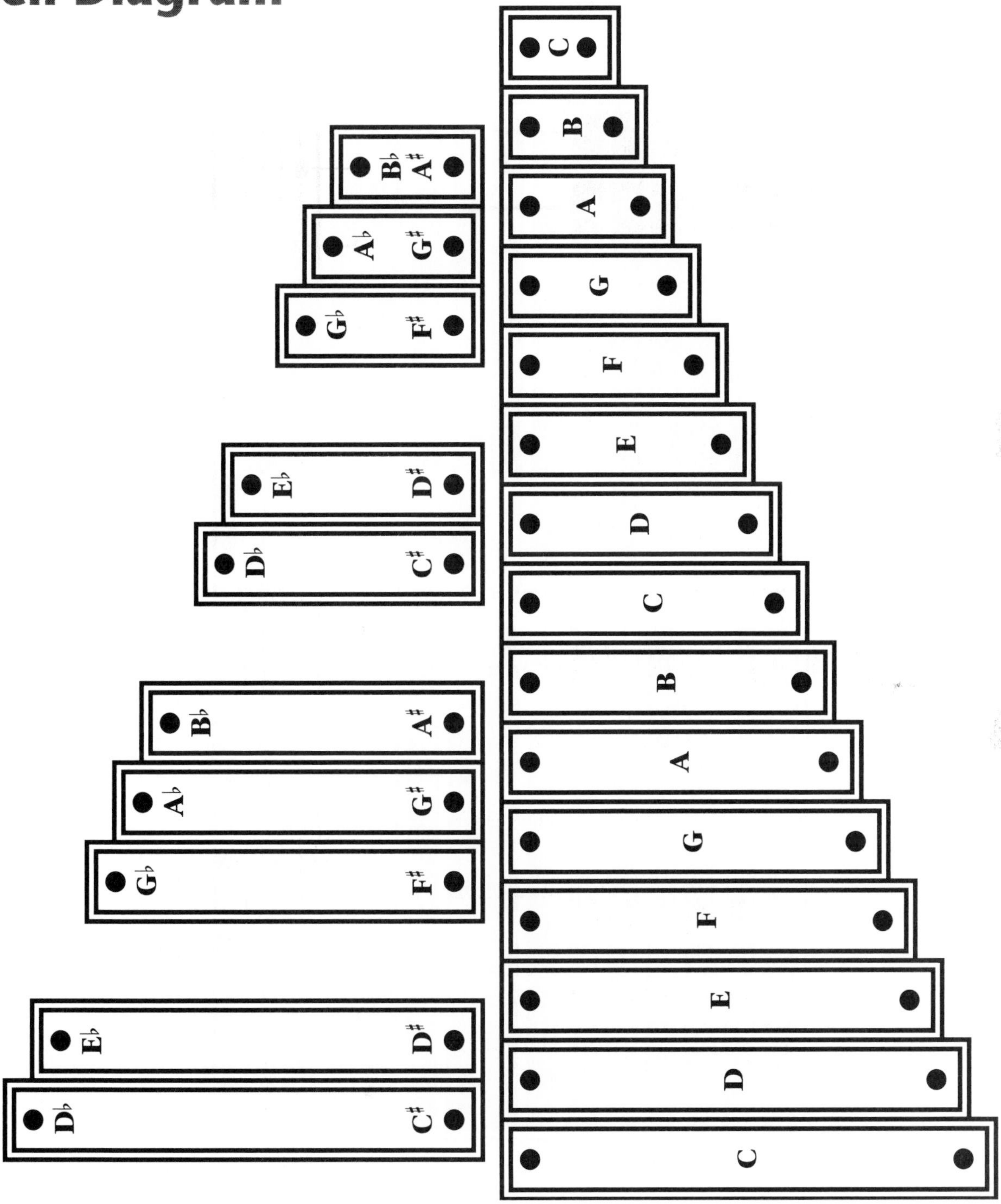

C
B
A
G
F
E
D
C
B
A
G
F
E
D
C

B♭ A♯
A♭ G♯
G♭ F♯
E♭ D♯
D♭ C♯
B♭ A♯
A♭ G♯
G♭ F♯
E♭ D♯
D♭ C♯

Name ______________________ Class ______________

ACTIVITY MASTER 18

Autoharp Diagram

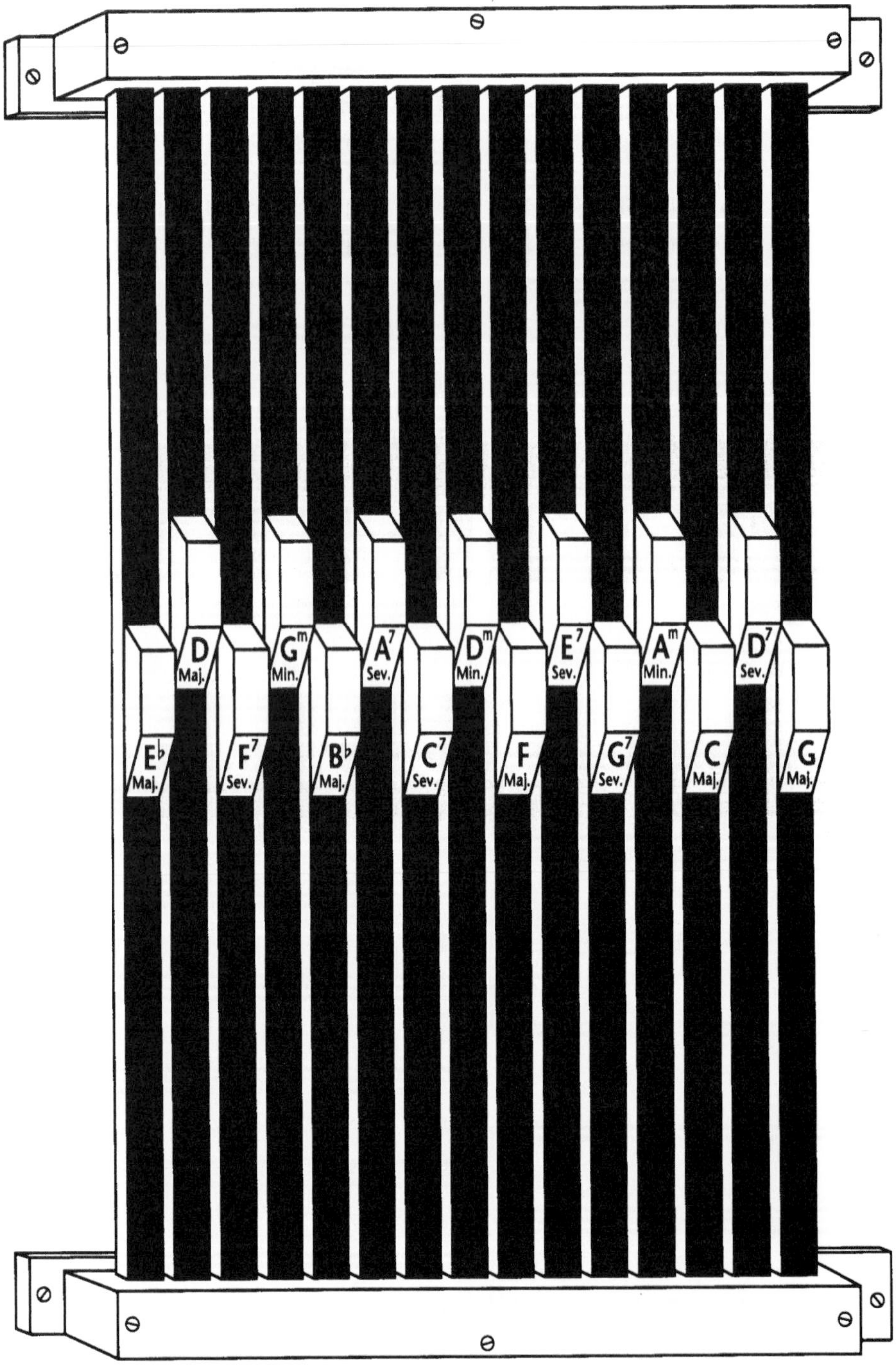

D Maj. | Gm Min. | A7 Sev. | Dm Min. | E7 Sev. | Am Min. | D7 Sev.

E♭ Maj. | F7 Sev. | B♭ Maj. | C7 Sev. | F Maj. | G7 Sev. | C Maj. | G Maj.

Activity Masters Answer Key

Activity Master 3: Real World Dynamics

Dynamic Marking	Definition	Environmental Sound
1. *pp*	very soft	a quiet babbling brook
2. *p*	soft	whispering
3. *mp*	moderately soft	a singing canary
4. *mf*	moderately loud	a busy store
5. *f*	loud	a factory floor
6. *ff*	very loud	a fire engine siren
7. *crescendo*	gradually getting louder	a jet airliner as it approaches you
8. *decrescendo*	gradually getting softer	a jet airliner as it passes overhead and leaves you

Activity Master 4: Twelve-Bar Blues

1. I
2. I
3. I
4. I
5. IV
6. IV
7. I
8. I
9. V
10. V or IV
11. I
12. I

Activity Master 5: Real World Dynamics

1. S
2. S
3. S
4. C
5. S
6. C
7. S
8. S
9. S
10. C

ACTIVITY MASTERS ANSWER KEY (CONTINUED)

Activity Master 6: Crossword Puzzle 1

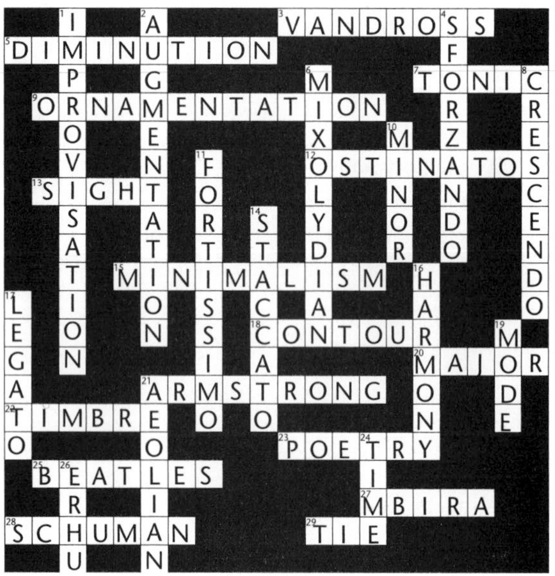

Activity Master 7: Notating Intervals

1. a. 2nd
   b. 5th
   c. 3rd
   d. 7th
   e. 6th
2. a. 6th
   b. 6th
   c. 6th
   d. 3rd
   e. 3rd
   f. 6th
   g. 6th
   h. 6th
   i. 6th
3.
4.
5. **a.** **4th** **b.** **5th** **c.** **2nd** **d.** **octave** **e.** **3rd**

Activity Masters Answer Key (continued)

Activity Master 11: Crossword Puzzle 2

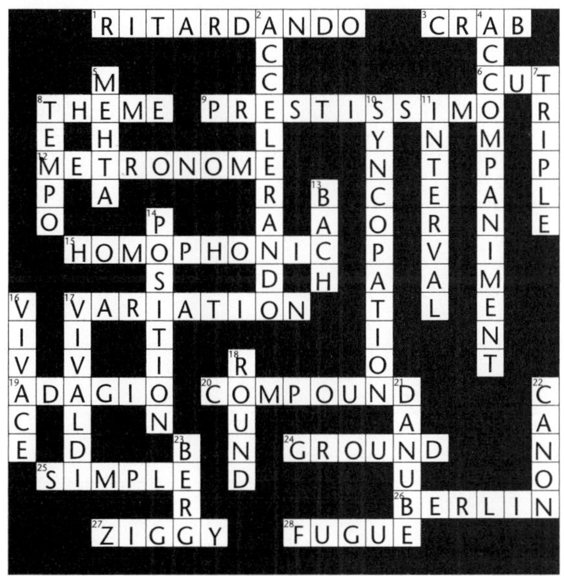

Activity Master 11: The Three "L's" of Pitch

1. Basson
2. Cello
3. Tuba
4. Large timpani
5. Trombone
6. pitch goes higher
7. pitch goes higher
8. pitch goes lower
9. pitch goes lower
10. pitch goes lower

Activity Master 13: Find the Motive

1. 1
2. 3
3. 5
4. 13
5. 5
6. 9

Teacher Notes

ART CREDITS

Reading
All art Burgandy Beam.

Keyboard
All art Burgandy Beam.

Activity Master
All art Burgandy Beam.

Orff icons
All art Tony Nuccio.

Signing
All art Burgandy Beam.

ACKNOWLEDGMENTS

Credits and appreciation are due publishers and copyright owners for use of the following:
A-3: "Magnolia" Words and music by Tish Hinojosa. © 1996 WB Music Corp. (ASCAP) & Manazo Music (ASCAP). All Rights administered by WB Music Corp. All Rights Reserved. Used by permission. WARNER BROS. PUBLICATIONS U.S. INC., Miami, FL 33014. **A-7:** "La paloma se fué" (The Dove that Flew Away) © 1988 Alejandro Jimenez/World Music Press. Publisher World Music Press/Judith Cook Tucker. **A-12:** "Lo yisa" **A-16:** "Así es mi tierra" (This Is My Land) Words and Music by Ignacío Fernandez Esperón. Copyright © 2003 by Promotora Hispano Americana De Musica, S.A. All Rights Administered by Peer International Corporation. International Copyright Secured. All Rights Reserved. Used by Permission. **A-19:** "Ise oluwa" Yoruba Folk Song From Nigeria, arranged by Nitanju Bolade Casel. © 1989 Nitanju Bolade Casel, Clear Ice Music. Used by permission. **A-20:** "Riendo el río corre" (Run, Run, River) WB MUSIC CORP. Warner Chappell Music Inc. **A-24:** "Asadoya" Used by permission of Bruce Saylor. **A-26:** "Oye" by Jim Papoulis. "Oye" is from the project Sounds of a Better World, all proceeds go to Children's Charities. soundsofabetterworld.org. Reprinted by permission. **A-35:** "Cantaré, cantaras" (I Will Sing, You Will Sing) Words and music by Albert Hammond, Anahi and Juan Carlos Calderón. Copyright © 1985 Irving Music, Inc., Calquin Music, EMI April Music, Inc. WARNER BROS. PUBLICATIONS U.S. INC., Miami, FL. 33014 and Hal Leonard Corporation. **A-36:** "Vem kan segla?" (Who Can Sail?) Finnish Folk Song. Reprinted by permission. Copyright Walton Music Corp. **A-40:** "Svivon" (Dreydl) verse by L. Kipnis from The New Jewish Song Book, compiled and edited by Harry Coopersmith, 1965. © Behrman House, Inc., reprinted with permission. **A-42:** "Eres tú" (Touch the Wind) Words and music by Juan Calderón, English Words by Michael Hawker. © 1972 (Renewed) Ed. Musicales PolyGram-Discorama. WARNER BROS. PUBLICATIONS U.S. INC., Miami, FL 33014. **A-45:** "Las mañanitas" from Children's Songs from Mexico. © Alfred Publishing Co. Inc. **D-5:** "Gonna Build a Mountain" From the Musical Production "Stop the World–I Want to Get Off." Words and Music by Leslie Bricusse and Anthony Newley. TRO–Ludlow Music, Inc., New York, New York. **D-6:** "Farewell to Tarwathie" (Adieu to My Comrades) from The Singing Islands by Peggy Seeger and Ewan McColl. © 1960 (Renewed) EMI Mills Music, Ltd. WARNER BROS. PUBLICATIONS U.S. INC., Miami, FL 33014. **D-10:** "Do, Re, Mi, Fa" from 150 Rounds and Canons. Reprinted by permission of Boosey & Hawkes, Inc. **D-19:** "Alleluia" responsory from Bernstein's Mass. Music by Leonard Berstein. **D-24:** "Paths of Victory" Words and music by Bob Dylan. Copyright © 1954 Warner Bros. Copyright Renewed 1992 by Special Rider Music. International Copyright Secured. All Rights Reserved. Reprinted by permission of Music Sales Corporation (ASCAP). **D-25:** "New Hungarian Folk Song" from Mikrokosmos (Bartok). © Copyright 1940 by Hawkes & Son (London) Ltd. **E-5:** "Gonna Build a Mountain" From the Musical Production "Stop the World–I Want to Get Off." Words and Music by Leslie Bricusse and Anthony Newley. TRO–Ludlow Music, Inc., New York, New York. **E-6:** "Farewell to Tarwathie" (Adieu to My Comrades) from The Singing Islands by Peggy Seeger and Ewan McColl. © 1960 (Renewed) EMI Mills Music, Ltd. WARNER BROS. PUBLICATIONS U.S. INC., Miami, FL 33014. **E-10:** "Do, Re, Mi, Fa" from 150 Rounds and Canons. Reprinted by permission of Boosey & Hawkes, Inc. **E-17:** "Alleluia" responsory from Bernstein's Mass. Music by Leonard Berstein. **E-22:** "Paths of Victory" Words and Music by Bob Dylan. Copyright © 1954 Warner Bros. Copyright Renewed 1992 by Special Rider Music, Music Sales Corporation (ASCAP). **E-23:** "New Hungarian Folk Song" from Mikrokosmos (Bartok). © Copyright 1940 by Hawkes & Son (London) Ltd. **F-2:** "Bury Me Not on the Lone Prairie' Cowboy Song from the United States. ORFF accompaniment © 2002 Pearson Education, Inc. **F-3:** "Hey, Ho! Nobody Home" Old English Round. ORFF accompaniment © 2002 Pearson Education, Inc. **F-4:** "Farewell to Tarwathie" (Adieu to My Comrades) from The Singing Islands by Peggy Seeger and Ewan McColl. © 1960 (Renewed) EMI Mills Music, Ltd. WARNER BROS. PUBLICATIONS U.S. INC., Miami, FL 33014. ORFF accompaniment by Pearson Education, Inc. **F-5:** "Barb'ry Allen" Folk Song from the British Isles. ORFF accompaniment © 2002 Pearson Education, Inc. **F-6:** "El cóndor pasa" Music by Daniel Almonica Robles. ORFF accompaniment by Pearson Education, Inc. **F-8:** "La paloma se fué" (The Dove that Flew Away) © 1988 Alejandro Jimenez/World Music Press. Publisher World Music Press/Judith Cook Tucker. ORFF accompaniment by Pearson Education, Inc. **F-10:** "Scarborough Fair" Folk Song from England. ORFF accompaniment © 2002 Pearson Education, Inc. **F-13:** "One Morning in May" Folk Song from the Appalachian Mountains. ORFF accompaniment © 2002 Pearson Education, Inc. **F-14:** "Lo yisa" (Vine and Fig Tree) Music by Shalom Altman. ORFF accompaniment © 2002 Pearson Education, Inc. **F-16:** "El payo" (The Cowpoke) (Folk Song from Mexico) ORFF accompaniment © 2002 Pearson Education, Inc. **F-18:** "Lost My Gold Ring" Singing Game from Jamaica. ORFF accompaniment © 2002 Pearson Education, Inc. **F-19:** "Paths of Victory" Words and music by Bob Dylan. Copyright © 1954 Warner Bros. Copyright Renewed 1992 by Special Rider Music, Music Sales Corporation (ASCAP). ORFF accompaniment by Pearson Education, Inc. **F-21:** "Siyahamba" Traditional Freedom Song from South Africa. ORFF accompaniment © 2002 Pearson Education, Inc. **F-22:** "The Water Is Wide" Folk Song from England. ORFF accompaniment © 2002 Pearson Education, Inc. **F-24:** "You Are My Sunshine" Words and music by Jimmie Davis and Charles Mitchell. Copyright 1930 by Peer International Corporation. ORFF accompaniment by Pearson Education, Inc. **F-26:** "Take Time in Life" Copyright © 1962 CRS, Transferred to World Around Songs, 20 Colberts Creek Rd., Burnsville, NC 28714. ORFF accompaniment by Pearson Education, Inc. **F-28:** "Everybody Loves Saturday Night" Folk Song from West Africa. ORFF accompaniment © 2002 Pearson Education, Inc. **F-29:** "Water Come a Me Eye" (Folk Song from Trinidad) ORFF accompaniment © 2002 Pearson Education, Inc. **F-31:** "Asadoya" Folk Song from Okinawa. ORFF accompaniment © 2002 Pearson Education, Inc. **F-32:** "Worried Man Blues" from Folk Blues by Jerry Silverman. © Saw Mill Music Corp. ORFF accompaniment by Pearson Education, Inc. **F-34:** "Tom Dooley" Folk Song from the United States. ORFF accompaniment © 2002 Pearson Education, Inc. **F-36:** "El carnavalito humahuaqueño" (The Little Humahuacan Carnival. ORFF accompaniment © 2002 Pearson Education, Inc. **G-2:** "Lean On Me" Words and Music by Bill Withers. © 1972 (Renewed) Interior Music (BMI). All Rights Reserved. Used by permission. WARNER BROS. PUBLICATIONS U.S. INC., Miami, FL 33014. **G-9:** "Ain't Gonna Let Nobody Turn Me 'Round" (African American Civil Rights Song) © 2002 Pearson Education, Inc. **G-13:** "Siyahamba" (Traditional Freedom Song from South Africa) Arrangement by Rick Baitz. **G-16:** "You Are My Sunshine" Words and Music by Jimmie Davis and Charles Mitchell. Copyright 1930 by Peer International Corporation. **G-24:** "I Am But A Small Voice" original words by Odina E. Batnag; English words and music by Roger Whittaker. Copyright © 1983 BMG Songs Inc. and BMG Music Publishing Ltd. Used by permission. **G-26:** "Free at Last" (African American Spiritual) Arrangement © 1995 Silver Burdett Ginn. **G-27:** "Love in Any Language" Words and Music by Jon Mohr and John Mays. Copyright © 1986 by Jonathan Mark Music, Birdwing Music, Sutton Hill Music. All rights reserved. Used by permission of Gaither Copyright Management and Music Services, Inc. **H-7:** "Bury Me Not on the Lone Prairie" (Cowboy Song from the United States) KEYBOARD accompaniment © 2002 Pearson Education, Inc. **H-9:** "Hey, Ho! Nobody Home" (Old English Round) KEYBOARD accompaniment © 2002 Pearson Education, Inc. **H-9:** "Give My Regards to Broadway" Music by George M. Cohan. Arranged by Lynn Freeman Olson from Piano for Pleasure, 3rd Edition by Martha Hilley & Lynn Freemann Olson. Copyright © 1998 by Wadsworth Publishing Company. Reprinted with permission of Wadsworth, an imprint of the Wadsworth Group, a division of Thomson Learning, Fax 800-730-2215. **H-11:** "Blue Skies" from Betsy featured in "Blue Skies." Words and music by Irving Berlin. Copyright © 1927 by Irving Berlin. Copyright Renewed. KEYBOARD accompaniment by Pearson Education, Inc. **H-12:** "Birthday" Words and Music by John Lennon and Paul McCartney. Copyright © 1968 Sony/ATV Songs LLC. Copyright Renewed. KEYBOARD accompaniment by Pearson Education, Inc. **H-13:** "Scarborough Fair" (Folk Song from England) KEYBOARD accompaniment © 2002 Pearson Education, Inc. **H-14:** "Swanee" Words by Irving Caesar, music by George Gershwin. © 1919 (Renewed) WB Music Corp. & Irving Caesar Music Corp. All Rights administered by WB Music Corp. WARNER BROS. PUBLICATIONS U.S. INC., Miami, FL 33014. KEYBOARD accompaniment by Pearson Education, Inc. **H-15:** "Dance for the Nations" Words and music by John (J) Krumm. KEYBOARD accompaniment by Pearson Education, Inc. **H-16:** "Así es mi tierra" (This Is My Land) Words and Music by Ignacío Fernandez Esperón. Copyright © 2003 by Promotora Hispano Americana De Musica, S.A. All Rights Administered by Peer International Corporation. KEYBOARD accompaniment by Pearson Education, Inc. **H-18:** "Peace Like a River" (African American Spiritual) KEYBOARD accompaniment © 2002 Pearson Education, Inc. **H-19:** "Paths of Victory" Words and Music by Bob Dylan. Copyright © 1954 Warner Bros. Copyright Renewed 1992 by Special Rider Music, Music Sales Corporation (ASCAP). KEYBOARD accompaniment by Pearson Education, Inc. **H-21:** "Kyrie" (Round from Suriname) KEYBOARD accompaniment © 2002 Pearson Education, Inc. **H-22:** "Sometimes I Feel Like a Motherless Child" (African American Spiritual) KEYBOARD accompaniment © 2002 Pearson Education, Inc. **H-20:** "Sun Gonna Shine" (Traditional Blues Song) Arranged and Adapted by John Fahey. Copyright © Tortoise Music (ASCAP). RECORDER accompaniment by Pearson Education, Inc.